THE MICROBIOLOGY OF
STARCH AND SUGARS

Uniform with this Volume

THE MICROBIOLOGY OF CELLULOSE, HEMICELLULOSES, PECTIN, AND GUMS. By A. C. THAYSEN and H. J. BUNKER. Demy 8vo. Cloth. Pp. viii + 363, with illustrations in the text and 9 plates. 25s. net.

OXFORD UNIVERSITY PRESS

THE MICROBIOLOGY OF STARCH AND SUGARS

By A. C. THAYSEN and
L. D. GALLOWAY

OXFORD UNIVERSITY PRESS
LONDON : HUMPHREY MILFORD
1930

OXFORD UNIVERSITY PRESS
AMEN HOUSE, E.C. 4
LONDON EDINBURGH GLASGOW
LEIPZIG NEW YORK TORONTO
MELBOURNE CAPETOWN BOMBAY
CALCUTTA MADRAS SHANGHAI
HUMPHREY MILFORD
PUBLISHER TO THE
UNIVERSITY

PRINTED IN GREAT BRITAIN AT THE UNIVERSITY PRESS, OXFORD
BY JOHN JOHNSON, PRINTER TO THE UNIVERSITY

PREFACE

THE treatise embodied in the following pages has been compiled as a complementary volume to the *Microbiology of Cellulose, Hemicelluloses, Pectin, and Gums* published by one of the writers (A. C. Thaysen) in collaboration with Mr. H. J. Bunker in 1927.

Taken together the two volumes endeavour to review the microbiology of the carbohydrates, a subject, it will be realized, which covers a very wide field, particularly the section which is now placed in the hands of the publishers under the title of the *Microbiology of Starch and Sugars*. Considerably more than three thousand original publications bearing on the subject have had to be examined in detail, and though it is hoped that the bulk of the relevant literature has been considered, the writers are anxious to acknowledge that some papers, even perhaps some quite important papers, may have escaped their notice, particularly any such which have been published in languages other than English, French, German, Dutch, Danish, Swedish, and Norwegian.

The volume has been written from the point of view of the research worker, and in addition to compiling existing knowledge it endeavours to point out paths which might be followed by workers who desire to extend their knowledge of the action of micro-organisms on starch and sugar.

As in the treatise on the microbiology of cellulose, the term 'micro-organisms' has been adopted to designate all microscopic organisms, whether belonging to the animal or to the vegetable kingdom. The word 'bacteria' has been used colloquially for all rod-shaped schizomycetes belonging to the *Eubacteriales*. Where a distinction in the Latin nomen-

clature has been necessary among the bacteria, the system
followed by Lehmann and Neumann and by Bergey has been
adopted, a spore producing rod being termed '*Bacillus*' and
a non-sporing rod '*Bacterium*'.

The writers are anxious to place on record the valuable
help rendered them by members of the staff of the Department of Scientific Research of the Admiralty and of the
Department of Scientific and Industrial Research.

They also greatly appreciate the permission granted them
by the Lords Commissioners of the Admiralty to publish
their treatise.

Last but not least they are most sincerely indebted to the
publishers, the Oxford University Press, for their never
failing patience, which must have been taxed to the utmost
by the long-delayed delivery of a promised manuscript. The
writers can only plead in their defence, that the task undertaken by them was found to be much greater than had been
originally anticipated.

HOLTON HEATH,
   September 1929.

CONTENTS

PART ONE

OUTLINE OF THE CONSTITUTION AND THE BIO-CHEMICAL PROPERTIES OF STARCH, GLYCOGEN, AND INULIN

Starch. The constitution of starch, its depolymerisation and its conversion through hydrolysis into simpler carbohydrates have long been favourite subjects for investigation. But though recent years have witnessed a certain simplification of the conception of these problems, much work has still to be done before the chemistry of starch and the constitution of this polysaccharide are fully understood.

The bulk of the existing literature on starch and starch hydrolysis is now of little more than historical interest and cannot be dealt with here. It must suffice briefly to refer to the few publications which have had a direct bearing on more recent fundamental researches. Among these must be mentioned Kirchoff's[1] observation in 1812 that boiling with dilute mineral acids converts starch into a sugar; de Saussure's[2] record in 1819 of the spontaneous decomposition of starch with the formation of sugars; and Dubrunfaut's[3] study of the action of malt extracts on starch, which led to Payen and Persoz's[4] isolation of diastase (malt amylase) in 1833. In 1847 Dubrunfaut[5] showed that the sugar, termed maltose by him, which he obtained from starch by the action of malt amylase, and which in the course of time had come to be regarded as identical with glucose, was in fact different from this sugar, yielded by starch on hydrolysis with dilute acids. Dubrunfaut's researches were considerably extended by O'Sullivan[6] from 1872 to 1876. O'Sullivan found that the maltose obtained from starch by the action of malt amylase was a disaccharide with about double the rotatory power of glucose, but with a lesser reducing action towards Fehling's solution.

During the eighty years following the discovery of malt

amylase, the study of the chemistry of starch became largely an investigation of the action of this enzyme mixture and of the nature of the dextrins, intermediate decomposition products of starch. Comparatively few of the publications dating from this period have proved of direct value to recent research. Of interest is Lintner's[7] observation in 1891 that a new sugar, isomaltose, is formed as a decomposition product of starch when the polysaccharide is subjected to the action of malt amylase. Lintner's statement was not accepted at the time, but subsequent investigations (Ling and Nanji[8] and Kuhn[9]) supported his view.

Another fruitful observation was reported by Maquenne and Roux[10] in 1906. These authors succeeded in decomposing the starch granule into two distinct substances, which they termed amylose and amylopectin respectively. The amylose was found to constitute from 80 to 85 per cent. of the starch granule, while amylopectin represented the bulk of the remaining 15 to 20 per cent. Amylose showed the characteristic blue iodine reaction of starch to an intensified degree, while the amylopectin gave no blue coloration with iodine. In this detail the French authors differ from Ling and Nanji, who find that their amylopectin, when dissolved, gives a blue-black colour and precipitate with iodine. Pringsheim,[11] on the other hand, records a brownish red colour for amylopectin, which he regards as identical with glycogen.

Amylose was shown by Maquenne and Roux to be soluble in boiling water. On treatment with malt amylase it was readily and completely converted into maltose. Amylopectin, on the other hand, had to be boiled to become dispersed in water and then yielded a viscous liquid. Amylopectin is thus responsible for the gelatinization of starch suspensions prepared with hot water. Treated with malt amylase, amylopectin was found to saccharify slowly, yielding dextrins. Nevertheless it was taken for granted by Maquenne and Roux[12] that amylopectin consisted entirely of maltose residues, since it was converted completely into maltose (using potato starch paste) when treated with malt amylase at a favourable hydrogen ion concentration. It should be added here that Ling[13] denies that amylopectin can be converted into maltose by amylase, which merely, he says, dephosphatises it and depolymerises it into a hexa-amylose. Maquenne and Roux's work, which demonstrated the presence of at least two substances in the starch granule, in many ways confirmed the views of the earliest investigators, for instance that of Nägeli,[14] who referred to two compounds in the starch granule, an interior 'granulose', the mother substance of maltose, and an exterior compound, 'starch-cellulose'. Meyer[15] shared the view of the presence of two substances in the starch granule, terming them α- and β-amylose, corresponding to Nägeli's granulose and starch cellulose respectively. But he regarded them as one and the same substance dehydrated to different degrees.

Gatin-Gruzewska's[16] researches demonstrated experimentally that the water-soluble amylose is identifiable with starch granulose and thus constitutes the interior substance of the starch grain, while the amylopectin, as mentioned above, represents the starch cellulose of earlier workers. It separates as empty shells of the original starch granule when a starch paste is subjected to the treatment required for the separation of its two composing substances. By the treatment evolved by Gatin-Gruzewska, as much as 40 per cent. of amylopectin can be obtained from potato starch. Tanret[17] examined a variety of other starch types and came to the conclusion that the yield of amylopectin may be much higher. In chestnut starch he found as much as 67 per cent. and in banana starch 79·5 per cent. amylopectin. Of other workers who have determined quantitatively the amount of amylopectin present in starch may be mentioned Ling and Nanji,[8] whose yields correspond to those of Maquenne and Roux; Pringsheim and Wolfsohn,[18] who report having obtained as much as 66 per cent. from potato starch, using the method recommended by Ling and Nanji; and Samec,[19] who reached a yield of 77 per cent. when carrying out the separation in a manner different from that used by Gatin-Gruzewska.

Other fruitful researches which should be mentioned are those of Fouard[20] and of Samec and his collaborators[21] on the phosphorus content of starch. Samec's investigations particularly have thrown light on the function of the phosphorus found associated with starch in the starch granule. It is now generally accepted that amylopectin represents the phosphoric ester of a polysaccharide, while amylose is free from chemically bound phosphorus.

Of interest are Clayson and Schryver's[22] and Schryver and Thomas's[23] observations on the presence of hemicelluloses in certain types of starch, in sago and maize starch, for instance, where these substances occur in quantities up to 3·8 per cent. These hemicelluloses are not acted upon by amylase, at least not by the enzyme present in taka-diastase. Potato starch does not appear to contain any hemicelluloses.

Additional work on the amylohemicelluloses has been carried out by Ling and his collaborators,[13] who find the percentages present considerably greater, reaching figures of 15 to 17 per cent. in potato tubers and rice respectively. It should be added also that Taylor and Lehrmann[24] have observed the presence of small quantities of fatty acids in maize starch, substances which they claim are organically combined with the amylopectin.

Special interest attaches to Schardinger's[25] observations, dating from 1909 to 1911, on the formation of crystalline decomposition products of starch by the action of *Bac. macerans*. In the hands of Pringsheim and his collaborators these observations have led to the elaboration of a possible interpretation of the chemical structure of amylose and of amylopectin. From the liquefied starch paste which *Bac. macerans* had acted upon for some days Schardinger obtained two crystalline substances which he termed α- and β-amylose respectively. In most of their physico-chemical properties these bodies resembled dextrins, substances to which reference will be made later. They were soluble in water but insoluble in alcohol, ether and choroform, and they did not reduce Fehling's solution. A solution of α-amylose gave a yellowish-green and of β-amylose a reddish-brown colour with iodine. Pringsheim and Langhans,[26] who repeated Schardinger's experiments, were able to confirm his results. They found that the α-amylose was composed of four groups of ($C_6H_{10}O_5$), a hypothetical hexosan to which they applied the term 'amylose'. The β-amylose of Schardinger was found to contain six of the hypothetical 'amylose' groups. Pringsheim and Langhans succeeded in depolymerising the tetra-amylose (Schardinger's α-amylose) into a diamylose, while the hexa-amylose (Schardinger's β-amylose) on depolymerisation gave a triamylose. The relationship between these polyamyloses (tetra- and hexa-amylose) and the amylose and amylopectin of Maquenne and Roux was studied by Pringsheim and Wolfsohn.[18] They found that Maquenne's amylose could be converted into the same diamylose which was obtained from Schardinger's α-amylose, while a triamylose, identical with that isolated from Schardinger's β-amylose, could be obtained from amylopectin either through acetylation or through heating the polysaccharides in glycerine at 200° C., a method used by Pictet and Jahn[27] for the depolymerisation of starch. Experimental evidence had thus been brought forward in support of Pringsheim's already expressed view[28] that the basic unit of Maquenne's amylose is a diamylose and that of amylopectin a triamylose. Pringsheim and Langhans also observed that diamylose and its polymers gave iodine addition products of metallic green needles, while triamylose and its polymers gave reddish-brown iodine compounds.

On treating the polyamyloses formed by *Bac. macerans* with cold concentrated hydrochloric acid, Pringsheim and Leibowitz[29] obtained a disaccharide $C_{12}H_{22}O_{10}$, which they termed amylobiose. It reduced Fehling's solution. The same substances could be obtained on treatment of amylose (Maquenne and Roux) with this reagent, while amylopectin yielded a reducing trisaccharide under these conditions, a substance to which Pringsheim and Leibowitz gave the name amylotriose.

Both amylobiose and amylotriose, when acted upon by malt diastase, were converted quantitatively into maltose.

Karrer and Nägeli,[30] from their study of the behaviour of Pringsheim's polyamyloses and of starch itself towards acetyl bromide, came to the conclusion that Pringsheim's diamylose as well as starch are maltose anhydrides, the starch having been polymerised to such an extent as to contain no less than eight amylose groups.[31] Karrer and his collaborators regard maltose anhydride as the fundamental unit of the whole of the starch molecule both of the amylose of Maquenne and Roux and of amylopectin.

Ling and Nanji,[8] on the other hand, regard both amylose and amylopectin as built up of hexosans as basic units, the amylose hexosan being of α-glucosidic nature, while the amylopectin hexosan shows both α- and β-glucoside linkings in addition to one phosphoric acid group in ester formation for every three hexose groups. By adopting this formula for amylopectin, Ling and Nanji claim to have explained the formation of isomaltose as a decomposition product of amylopectin.

Finally Irvine and Macdonald[32] have come to the conclusion from their study of methylated starch and starch derivatives that the ultimate unit of the starch molecule is a trihexosan, thus supporting, in some measure at least, Ling and Nanji's contention. Their researches do not indicate, however, whether starch is to be considered as two different constituents embodied in the amylose and amylopectin respectively of Maquenne and Roux, or whether it is to be assumed that starch is a polymer of maltose anhydride only.

In the following pages the subject of the hydrolysis of starch will be dealt with on the assumption that it consists of two definite components, amylose and amylopectin, as defined by Maquenne and Roux.

One of the most characteristic physical properties of starch is its swelling to form a viscous opalescent paste when heated in water above a certain temperature. This property is attributed to the amylopectin, while another property of the carbohydrate, the formation of a deep blue compound with iodine, is ascribed to the amylose. If a very dilute solution of a starch-hydrolysing enzyme, an amylase, is allowed to act on a starch paste under favourable conditions, the viscous nature of the paste diminishes and disappears without the resulting solution losing its property of staining blue with iodine. Samec[21] observed this and pointed out that, as a result of the enzyme action, the amylopectin, the bearer of the viscous properties of the paste, must have undergone changes either through saponification of its ester linkings or through depolymerisation into non-viscous soluble products. That the latter has actually occurred is clear from the fact that the carbohydrates of the paste still contain their phosphorus chemically bound. The first stage in the action of enzymes upon starch is therefore a depolymerisation of at least one constituent of the starch granule. For this reaction to take place, a reaction which does not lead to the formation of Fehling-reducing substances (since the elements of water do not enter the polyamylose molecule), Pringsheim assumes the presence of specific depolymerising enzymes in amylase.

This view is not accepted by Nishimura,[33] who regards amylase as being composed of one enzyme only, having the ability to perform both the saccharification and the depolymerisation, the latter notably in the presence of an activator, perhaps identical with Pringsheim and Beiser's[34] co-enzyme.

Earlier investigators had interpreted the conversion of the viscous opalescent starch paste into a clear solution in a different manner. The resolution was connected by them with a partial hydrolysis of the starch granule through an enzyme, sometimes termed dextrinase (Pottevin[35]), leading to the formation of a series of dextrins ranging from the amylodextrins, which showed comparatively small Fehling-reducing powers, and retained the faculty of giving a blue reaction product with iodine, to the achroodextrins, or simply dextrins (Czapek[36]), where the Fehling-reducing properties had increased considerably and the iodine coloration had been lost. Between these extremes were found other dextrins, sometimes termed erythrodextrins, which showed an intermediate Fehling reduction and stained reddish-brown with iodine. How far it is justifiable to assume with Pringsheim that amylase contains both a depolymerising and a dextrinising enzyme in addition to saccharifying enzymes remains an open question. The assumption does not appear essential, since the opening of the depolymerised amylose and amylopectin through the introduction of the elements of water might well be due to a saccharifying enzyme if present in the amylase. That this saccharifying enzyme is different from the liquefying enzyme is clear from the work of Olsson,[37] who found that addition of certain poisons reduced its action without interfering with the activity of the liquefying enzyme.

The saccharification of the depolymerised amylose and amylopectin does not proceed at the same rate. This was noted very early in the history of starch saccharification. The amylose always becomes smoothly and rapidly converted into the theoretical amount of maltose, a disaccharide which under normal conditions represents the final stage of starch hydrolysis by many types of amylase. The saccharification of the amylopectin, on the other hand, is slower, and usually ceases when about 78 per cent. of the theoretical amount of maltose has been formed. The residue, a 'residual dextrin', was found by Pringsheim and Beiser[34] to be a trisaccharide identical with trihexosan. But even this, according to Pringsheim and Beiser, may be converted into maltose by the saccharifying enzyme when a co-enzyme or complement, in the form of yeast extract, is added. The formation of this residual dextrin and its saccharification to maltose in the presence of a complement lend considerable weight to Pringsheim's suggestion that amylopectin is composed of a triglucose as basic unit. The nature of the complement has been studied by Pringsheim, Bondi, and Thilo[38]. It would appear to be a trypsin decomposition product of albumin, and it is present in yeast owing to autolysis of the yeast cells.

Pringsheim[11] visualizes the conversion of a triglucosan into maltose by assuming that the active enzyme splits off one molecule of maltose, leaving the remaining glucose radical to condense with another glucose radical liberated from another molecule of the triglucosan. In support of this explanation he quotes Hess, Weltzien, and Messmer's[39] researches on the auto-condensation of glucose anhydride to form cellobiose, a view which is not accepted by Kuhn.[40] That the incomplete conversion of amylopectin into maltose may sometimes be due to the absence of optimal hydrogen-ion concentrations was shown by Maquenne and Roux.[41]

Interesting light has subsequently been thrown on the nature of the various existing amylases by the researches of Kuhn.[42] He bases his investigations on the observations of Brown and Heron[43] that the hydrolysis of starch by malt amylase at 50° C. proceeds at the same rate both as regards increase in copper-reducing properties and polarimetric changes, and on Brown and Morris's[44] conclusions that this is not the case when the hydrolysis takes place at a low temperature. Kuhn brings forward evidence to show that these divergences are due to the fact that malt amylase liberates maltose in the β-glucosidic form. At low temperatures and at the optimal hydrogen-ion concentration of malt amylase this β-maltose is converted comparatively slowly into the stable α-β-maltose mixture. The establishment of a polarimetric equilibrium in the hydrolysed starch paste will therefore lag behind the changes in copper-reducing powers in this case.

Where pancreas amylase or taka-diastase is used to hydrolyse starch, Kuhn finds that the maltose is initially liberated in the α-glucosidic form. This shows that two distinct types of amylase exist, an α-amylase originating from animal sources and from taka-diastase, and a β-amylase from vegetable sources other than taka-diastase and present in emulsin and in malt amylase.

In a later paper Kuhn[42] remarks that in view of its behaviour towards animal and vegetable amylases the starch granule probably consists of carbohydrates in which α- and β-linkings occur in regular sequence between the glucose residues composing them. This, as will be recollected, had been already suggested by Ling and Nanji in the case of amylopectin. Kuhn does not accept the view that Pringsheim's polyamyloses or hexosans are the basic units of the starch molecule, since each of them only shows the characteristics of starch to a limited extent.

A deduction which is of interest from the point of view of the microbiologist was made by Pringsheim and Leibowitz[45] from Kuhn's earlier work. They considered that if both a- and β-glucosidic linkings occur in the carbohydrates of starch it should be possible to obtain glucose direct from starch if a mixture of a- and β-amylase is made to act on a starch paste. That this was possible they demonstrated experimentally, thus showing that it is not essential to assume, as had been done by earlier investigators (Beijerinck[46]), that a special maltase must be present in an amylase which saccharifies starch with the production of both maltose and glucose.

Before leaving the subject of the chemistry of starch, a few words must be devoted to the observations of Wolff and Fernbach[47] that unripe cereals and leaves contain an enzyme which precipitates soluble starch from its solutions. This enzyme they term amylocoagulase. Beyond the observations by Joszt[48] that amylocoagulase is destroyed on heating to 63° C. for six minutes, and that it differs markedly from the saccharifying enzyme, little is known of this interesting substance, which in the writers' view probably plays a considerable role in the action of micro-organisms on starch, since it frequently occurs that a starch paste inoculated with starch hydrolysing micro-organisms has its colloidal properties destroyed long before the production of acidic fermentation products can have accumulated sufficiently to cause this change.

Glycogen. Glycogen, the reserve carbohydrate of animals and of many lower saprophytic and parasitic plants, resembles starch in some of its properties. It forms a white amorphous powder which yields opalescent colloidal suspensions in water. With iodine it forms a reddish-brown compound resembling that of the erythrodextrins. When acted upon by amylase it undergoes decomposition processes similar to those of starch (Musculus and Mering),[49] and yields dextrins and maltose. These changes, according to Cremer,[50] proceed slower than in the case of starch. According to Harden and Young[51] the rate seems to vary with the type of glycogen used. The glycogen-hydrolysing enzyme, glycogenase, was found by Pick[52] in various animal tissues, and was observed as an endo-enzyme in yeast by Buchner and Rapp.[53] Norris [54] found that the hydrolysis proceeded much faster during the early stages and seldom converted the carbohydrate quantitatively. The presence or absence of electrolytes in the enzyme was shown by him to have a considerable effect on the rate of hydrolysis, dialysed enzymes having practically no action at all. An interesting account of the constitution of glycogen has been given by Pringsheim and Beiser,[34] who suggest that, apart perhaps from its content of electrolytes, it is identical with amylopectin. They arrive at this conclusion from their observations that both glycogen and amylopectin yield the same depolymerisation products on heating with glycerin and by treatment with hydrochloric acid.

Inulin. This, the third important polysaccharide which will be touched upon in subsequent pages, forms white spherocrystals and occurs as a reserve carbohydrate in the roots and tubers of certain plants. Czapek[36] records its presence in certain algae. On hydrolysis it is converted quantitatively into fructose. The determinations of the molecular weight of its acetyl ester led Pringsheim and Aronowsky[55] to conclude that its molecule contains nine fructose residues. Karrer[56] assumes that these are present without internal polymerisation, but Pringsheim and Aronowsky see in its molecule an aggregation of three groups of an anhydro-tri-fructosan, a view which appears to have been accepted by Irvine.[57] A characteristic of inulin is its rapid hydrolysis to fructose without the formation of detectable intermediate decomposition products. This would appear to indicate that the individual fructose radical occurs in a particularly active form, as a so-called γ-sugar (Irvine[58]). Intermediate condensation products between fructose and inulin have been shown by Tanret[59] to occur in tissues of certain plants.

LITERATURE

1. S. R. Kirchoff, Account by Nasse, *J. f. Chem. and Physik*, vol. 4, p. 111, 1812.
2. Th. de Saussure, *Ann. Chim. Phys.*, vol. 11, p. 379, 1819.
3. P. Dubrunfaut, *Jour. für technische und ökonomische Chemie* (Erdmann), vol. 4, p. 156, 1830.
4. A. Payen and J. Persoz, *Ann. Chim. Phys.*, vol. 53, p. 73, 1833.
5. P. Dubrunfaut, *Ann. Chim. Phys.*, vol. 3, p. 178, 1847.
6. C. O'Sullivan, *J. Chem. Soc. Trans.*, vol. 25, p. 579, 1872; vol. 29, p. 479, 1876; vol. 30, p. 125, 1876.
7. C. J. Lintner, *Zeitsch. f. d. gesamt. Brauwesen*, vol. 15, p. 284, 1891.
8. A. R. Ling and D. R. Nanji, *J. Chem. Soc. Trans.*, vol. 123, p. 2666, 1923.
9. R. Kuhn, *Berichte*, vol. 57, p. 1965, 1924.
10. L. Maquenne and E. Roux, *Ann. Chim. Phys.*, vol. 9, p. 179, 1906.
11. H. Pringsheim, *Berichte*, vol. 57, p. 1581, 1924.
12. L. Maquenne and E. Roux, *Comptes rend.*, vol. 142, p. 1059, 1906.
13. A. R. Ling, *J. Soc. Chem. Ind.*, vol. 46, p. 279 T, 1927.
14. W. Nägeli, *Die Stärkekörner*, Zürich, 1858.
15. A. Meyer, *Untersuchungen über die Stärkekörner*, Jena, 1895.
16. Z. Gatin-Gruzewska, *Comptes rend. soc. biol.*, vol. 64, p. 178, 1908; *Comptes rend.*, vol. 146, p. 540, 1908.
17. C. Tanret, *Comptes rend.*, vol. 158, p. 1353, 1914; vol. 159, p. 530, 1914.
18. H. Pringsheim and K. Wolfsohn, *Berichte*, vol. 57, p. 887, 1924.
19. M. Samec, *Kolloidchem. Beihefte*, vol. 4, p. 23, 1914.
20. E. Fouard, *Comptes rend.*, vol. 144, p. 146, 1907–8; *Intern. Cong. Appl. Chem.* London, vol. 7, VI. B. Fermentation, p. 129, 1909.
21. M. Samec and F. v. Hoefft, *Kolloidchem. Beihefte*, vol. 4, 132, 1912; vol. 5, p. 141, 1913; vol. 6, p. 291, 1914.
    M. Samec and H. Haerdtl, *Kolloidchem. Beihefte*, vol. 12, p. 281, 1920.
    M. Samec and A. Meyer, *Kolloidchem. Beihefte*, vol. 16, p. 89, 1922.
    M. Samec, *Kolloidchem. Zeitschr.*, vol. 47, p. 81, 1929.
22. D. H. F. Clayson and S. B. Schryver, *Biochem. J.*, vol. 17, p. 493, 1923.
23. S. B. Schryver and E. M. Thomas, *Biochem. J.*, vol. 17, p. 497, 1923.
24. F. C. Taylor and L. Lehrmann, *J. Am. Chem. Soc.*, vol. 48, p. 1739, 1926.
25. F. Schardinger, *Zentrbl. f. Bakt.*, Abt. II, vol. 22, p. 98, 1909; II, vol. 29, p. 188, 1911.

26. { H. Pringsheim and A. Langhans, *Berichte*, vol. 45, p. 2533, 1912.
     { H. Pringsheim and F. Eissler, *Berichte*, vol. 46, p. 2959, 1913.

27. A. Pictet and R. Jahn, *Helv. Chim. Acta*, vol. 5, p. 640, 1922.

28. H. Pringsheim, *Berichte*, vol. 57, p. 1581, 1924.

29. H. Pringsheim and J. Leibowitz, *Berichte*, vol. 57, p. 884, 1924.

30. P. Karrer and C. Nägeli, *Helv. Chim. Acta*, vol. 4, pp. 169, 185, 263, 1921.

31. P. Karrer, C. Nägeli, O. Hurwitz and A. Walti, *Helv. Chim. Acta*, vol. 4, p. 678, 1921.

32. { J. C. Irvine, *J. Chem. Soc. Trans.*, vol. 123, p. 898, 1923.
     { J. C. Irvine and J. Macdonald, *J. Chem. Soc. Trans.*, vol. 129, p. 1502, 1926.

33. S. Nishimura, *Biochem. Zeit.*, vol. 200, p. 81, 1928.

34. H. Pringsheim and A. Beiser, *Biochem. Zeits.*, vol. 148, p. 336, 1924.

35. H. Pottevin, *Ann. Inst. Pasteur*, vol. 13, p. 665, 1899.

36. F. Czapek, *Die Biochemie der Pflanzen*, Gustav Fischer, Jena, 1913–21.

37. U. Olsson, *Z. physiol. Chem.*, vol. 126, p. 29, 1923.

38. H. Pringsheim, J. Bondi, and E. Thilo, *Biochem. Zeit.*, vol. 197, p. 143, 1928.

39. K. Hess, W. Weltzien, and E. Messner, *Liebig's Ann.*, vol. 435, p. 1, 1923.

40. R. Kuhn, *Ann. d. Chem.*, vol. 443, p. 1, 1925.

41. L. Maquenne and E. Roux, *Comptes rend.*, vol. 142, p. 124, 1906.

42. R. Kuhn, *Berichte*, vol. 56, p. 857, 1923; vol. 57, p. 1965, 1924.

43. H. T. Brown and J. Heron, *J. Chem. Soc. Trans.*, vol. 35, p. 596, 1879.

44. H. T. Brown and G. H. Morris, *J. Chem. Soc. Trans.*, vol. 67, p. 309, 1895.

45. H. Pringsheim and J. Leibowitz, *Berichte*, vol. 58, p. 1262, 1925.

46. M. W. Beijerinck, *Zentrbl. f. Bakt.*, Abt. II, vol. 1, p. 221, 1895.

47. J. Wolf and A. Fernbach, *Comptes rend.*, vol. 137, p. 718, 1903.

48. A. Joszt, *Chem. Zentralbl.*, vol. 96, p. 1327, 1925.

49. F. Musculus and von Mering, *Zeitschrift physiol. Chem.*, vol. 2, p. 413, 1882.

50. M. Cremer, *Münch. med. Wochenschr.*, vol. 41, p. 525, 1894.

51. A. Harden and W. J. Young, *J. Chem. Soc. Trans.*, vol. 81, p. 1225, 1902.

52. F. Pick, *Hofmeisters Beiträge*, vol. 3, p. 4, 1902.

53. E. Buchner and R. Rapp, *Berichte*, vol. 31, p. 214, 1898.

54. R. U. Norris, *Biochem. J.*, vol. 7, pp. 26 and 622, 1913.

55. H. Pringsheim and A. Aronowsky, *Berichte*, vol. 54, p. 1281, 1921.

56. P. Karrer, *Helv. chim. acta*, vol. 5, p. 130, 1922.

57. J. C. Irvine, *Brit. Assoc.*, Hull, p. 33, 1922.

58. J. C. Irvine, *Chemical Reviews*, vol. 1, p. 45, 1925.

59. C. Tanret, *Bull. Soc. Chim.*, Paris, vol. 9, p. 622, 1893.

CHAPTER II

MICROBIOLOGICAL HYDROLYSIS OF STARCH, GLYCOGEN, AND INULIN

It was mentioned in Chapter I that de Saussure[1] had observed that a starch paste left exposed to the atmosphere became spontaneously decomposed. This is probably the first record of a hydrolysis of starch by micro-organisms. Six decades later, in 1877 and in 1878, Fitz[2] studied the schizomycete fermentation of starch and dextrin, while Wortmann[3] succeeded in isolating enzymes from a crude culture of *Bact. termo*, a species which is now considered synonymous with the putrefying *Bact. vulgare* Lehmann and Neumann. These investigations were followed in rapid succession by a large number of publications, illustrating the widespread property among micro-organisms of hydrolysing starch.

Following the procedure adopted by Thaysen and Bunker[4] in their treatise on the microbiological decomposition of cellulose, the writers have grouped the existing information on microbiological starch hydrolysis under three headings, as caused by bacteria, by actinomycetes, and by fungi.

No reference will be made to the amylolytic properties of the myxomycetes and of the algae, a subject which is dealt with in several leading text-books on plant physiology and plant chemistry. Even among the three classes of micro-organisms selected it has been found necessary to restrict the discussion to the most important groups. The fact that most, if not all, existing fungi, a very large number of bacteria, and many actinomycetes hydrolyse starch makes it quite impossible within the scope of the present volume to give a detailed description of each individual type producing amylase.

THE HYDROLYSIS OF STARCH BY BACTERIA

Following the first more or less incidental observations of Fitz,[2] Marcano,[5] Wortmann,[3] Prillieux,[6] and Bitter,[7] Fermi[8] undertook a more comprehensive study of the behaviour of a number of well-known bacteria towards starch. The list in Table I contains those types found by him to produce starch-hydrolysing enzymes as well as some additional forms which from time to time have been studied from this point of view. The list is not complete, and could not claim to be complete, since the whole subject of the action of individual species of bacteria on starch, glycogen, and inulin is one which has not yet been systematically explored.

The nature of bacterial amylase has not been studied in detail. The isolation of the enzyme appears to have been carried out only in a few cases, for instance in those of *Bac. mesentericus* (Effront[34]), and of *Bact. termo*, now known as *Bact. vulgare*. Here Wortmann obtained an amylase by the addition of alcohol to a culture of the test organism. He found that the enzyme, when dissolved in water, acted both at neutral and at acid reactions, the latter being the more favourable.

In most cases where bacterial amylase has been studied, the investigators have employed, not the isolated enzyme, but a bacterial culture, added to a starch paste or a solidified mixture of starch paste and gelatine (Beijerinck[32]), often after the addition of an antiseptic such as toluene (Gottheil[16]). A technique such as this cannot be regarded as altogether satisfactory, particularly where no care is taken to destroy the living cells producing the enzyme. And even with this ensured it cannot *a priori* be assumed that the cultures do not contain other enzymes, in addition to the amylase, which would seriously influence the nature of the products of hydrolysis. This deficiency in technique is conceivably responsible for the great difference of opinion which prevails as to the changes suffered by starch through the action of bacterial amylase. Leaving out of account Fitz's assertion that only the amylose of the starch granule becomes affected by the

TABLE I

Name of Organism.	Hydrolysis of Starch.	Reaction of medium at which hydrolysis occurred.	Name of Investigator.
Azotobacter croococcum	+	?	Omeliansky[9]
Bac. anthracis	+	neutral	Fermi[8]; Maumus[10]
Bac. amylobacter species	+++	pH 3·9–4·6	Villiers[11]; Behrens[12] Bredemann[13]; Makrinov[14]
Bac. amylozyma	++	?	Perdrix[15]
Bac. asterosporus	+++	—	Gottheil[16]
Bac. botulinus	++	—	Holland[17]
Bac. Fitzianus	++		Fermi[8]
Bac. graveolens	++	—	Gottheil[16]
Bac. macerans	+++	pH 5·75–6·0	Schardinger[18]
Bac. Megatherium	++	very acid	Fermi[8]
Bac. mesentericus ruber	+++	acid	Dupont[19]
Bac. mycoides Flügge	+++	neutral	Fermi[8]
Bac. oedematis maligni	++	acid	Kerry and Fränkel[20]
Bac. petasites	++	—	Gottheil[16]
Bac. polymyxa	++	—	Gruber[21]
Bac. ruminatus	++	—	Gottheil[16]
Bac. subtilis	++ When peptone is present as a food	neutral	Fermi[8]
Bac. tenuis Duclaux (Tyrothrix tenuis)	++	neutral	Fernbach[22]
Bac. thermoamylolyticus	+++	acid	Coolhaas[23]
Bac. Welchii	+	—	Fleming and Neill[24]
Bact. dysenteriae	++	?	Eijkman[25]
Bact. fluorescens liquefaciens	+	?	Emmerling and Reiser[26]
Bact. industrium (an acetic acid bacterium)	+	acid	Henneberg[27]
Bact. lactis aerogenes	+ in some strains	?	Laybourn[28]
Bact. pestis	+	?	Eijkman[25]
Bact. phosphorescens	+++	very acid	Fermi[29]

Name of Organism.	Hydrolysis of Starch.	Reaction of medium at which hydrolysis occurred.	Name of Investigator.
Bact. pyogenes foetidum	+	acid	Fermi[8]
Bact. typhosum	traces	neutral	Fermi[8]
Bact. violaceae	+	very acid	Fermi[8]
Bact. vulgare	++	neutral to acid	Sclavo and Gosio[30]
Bact. Zopfii	traces	neutral	Fermi[8]
Glycobacter species	+++	?	Wollman[31]
Granulobacter species	++	acid	Beijerinck[32]
Micrococcus gonorrhoeae	+	?	Vedder[33]
Micrococcus mastitidis gangraenosae	+++	?	Fermi[29]
Micrococcus tetragenus	++	acid	Fermi[8]
Staphylococcus pyogenes aureus	+	neutral	Fermi[8]
Vibrio cholerae	+++	acid	Bitter[7]; Fermi[8]

enzyme, an assertion which is contradicted by all subsequent investigators, the available information indicates that the attacked starch may be decomposed in different ways. It may be depolymerised to lower hexosans (Schardinger[18]), and these be converted into the final fermentation products with the formation of but a slight excess of reducing sugars (Euler and Svanberg[35]). In other cases dextrins may be formed and no reducing sugars (Villiers[11]), Kerry and Fränkel[20] and Siedish[36]. Finally, in some cases both dextrins and reducing sugars may be produced, the latter composed either of maltose (Beijerinck[32]) or of glucose (Bitter[7] and Dupont[19]). Further work is evidently required to elucidate the nature of the decomposition products, particularly as the same type of bacterium is sometimes recorded to have yielded one set of products and sometimes another. At the moment the changes caused by bacterial amylase are obscure. On one point only do the various investigators appear to agree, and that is in allotting two enzymes to the bacterial amylases, a depolymerising enzyme and a saccharifying enzyme. Whether the latter is of an α- or a β-glucosidic nature or a mixture of both remains to be decided. The reported conversion of starch into glucose as the final product of hydrolysis (Dupont[19], and Sclavo and Gosio[30]) might conceivably point to the latter being the case.

Very little additional information is available on bacterial amylases. Effront[37] records that they are readily extractable by maceration. The enzymes studied by Fermi were active between the temperatures of 4° and 50° C. Effront's work indicates that their optimum temperature lies at 40° C. Heating to 60° C., and in some cases to 70° C., was sufficient in Fermi's experiments to destroy them. They would nevertheless appear to be more thermolabile than malt amylase. On the subject of the range of their hydrogen ion concentrations little is known beyond Fermi's observations recorded in Table I. It should be mentioned also that 5 per cent. of phenol, or saturation of their solutions with salicylic acid, or addition of 10 per cent. sodium carbonate, were found by Fermi not to interfere with their action. The latter statement is interesting since it indicates that a hydroxyl ion concentration equal to a pH value of about pH 11·0 should be unable to affect the normal functioning of the enzyme.

Of interest from the point of view of pathological bacteriology are Kodama and Takeda's[38] observations on the starch hydrolysing properties of *Vibro cholerae* and Vedder's[33] on those of *Micrococcus gonorrhoeae*. In the case of *Vibrio cholerae* the observations have inspired the elaboration of a method for detecting this micro-organism in faecal matter, and in the case of *Micrococcus gonorrhoeae* the preparation of a suitable culture medium.

Kodama and Takeda recommend the inoculation of cholera suspected excreta into peptone water containing starch, followed by incubation for 7 to 24 hours. If, after this time, the addition of iodine indicates the disappearance of the starch, through the absence of the typical blue reaction with iodine, the suspicion is justified that *Vibrio cholerae* was present in the faecal matter tested. The brief incubation period allowed is necessary to avoid interference by other starch hydrolysing micro-organisms, such as *Vibrio Metchnikoff* for instance, which is less active than Koch's vibrio.

For the cultivation of *Micrococcus gonorrhoeae* Vedder recommends a beef infusion agar to which 1 per cent. of maize starch is added. He finds that the gonococcus remains alive for two to three weeks on this medium as against two to three days on the usual salt-free veal agar.

The utilization of bacterial enzymes for the removal of starchy matter from textile materials has been recommended by Boidin,[39] and by Boidin and Effront,[40] who use the amylases secreted by *Bac. mesentericus* and *Bac. subtilis* for this purpose.

Bac. mesentericus has been recommended also by Effront[34] for the liquefaction of starch-containing mashes in the distillery. He grows the organism on distillery residue, a medium which appears to be highly suitable, since 1 kg. of the residue on which *Bac. mesentericus* has been allowed to develop is stated to be equal in starch liquefying power to 20 kg. of malt. The optimum temperature of this amylase is given as 40° C. It is very resistant to alkali but somewhat more sensitive to acid, a 1 per mille concentration of hydrochloric acid (pH value about 2·9) arresting its action completely. Like Fermi, Effront isolates the enzyme from the culture of the organism by precipitation with alcohol. Ammonium sulphate also appears suitable for this purpose. The products of hydrolysis are stated to consist of dextrins and maltose—41·2 per cent. of the latter.

For the saccharification of starch mashes in distilleries Joucla[41] advocates the use of *Bac. burdigalense*, a type related to *Bac. tenuis*, Duclaux, Lehmann and Neumann, and recommended also by Bettinger[42] for this purpose. This organism is used either alone or in symbiosis with a Mucor species, *Mucor eloeis*, which is claimed to possess twice the saccharifying power of *Mucor Rouxii*. Though *Bac. burdigalense* is capable of developing even at 50° C. the mash must be cooled to 36° C., when a mixed culture of the rod and *Mucor eloeis* is employed, since the fungus is unable to develop at the higher temperature.

Other thermophilic or thermotolerant amylase producing bacilli have been isolated by Coolhaas[23] from mud. The most active form, *Bac. thermoamylolyticus*, penetrates the starch granules attacked by it, gradually dissolves them, and converts them into maltose. In the course of 9 days this organism was capable of converting 80 per cent. of the starch into maltose, a conversion equal in magnitude, though not in speed, to that of malt amylase. The maltose is subsequently converted into various fermentation products the nature of which indicates that *Bac. thermoamylolyticus* belongs to the group of butyric acid bacilli.

THE HYDROLYSIS OF STARCH BY ACTINOMYCETES

Beyond the observation that a great many Actinomycetes hydrolyse starch, little is known on the subject. Of interest is Fermi's[8] observation that such important species as *Corynebacterium diphtheriae* and *Mycobacterium tuberculosis* actively hydrolyse starch. The hydrolysing properties of the latter are regarded by Fermi[43] as an additional proof for its relationship to the Actinomycetes. Of other species producing amylase may be mentioned *Actinomyces bovis* and *Actinomyces diastaticus*. In their studies on the classification of the Actinomycetes both Waksman and Curtis[47] and Krainsky[45] have paid attention to the amylolytic properties of the various species examined. It should be recorded also that Rullmann[46] found that the presence of starch in cultures of *Actinomyces odorifera* gave rise to the emanation of an intensified odour of damp earth.

HYDROLYSIS OF STARCH BY FUNGI

Commensurate with its greater industrial importance starch hydrolysis by fungi has received more attention in the past than saccharification through bacteria or through actinomycetes. In the Far East certain fungi have been used for many centuries (Kozai[47]) for purposes where in the West malt is employed. The preparation of alcoholic beverages such as saké, and of the aromatic sauce soya, is based on the saccharification of starch by species of lower fungi. The value of these products, taking Japan alone, was stated by Taka-mine[48] to amount to £40,000,000 in 1914.

Both in the case of saké and of soya manufacture, the first operation consists in the preparation of a 'koji', or culture of the micro-organisms active in the hydrolysis of the starch. The following description of this process is taken from Atkinson's[49] classic account in 1881, though Korschelt[50] can lay claim to a still earlier description:

After removing the husks and the inner skin the cleaned grain, usually rice, is soaked in water overnight and heated on the following morning in a current of steam until the grains have become elastic to the touch. This operation takes from four to five hours. The soft grain is then placed on mats and cooled with stirring till its temperature has fallen to 28–30° C. To every 75 kgs. of the cooked grain 'three salt spoons full' of spores of the active fungus, usually *Aspergillus oryzae*, are added. The spores are first mixed with a small proportion of the steamed grain, and this mixture then scattered over the rest. The inoculated rice is gathered in baskets and carried to the coolest part of the growing chamber, which normally is built underground. The grain is thrown in a heap on the floor, covered with mats and left overnight. After about 20 hours it is removed and sprinkled with water. The temperature of the grain thereby falls to about 23° C. Where the koji is to be used for saké brewing this sprinkling process is omitted. In this case the preparation is termed raw koji. In the afternoon of the second day the sprinkled grain is spread thinly on trays, placed in the growing chamber underneath other trays containing nearly finished koji. The temperature of the grain rises during the night, and by the following morning has reached a figure of about 25° C. It is now gathered in small heaps on the trays and allowed to remain undisturbed for about three to four hours. By then its appearance has changed. Through the development of mycelium it has become woolly. The temperature of the heaps has reached 40°–41° C. In order to cool the grain the heaps are broken up, aerated, and again built up, to be left for another four to five hours until the temperature has risen to 40° C. The grain is now finally scattered in thin layers on trays and the fungus allowed to spread its silky threads of mycelium throughout the mass. The koji is left on the trays for about 20 hours until it has set to a solid cake, the form in which it is disposed of for industrial purposes.

For other types of koji, bean flour, millet or roasted barley are used, and other species of fungi, among them *Aspergillus batatae*, which yields a black koji, coloured by the dark pigmented conidiospores of the fungus (Saito[51]).

In India, according to Hutchinson and Ramayyar,[52] an enzyme similar to koji is prepared from rice, powdered roots, and other parts of certain plants. It is known under the name of Bákhar, and is used in the manufacture of rice beers. It contains a great variety of fungi, the most active being *Aspergillus oryzae*. Its saccharifying powers are markedly less than that of koji, and its alcohol-producing properties equally deficient owing to the inferior fermenting power of the yeast types present.

In Formosa a species of *Rhizopus* is used for a similar purpose in the preparation of an alcoholic beverage, ' Biityn ' (Takeda[53]), and in the Malay States the Chinese inhabitants prepare a distilled beverage, using *Mucor Rouxii* (Bishop and Feik[54]) as the fungus for the hydrolysis of the raw material, rice.

From the fact that various Asiatic countries have acquired what amounts to a monopoly in the industrial application of fungi to the hydrolysis of starch, it is not to be deduced that the fungi met with in Asia are exceptionally vigorous amylase producers. Nill,[55] who undertook to ascertain whether this might be the case, found that a number of *Rhizopus* species could be isolated from German cereals which produced amylase to the same extent as the well-known Asiatic species, *Rhizopus tonkinensis*, and *Aspergillus oryzae*.

In soya koji, Saito[51] found a number of other fungi besides *Aspergillus oryzae*; among them *Rhizopus japonicus*, *Cladosporium herbarum*, and *Penicillium glaucum*. The active type was considered to be *Aspergillus oryzae*. Nishiwaki[56] reports the preparation of a soya koji, using *Monilia sitophila* as active fungus.

A description of the preparation of soya is given by Saito. The previously prepared koji, for which bean flour and wheat flour are frequently used in the proportions of 50 parts to 46 parts, is mixed with a steam-boiled solution of 2·8 per cent. sodium chloride in the proportions of equal parts of koji and salt-water, and the mixture stirred from time to time during the whole process of fermentation, which takes from one to one-and-a-quarter years to complete. The mash gradually acquires a deep reddish-brown colour. When the fermentation is finished the mash is pressed in bags, previously soaked in the tannin containing juice of unripe date plums (*Diospyros Kaki*). On standing the filtrate separates into an oily and a watery layer. The latter, the soya, is left standing for a few days after separation from the oil and, when clear, is bottled and heated to 50° C. for the purpose of sterilization.

In the preparation of taka-koji, a substance which has become widely known in the form of an extract termed taka-diastase, Takamine[48] uses wheat bran instead of grain. The bran is mixed in a rotatory drum with an antiseptic and a requisite amount of warm water, and is gelatinized by live steam. After cooling, the mass is inoculated with spores of *Aspergillus oryzae*, acclimatized to the antiseptic used, and cool air is passed through the drum to prevent excessive heating. After 48 hours' incubation the koji is finished. Takamine reports that Ortved found 4 per cent. of this koji capable of hydrolysing a starch paste in 15 to 20 minutes.

The types of antiseptics suitable for the suppression of infections in preparations of taka-diastase have been investigated by Oshima,[57] who recommends cresol in concentrations of 0·15 to 0·4 per cent., calculated on the solution of taka-diastase, lysol 0·5 to 2·0 per cent., phenol 0·4 to 1·5 per cent., thymol 0·05 to 0·2 per cent., and mixtures of phenol and cresol.

Chloral hydrate, chloroform, clove oil, formalin, potassium cyanide, mercuric chloride, sodium fluoride, sodium benzoate, salicylic acid, toluene, and xylol were all found unsuitable.

By extracting the koji with water and precipitating the extract with alcohol, for which purpose Sherman and Tanberg[58] recommended a strength of 60 to 65 per cent. by volume, the active enzyme is obtained in dry form. This substance has been extensively investigated during the last decade. A review of the more important literature is given in the following lines.

Takamine states that taka-diastase is a mixture of several enzymes, the amylase being considerably more resistant to acids than malt diastase and more stable on storage. A fuller account of the various enzymes present in taka-diastase is given by Wohlgemuth,[59] who identified amylase, maltase, trypsin, rennet, erepsin, lipase, and haemolysin—all the enzymes of the pancreatic juice except peptolytic enzymes. He found that one gram of taka-diastase contained as much trypsin as 10 cc. of active pancreatic juice. In addition to the above enzymes Nishimura[60] records the presence in taka-diastase of saccharase, protease, lactase, catalase, inulase, sulphatase, and amidase. The experimental data of a number of investigations support the view that the amylase of taka-diastase is a mixture of depolymerising and saccharifying enzymes. Thus Sherman and Tanberg[58] record that the amyloclastic enzyme is considerably more active than that of the best malt amylase, while the saccharifying enzyme is less active than that of malt amylase. Expressed in figures, Waksman[61] gives the ratio of amyloclastic to saccharifying enzymes as 1:1, or even 1·5:1, as against 1:4 or 1:5 for malt amylase.

A comparative study of the hydrogen ion concentration ranges of taka-diastase—or rather of the amylase of *Aspergillus oryzae*—malt amylase, and pancreas amylase was undertaken by Sherman, Thomas, and Baldwin.[62] They found that *Aspergillus* amylase was active between the pH values of

2·6 and 8·0, with an optimum at 4·8. Malt amylase was active between pH values 2·5 and 9·0, with an optimum between 4·4 and 4·5. These ranges, however, should not be regarded as fixed and typical for this particular enzyme. According to Chrzaszcz, Bidzinski, and Krause,[63] they will vary with the prevailing temperature, with the protective action of the starch, and with the presence or absence of substances acting as buffers. Conditions, these writers found, which are unfavourable to the action of amylase activity shifted the hydrogen ion concentration towards the alkaline side of the neutral point, while favourable conditions moved it towards the acid side.

The resistance of taka-diastase to acids is emphasized by Okada,[64] who states that the enzyme regains its former activity on neutralization after having been kept for some time at a pH value not exceeding that which usually obtains in the gastric juice of man (0·9–1·6).

The temperature range for 'polyzime', another preparation of the enzymes of *Aspergillus oryzae*, was investigated by Takamine jun. and Oshima.[65] They record a maximum activity at 40° C. Kept at 50° C. for three hours the preparation lost 55 per cent. of its diastatic powers. At 40° C. and less it could be kept for six months in a closed vessel without any loss of activity.

The action of electrolytes on the enzymes of *Aspergillus oryzae* and on their preparations has been studied by a number of investigators. Effront[66] finds that phosphates and aluminium salts have an accelerating action, and he has noted a similar action by asparagin.

Sodium chloride and potassium chloride had no action on the enzymes in Sherman and Tanberg's experiments, while acid phosphates accelerated, and alkaline phosphates retarded, the activity of taka-diastase. For the protection of the enzymes on storage Kita[67] recommended concentrated solutions of sodium chloride. Calcium salts in Kita and Kyoto's[68] experiments accelerated the amyloclastic enzyme but sometimes retarded the saccharifying enzyme.

Under optimum conditions taka-diastase converts from 70 to 80 per cent. of the available starch into the reducing sugars maltose and glucose, and attains a degree of conversion therefore similar to that of malt diastase. Taken in large excess, however, Nishimura[69] found that an extract from *Aspergillus oryzae*, and therefore presumably also taka-diastase, was able to hydrolyse 95 per cent. of the available starch, irrespective of whether a complement (Pringsheim and Otto[70]) was present or not.

The incomplete conversion of the starch by taka-diastase under ordinary conditions is therefore perhaps not caused by the absence of a complement, but may be due to the accumulation of reducing sugars and even of saccharose substances which various investigators, Grezes,[71] Katz,[72] Funke,[73] and Yamagishi,[74] have found to inhibit the progress of the hydrolysis in proportion to their concentration.

For the quantitative determination of the diastatic power of taka-diastase a number of methods have been recommended. Those recommended by Lintner[75] or by Wohlgemuth[76] for malt diastase might of course be used. A more satisfactory method appears to be that evolved by Waksman[61]. It is based on the resolution of the starch of a potato starch paste by the enzyme to be tested without considering the question of how much of the starch is converted into polyamyloses, how much into dextrins, and how much into reducing sugars. The potato starch used is first stained red with neutral red and then made into a 2 per cent. starch paste. The paste is filled into test tubes, 100 c.cms. in each, and these placed in an incubator at 40° C. When the paste has reached this temperature sufficient enzyme is added to the tube to cause a resolution of the starch in not less than one minute, and in not more than fifteen minutes. Tubes liquefied outside these limits are rejected. The resolution of the starch is easily recognized by the liquid becoming clear and reddish coloured. The various tubes must be shaken from time to time during digestion to ensure thorough mixing. As each tube clears the time taken is recorded.

The enzymatic power is deduced from the following formula:

$$F = \frac{D \times t}{E \times T}$$

where F represents the enzymatic power at $40°$ C.; D the dilution of the enzyme; t the time taken for the standard unit of enzyme to resolve the starch (t 30 min.); E the quantity of diluted enzyme; and T the time taken by the actual amount of enzyme added to liquefy the starch. Thus if the enzyme has been diluted ten times and 0·2 c.cms. of this dilution has been found to liquefy 10 c.cms. of the starch paste in six minutes the enzymatic power expressed as units would be

$$F \left\{ \begin{array}{l} 30 \text{ min.} \\ 40° \text{ C.} \end{array} \right. = \frac{10 \times 30}{0·2 \times 6} = 350 \text{ units.}$$

Attempts to increase the diastatic properties of taka-diastase through precipitation were made by Sherman and Tanberg.[58] They found that extraction of the commercial product with water, precipitation of the solution with ammonium sulphate, subsequent removal of the salt by dialysis, and final precipitation of the resulting solution of the enzyme by alcohol yielded an amylase which in some cases showed an increased activity of nearly thirty times that of the commercial product.

In addition to *Aspergillus oryzae*, a number of other *Aspergillus* and *Penicillium* species have been studied from the point of view of their amylolytic enzymes. Among them may be mentioned *Aspergillus niger*, investigated by Gayon[77] and by Fernbach,[78] *Aspergillus batatae* and *Aspergillus pseudoflavus* by Saito,[51] *Aspergillus albus*, *Aspergillus candidus*, and *Aspergillus Okazakii* by Okazaki,[79] *Aspergillus terricola* by Scales,[80] and *Aspergillus glaucus* and *Penicillium glaucum* by Duclaux.[81]

Though all of these species hydrolyse starch and many of them are used in the East for the manufacture of alcoholic beverages, they do not convert carbohydrates into alcohol—at least not to any appreciable extent. Sanguinetti[82] reports a yield of 4 per cent. on the carbohydrates converted in the case of *Aspergillus oryzae*. Far more active in this respect are a number of *Mucor* species used in the East for fermentation purposes. The first *Mucor* species reported capable of hydrolysing starch and dextrins and converting the resulting saccharides into alcohol were *Mucor circinelloides* and *Mucor alternans*, studied by Gayon and Dubourg[83] in 1886 and 1887. The utilization of Mucor species for industrial purposes was not seriously considered, however, until after Calmette's[84] publication on 'Chinese yeast' in 1892. This 'yeast' was found by Calmette to be a Mucor species, which he named *Amylomyces Rouxii*, and which is now usually referred to as *Mucor Rouxii*. It produces a very active amylase when grown aerobically. On elimination of the oxygen supply it utilizes the available carbohydrates as hydrogen acceptors* in the place of oxygen and converts them to ethyl alcohol, as much as 35 per cent. of alcohol being formed from the sugar fermented.

Calmette succeeded in isolating the amylase produced by *Mucor Rouxii*, using Duclaux's method—a method to which a few lines must be devoted here, since it is often advocated as suitable for the isolation of fungus enzymes. Duclaux[85] inoculates a culture medium containing inorganic and organic food substances—Raulin's medium, for instance—with spores of the fungus from which he desires to obtain an enzyme, and allows growth to proceed to maturity. This is usually reached after 96 hours' incubation at the optimum temperature. At this stage the fungus covers the culture medium with a densely matted layer of mycelial growth containing numerous sporangia. The accumulation of enzyme in the medium is now particularly rapid, and the spent culture medium, with its salts and decomposition products, is therefore replaced by distilled water, into which the enzyme continues to diffuse. An aqueous solution of the enzyme is thus obtained and can be concentrated by evaporation in vacuo. Or the enzyme may be separated from the aqueous solution by precipitation

* See Chapter V.

with alcohol. Duclaux in his account of the secretion of enzymes emphasizes the need for the presence in the culture medium of the substance specifically decomposed by the enzyme to be collected. This, however, does not appear to be essential in all cases. Thus taka-diastase has been found to contain both rennet and haemolysin, though its mode of preparation precludes the presence of either milk or red blood corpuscles during its secretion by *Aspergillus oryzae*. Katz[72] in his studies on the amylolytic properties of *Aspergillus niger*, *Penicillium glaucum*, and *Bac. Megatherium* found that amylase was secreted by these types even where starch was absent from the culture medium. The secretion of the enzyme could, however, be influenced by the composition of the medium. If for example the medium contained 5 per cent. of saccharose or 2 per cent. of glucose, amylase secretion became completely inhibited in the case of *Penicillium glaucum* and *Bac. Megatherium*, while even 30 per cent. of saccharose was insufficient completely to check the secretion of amylase in the case of *Aspergillus niger*. This observation confirms the experimental evidence discussed in Chapter XXIII on the action of species of *Aspergilli* on sugar stored in bulk.

Maltose was found to be less inhibitory to the secretion of amylase than glucose or saccharose, and erythrodextrin even less. Peptone was found to accelerate amylase production in the case of all three types of micro-organisms with which Katz experimented. The addition of tannin, which removed by precipitation the enzyme secreted, was also found to increase its production by the test organism.

In discussing the question of the influence of the medium on the secretion of enzymes it is interesting to recall that Duclaux[81] found that a typical starch hydrolysing fungus, such as *Aspergillus niger*, did not germinate from its spore in a medium consisting exclusively of ungelatinized starch. To achieve growth it was necessary to add traces of water soluble carbohydrates, such as maltose or saccharose. In starch pastes, however, germination took place within the normal time, even when no traces of copper-reducing substances could be detected in the paste.

The available information on the physical and chemical properties of the amylase isolated by Calmette from *Mucor Rouxii* is not very definite. Calmette himself states that the optimum activity of the enzyme is reached between 35° C. and 38° C., and that heating to 72° C. destroys it. The addition of calcium carbonate is claimed by Calmette to impede its activity. An indication of its acidity range is supplied by Bellinger and Delaval.[86] They found that optimal conditions prevailed when *Mucor Rouxii* acted in a mash containing 5 litres of concentrated hydrochloric acid per 1,000 kg. of grain. Assuming their mash to have been of 10 per cent. strength, the acid added would be sufficient to establish a hydrogen ion concentration equal to a pH value of about 4·0 in the mash.

Subsequent to Calmette's publication a number of descriptions of other amylolytic *Mucoraceae* have been given. Among these may be mentioned *Mucor Cambodia* (Chrzaszcz[87]), *Mucor eloeis* (Joucla[88]), and *Mucor batatas* (Nakazawa[89]). The amylase in *Mucor stolonifer* was studied by Durandard,[90] who records a temperature range for this enzyme from 10° C. to 65° C., with an optimum at 45° C.

Though this is not the place to enter into a discussion of the alcohol-producing properties of the various *Mucor* species, a brief account has been included of the methods adopted for the utilization of mucor species in distilleries, in the processes frequently described under the names of the Amylo process and the Boulard process. Most of the literature dealing with this subject is difficult of access owing to patent restrictions, and Galle's[91] account in 1923 therefore fills a long-felt want. The data supplied here are taken from Galle's paper, which is based on practical experience with the working of the Amylo process. For the laboratory cultivation of the fungus a mash containing 16 to 17 per cent. of starch is filled in test tubes to 5 c.cms. and in litre flasks to 250 c.cms. and sterilized for 20 min. at 1·5 atm. After 24 hours' standing the media are sterilized

again. A further medium used consists of rice (20 gr.) mois-
tened with 1 c.cm. of water and contained in sufficiently large
containers to allow abundant air-space. This medium, like
the liquid mash, is sterilized in the autoclave on two con-
secutive days at 1·5 atm. for 20 min.

When required for starting large-scale fermentations the
sterile tubes containing liquid mash are inoculated with a
pure culture of *Mucor Rouxii*, or any other *Mucor* strain
which may have been chosen, and incubated at 38° C. After
four to five days' incubation these cultures are fully developed
and the surface of the liquid is covered with a mass of black
sporangia. The ripe cultures are placed in a dark, cool place
when not required for immediate use. Before the inoculation
of the sterilized rice grains the contents of a tube are carefully
shaken until the spores contained in the sporangia have been
distributed throughout the liquid in the tube. The rice is
then sprinkled with this liquid and incubated at 38° C. for
eight days. After satisfactory development it is shaken with
250 c.cms. of sterile mash and left at 38° C. for 24 hours for
the spores to germinate. If free from infecting bacteria this
material is used to inoculate a seed tank holding a quantity
of mash equal to 10 per cent. of that finally to be fermented.
The mash in the seed tank is sterilized by live steam for one
hour at 110° C. (0·9 atm.) and cooled to 39° C. before inoculation. After 15 hours' incubation the first hyphae become
visible. For the satisfactory development of the fungus it is
essential that the reaction of the mash, as well as its temperature, should be maintained at the optimum. The acidity of
the mash must not be allowed to increase beyond a concentration which requires 2 to 3 c.cms. of $\frac{n}{10}$ NaOH for neutralization of 20 c.cms. of the mash. After 18 hours in the seed tank
the mash is used as inoculant for the mash in the fermenting
vat. Here the acidity must be checked every six hours and
not allowed to increase beyond 5 c.cms. of $\frac{n}{10}$ NaOH per
20 c.cms. of the mash. Twenty-four hours after inoculation the

mash in the fermenting vat is cooled to 32° C. and inoculated with a yeast mixture. Thereupon the mash is aerated for about six hours. After 48 hours the fermentation is completed. The whole process in the factory therefore takes three days. At the end of the fermentation the acidity may have risen to 7 c.cms. $\frac{n}{10}$ acid per 20 c.cms. of mash.

In many factories where the Amylo and the Boulard process are worked it is customary to assist the liquefaction of the grain by soaking it at 70° C. with the requisite amount of water to which 0·8 per cent. of sulphuric acid have been added, calculated on the weight of the grain taken. During the subsequent cooking the mash becomes more liquid than if no acid had been used. In consequence higher concentrations of grain than would normally be possible can be used. Bellinger and Delaval in their publication already referred to mention that the addition of acid is more favourable for the subsequent activity of the amylase than the use of a small amount of malt added for the purpose of liquefaction of the mash.

The production of amylase by higher fungi cannot be dealt with in these pages. It has already been mentioned that very few species belonging to the order of the *Eumycetes* lack the property of amylase secretion. Its presence in the mycelium of the higher fungi has frequently been recorded, for instance by Zellner.[92] The importance of starch hydrolysis in the microbiological destruction of wood was referred to in Thaysen and Bunker's[4] treatise on the microbiology of cellulose.

It remains to draw attention to the connexion which must exist between the amylase-producing properties of many fungi and the discoloration and destruction of starch in storage. In this destruction fungi participate and may perhaps even be solely responsible. It would seem that they are capable not only of spreading throughout the mass of the starch but actually of penetrating the individual starch grains. Lindner's[93] observations on mouldy potatoes at least indicate that this is what may occur.

Before leaving the subject of starch hydrolysis reference must be made to the interesting observation of Gramenitzki[94] on the regeneration of amyloclastic enzymes after exposure to high temperatures. It has already been mentioned that temperatures of from 70° C.–80° C. destroy the characteristic properties of starch hydrolysing enzymes. Gramenitzki finds that this destruction in many cases is an inactivation rather than a destruction—an inactivation from which the enzymes may recover. Thus a solution of taka-diastase heated for a short time to 80–85° C. will show an appreciable regeneration of its amyloclastic properties when left at room temperature for one or two days. When left at 40° C. the recovery of its specific properties is more rapid, though less complete, and is maintained for only four to six hours. Kept at 45° C. there is only a slight regeneration, which is lost again after two to three hours. Kept at 50° C. no regeneration at all takes place. The degree of regeneration therefore depends on the temperature at which the enzyme is kept after exposure. But in addition it is governed also by the degree to which the enzyme has been heated, a short exposure to 115° C. being the maximum beyond which no regeneration occurs. The more active an enzyme the more readily will it become regenerated, and as a general rule dilute solutions of taka-diastase are more easily regenerated than concentrated solutions. Whether the enzyme solution has been previously dialysed or not does not appear to affect its regenerative powers, which therefore must be regarded as independent of the conductivity of the enzyme solution.

It is interesting to note that Gramenitzki found the saccharifying enzyme of taka-diastase less resistant to heat than the amyloclastic enzyme, and that it lost its regenerative power at a lower temperature (100° C.) than the amyloclastic enzyme. This observation offers additional proof for the contention that the two enzymes are different.

Glycogen. The hydrolysis of glycogen by micro-organisms has been investigated in the past almost exclusively from the point of view of the *Saccharomycetes,* in the cell of which it occurs as a reserve carbohydrate. Occasionally a reference is met with in the literature, such as that of Heinze[95] or that of Pringsheim and Lichtenstein,[96] which deals in some detail with the action on glycogen of specific micro-organisms other than yeast. In such cases the conclusion is invariably arrived at that this polysaccharide is hydrolysed by those micro-organisms which produce amylolytic enzymes. Realizing the close relationship, bordering on identity, which exists between glycogen and amylopectin this result is not surprising.

Inulin. Even more unsatisfactory is the existing knowledge of the microbiological decomposition of inulin. No systematic investigation like that of Fermi's on the amylolytic micro-organisms has so far been carried out, and the occasional reference to inulin decomposition leaves no impression as to the extent to which this polysaccharide is utilized for instance by bacteria and actinomycetes. Among fungi the secretion of an inulase appears to be fairly widespread, and inulin decomposition has been observed both among higher and lower types. Thus Bourquelot[97] found inulase in *Aspergillus niger*, Grüss[98] in *Ustilago Maydis*, Dean[99] in *Aspergillus niger* and a *Penicillium* species, Frou[100] in *Morchella*, Wehmer[101] in some *Mucor* species, Hanzawa[102] in *Rhizopus Delemar*, introduced by Boidin into the Amylo process, and Castellani and Taylor[103] in *Monilia macedoniensis*.

The physical constants of the inulase of *Aspergillus niger* were studied by Boselli,[104] who determined the optimum temperature as 51° C. and the optimum acidity at this temperature as $\frac{n}{200}$ H_2SO_4, equal to a hydrogen ion concentration of the pH value 2·3. A 'slight' alkalinity was found by him to arrest the action of the enzyme. In Dean's experiments the optimum temperature of the enzyme is given as 55° C. and the optimum hydrogen ion concentration at a pH value of 4·0. Dean also determined the alkalinity capable of arresting the action of the enzyme. It was equal to a pH value of 10–14. In its sensitiveness to alkalies the microbiological inulase greatly resembles the inulase isolated by Green[105] from Jerusalem artichokes.

LITERATURE

1. Th. de Saussure, *Ann. Chim. Phys.* (2), vol. 11, p. 379, 1819.
2. A. Fitz, *Berichte*, vols. 10 and 11, pp. 276 and 42, 1877 and 1878.
3. J. Wortmann, *Z. f. physiol. Chem.*, vol. 6, p. 287, 1882.
4. A. C. Thaysen and H. J. Bunker, *Microbiology of Cellulose, etc.*, Oxford University Press, 1927.
5. V. Marcano, *Comptes rend.*, vol. 95, pp. 345, 357, 856, 1882.
6. E. Prillieux, *Bull. Soc. Botan.*, vol. 26, pp. 31 and 187, 1879.
7. H. Bitter, *Arch. f. Hygiene*, vol. 5, p. 241, 1886.
8. Cl. Fermi, *Arch. f. Hygiene*, vol. 10, p. 1, 1890.
9. V. L. Omeliansky, *Abstr. Bacteriol.*, vol. 7, p. 288, 1923.
10. —. Maumus, *Comptes rend. soc. biol.*, vol. 5, Series 9, p. 107, 1893.
11. A. Villiers, *Comptes rend.*, vol. 112, p. 435, 1891.
12. J. Behrens, *Zentrbl. f. Bakt.*, Abt. II, vol. 8, p. 114, 1902.
13. G. Bredemann, *Zentrbl. f. Bakt.*, Abt. II, vol. 23, p. 384, 1909.
14. I. A. Makrinov, *Abstr. Bacteriology*, vol. 7, p. 172, 1923.
15. L. Perdrix, *Ann. Inst. Pasteur*, vol. 5, p. 287, 1891.
16. O. Gottheil, *Zentrbl. f. Bakt.*, Abt. II, vol. 7, p. 430, 1901.
17. D. F. Holland, *J. Bacteriology*, vol. 5, p. 215, 1920.
18. F. Schardinger, *Zentrbl. f. Bakt.*, Abt. II, vol. 22, p. 98, 1909.
19. C. Dupont, *Comptes rend.*, vol. 134, p. 1449, 1902.
20. R. Kerry and S. Fränkel, *Monatshefte f. Chem.*, vol. 12, p. 350, 1891.
21. T. Gruber, *Zentrbl. f. Bakt.*, Abt. II, vol. 14, p. 353, 1905.
22. A. Fernbach, *Comptes rend.*, vol. 151, p. 1004, 1910.
23. C. Coolhaas, *Zentrbl. f. Bakt.*, Abt. II, vol. 75, p. 344, 1928; vol. 76, p. 38, 1928.
24. W. L. Fleming and J. M. Neill, *J. Exp. Med.*, vol. 45, p. 947, 1927.
25. C. Eijkman, *Zentrbl. f. Bakt.*, Abt. I, vol. 29, p. 841, 1901.
26. O. Emmerling and O. Reiser, *Berichte*, vol. 35, p. 700, 1902.
27. W. Henneberg, *Zentrbl. f. Bakt.*, Abt. II, vol. 4, p. 14, 1898.
28. R. L. Laybourn, *J. Inf. Dis.*, vol. 26, p. 418, 1920.
29. Cl. Fermi, *Zentrbl. f. Bakt.*, vol. 12, p. 713, 1892.
30. A. Sclavo and B. Gosio, *Jahresber. d. Agricult. Chem.*, vol. 34, p. 658, 1891.
31. E. Willman, *Ann. Inst. Pasteur*, vol. 26, p. 610, 1912.
32. M. W. Beijerinck, *Rec. d. trav. chim. des Pays-Bas*, vol. 12, p. 141, 1893.
33. E. B. Vedder, *J. Inf. Dis.*, vol. 16, p. 385, 1915.
34. J. Effront, *Comptes rend.*, vol. 164, p. 415, 1917.
35. H. v. Euler and O. Svanberg, *Biochem. Z.*, vol. 128, p. 323, 1922.
36. A. S. Siedish, *Chem. Abstr.*, vol. 19, p. 2683, 1925.
37. J. Effront, *Comptes rend. soc. biol.*, vol. 86, p. 274, 1922.
38. H. Kodama and H. Takeda, *Zentrbl. f. Bakt.*, Abt. I, vol. 88, p. 513, 1922.
39. A. Boidin, *Fr. Pat.*, No. 399087, 1908.
40. A. Boidin and J. Effront, *Fr. Pat.*, No. 475431, 1914.

41. H. Joucla, *Fr. Pat.*, 474948, 1914.

42. M. Bettinger, *Bull. ass. chim. sucr. et dist.*, vol. 38, p. 463, 1921.

43. Cl. Fermi, *Zentrbl. f. Bakt.*, Abt. I, vol. 40, p. 187, 1906.

44. S. A. Waksman and R. E. Curtis, *Soil Science*, vol. 1, p. 99, 1916.

45. A. Krainsky, *Zentrbl. f. Bakt.*, Abt. II, vol. 41, p. 649, 1914.

46. W. Rullman, *Zentrbl. f. Bakt.*, Abt. II, vol. 2, p. 116, 1896.

47. Y. Kozai, *Zentrbl. f. Bakt.*, Abt. II, vol. 6, p. 385, 1900.

48. J. Takamine, *Chem. News*, vol. 110, p. 215, 1914.

49. A. W. Atkinson, *Proc. Roy. Soc.*, vol. 32, p. 299, 1881.

50. O. Korschelt, quoted by C. Wehmer in Lafar's Textbook on *Technische Mykologie*, vol. 4, p. 240, 1905–7, Gustav Fischer, Jena.

51. K. Saito, *Zentrbl. f. Bakt.*, Abt. II, vol. 18, p. 30, 1907.

52. C. M. Hutchinson and C. S. Ramayyar, *Memo. of the Dept. of Agric. India, Bacteriol. Series*, vol. 1, p. 137, 1915.

53. Y. Takeda, *Rept. Dept. Research Inst. Formosa*, 1924.

54. R. O. Bishop and G. R. Feik, *Malay Agric. J.*, vol. 16, p. 14, 1928.

55. W. Nill, *Zentrbl. f. Bakt.*, Abt. II, vol. 72, p. 21, 1927.

56. Y. Nishiwaki, *Zentrbl. f. Bakt.*, Abt. II, vol. 63, p. 25, 1924.

57. K. Oshima, *The Analyst*, vol. 53, p. 612, 1928.

58. H. C. Sherman and A. P. Tanberg, *Am. Chem. Soc.*, vol. 38, p. 1638, 1916.

59. J. Wohlgemuth, *Biochem. Z.*, vol. 39, p. 324, 1912.

60. S. Nishmura, *Chem. Zelle und Gewebe*, vol. 12, p. 212, 1925.

61. S. A. Waksman, *J. Am. Chem. Soc.*, vol. 42, p. 293, 1920.

62. H. C. Sherman, A. W. Thomas, and M. E. Baldwin, *J. Am. Chem. Soc.*, vol. 41, p. 231, 1919.

63. T. Chrzaszcz, Z. Bidzinski and A. Krause, *Biochem. Z.*, vol. 160, p. 155, 1925.

64. S. Okada, *Biochem. J.*, vol. 10, p. 130, 1916.

65. J. Takamine Jr. and K. Oshima, *J. Am. Chem. Soc.*, vol. 42, p. 1261, 1920.

66. J. Effront, *Comptes rend.*, vol. 115, p. 1324, 1892.

67. G. Kita, *J. Ind. Eng. Chem.*, vol. 5, p. 220, 1913.

68. G. Kita and E. Kyoto, *Mem. Coll. Imp. University, Tokyo*, vol. 2, p. 1, 1918.

69. S. Nishimura, *Chem. Absts.*, vol. 22, p. 2233, 1928.

70. H. Pringsheim and G. Otto, *Biochem. Z.*, vol. 173, p. 399, 1926.

71. G. Grezes, *Ann. Inst. Pasteur*, vol. 26, p. 556, 1912.

72. J. Katz, *Jahrb. Wiss. Botanik*, vol. 31, p. 599, 1898.

73. G. L. Funke, *Rec. trav. bot. Neerland.*, vol. 23, p. 200, 1926.

74. H. Yamagishi, *Japan. J. Biol.*, vol. 4, p. 51, 1928.

75. C. J. Lintner, *Z. gesamm. Brauwesen*, vol. 8, p. 281, 1885.

76. J. Wohlgemuth, *Biochem. Z.*, vol. 9, p. 1, 1908.

77. U. Gayon, *Comptes rend.*, vol. 86, p. 52, 1878.

78. A. Fernbach, *Ann. d. brasserie et distillerie*, vol. 2, p. 409, 1889.

79. K. Okazaki, *Zentrbl. f. Bakt.*, Abt. II, vol. 42, p. 225, 1914.

80. F. M. Scales, *J. Biol. Chem.*, vol. 19, p. 459, 1914.

81. E. Duclaux, *Ann. Inst. Pasteur*, vol. 3, p. 97, 1889; vol. 6, p. 97, 1889.

82. J. Sanguinetti, *Ann. Inst. Pasteur*, vol. 11, p. 264, 1897.

83. U. Gayon and E. Dubourg, *Comptes rend.*, vol. 103, p. 885, 1886. *Ann. Inst. Pasteur*, vol. 1, p. 532, 1887.

84. A. Calmette, *Ann. Inst. Pasteur*, vol. 6, p. 604, 1892.

85. E. Duclaux, *Frémy's Encyclopédie Chimique*, vol. 9, part I, p. 191, 1883. Dunot, Paris.

86. P. Bellinger and H. Delaval, *Bull. assoc. chim. sucr. et dist.*, vol. 37, p. 254, 1920.

87. T. Chrzaszcz, *Zentrbl. f. Bakt.*, Abt. II, vol. 7, p. 326, 1901.

88. H. Joucla, *Fr. Pat.*, 474948, 1914.

89. R. Nakazawa, *Zentrbl. f. Bakt.*, Abt. II, vol. 24, p. 482, 1909.

90. M. Durandard, *Comptes rend.*, vol. 157, p. 471, 1913.

91. E. Galle, *Z. angew. Chem.*, vol. 30, p. 231, 1909.

92. J. Zellner, *Monatshefte d. Chem.*, vol. 30, p. 231, 1909.

93. P. Lindner, *Z. f. Spiritusind.*, vol. 43, p. 213, 1920.

94. M. J. Gramenitzki, *Z. f. physiol. Chem.*, vol. 69, p. 286, 1910.

95. B. Heinze, *Zentrbl. f. Bakt.*, Abt. II, vol. 12, p. 43, 1904.

96. H. Pringsheim and S. Lichtenstein, *Berichte*, vol. 49, p. 364, 1916.

97. E. Bourquelot, *Comptes rend.*, vol. 116, p. 1143, 1893.

98. J. Grüss, *Berichte d. deutsch. botan. Gesellsch.*, vol. 20, p. 213, 1902.

99. A. L. Dean, *Botanical Gazette*, vol. 35, p. 24, 1903.

100. G. Frou, *Comptes rend.*, vol. 140, p. 1187, 1905.

101. C. Wehmer, *Lafar's Handbuch der techn. Mykologie*, vol. 4, p. 527, 1905–7. Gustav Fischer, Jena.

102. J. Hanzawa, *Mykolog. Zentrbl.*, vol. 1, p. 76, 1912.

103. A. Castellani and F. E. Taylor, *Biochem. J.*, vol. 16, p. 655, 1922.

104. J. Boselli, *Ann. Inst. Pasteur*, vol. 25, p. 695, 1911.

105. J. R. Green, *Annals of Botany*, vol. 1, p. 223, 1888.

CHAPTER III

THE HYDROLYSIS OF TETRA-, TRI-, AND DISACCHARIDES

IT seems obvious that before starch, glycogen, and inulin can be assimilated by micro-organisms they must undergo a depolymerisation and hydrolysis to soluble carbohydrates. This has not been seriously disputed. But in the case of soluble carbohydrates among those saccharides which Pringsheim[1] terms polysaccharides of the first order, the conception of a preliminary hydrolysis before assimilation has never been generally accepted although a vast amount of evidence has been accumulated demonstrating the frequent occurrence of hydrolysis of such saccharides. Abderhalden's[2] theory, therefore, that a food substance must be decomposed to its simplest units before it can be assimilated has not always been accepted for the tetra-, tri-, and disaccharides. For instance it has occasionally been maintained that a disaccharide might readily be assimilated by micro-organisms but its component monosaccharides be of little or no value as a food substance. Thus Rose[3] found that *Endomyces Magnusii* could assimilate maltose, while glucose, though fermented, did not promote growth. Similar observations were recorded by Lindner and Saito[4] for certain types of yeasts. Kluyver,[5] who reinvestigated this question and confirmed that certain yeasts showed better development in maltose than in glucose solutions, was able to trace this anomaly to the presence of small amounts of nitrogenous impurities in the pure maltose used. On removal of these, maltose was found to behave exactly like glucose, thus showing that the readier assimilation of maltose was due not to the greater suitability of the carbohydrate, but to the presence of nitrogen which, when added to glucose, rendered the latter as readily assimilable as the disaccharide.

A direct assimilation of saccharose is stated by Pringsheim and Zemplén[6] to be possible in the case of certain fungi. The experimental evidence given in support of this statement is not altogether convincing, and is based solely on the failure of the investigators to demonstrate the presence of a hydrolysing enzyme in the press juice and in the dried mycelium of some of the fungi studied which were capable of hydrolysing saccharose in vitro. It is conceivable, as Kluyver points out in the paper referred to above, that the hydrolysis in this case in some way had been connected with the life function of the fungi and therefore evaded detection. But it might be also that the technique adopted by the investigators for the preparation of the mycelial extracts was unsuitable and had destroyed the inverting enzyme responsible for the hydrolysis. Whatever the explanation, Pringsheim and Zemplén's investigations do not suffice to dispose of the theory that a soluble polysaccharide must be decomposed to its basic units before it can be assimilated by micro-organisms. No more convincing is Violle's[7] observation on a certain lactic acid-producing *Streptococcus*, the behaviour of which has been quoted in support of the theory that polysaccharides may be assimilated without preliminary hydrolysis. Violle finds that his organism develops exceptionally well on media containing saccharose, and reports that it is unable to utilize either glucose or fructose. He emphasizes, however, that an inverting enzyme is contained in such cultures, and thus indirectly admits that the surprising results of his experiments with glucose and fructose must have been due to faulty technique and not to an abnormal behaviour of the micro-organisms studied. More important evidence in favour of a direct assimilation of saccharose was brought forward by Gayon and Dubourg,[8] who observed that certain mannitol-producing bacteria could ferment saccharose readily without producing mannitol, but yielded considerable quantities of this alcohol when acting on fructose. But even here it remains to be shown that fructose as liberated from saccharose cannot act differently *in statu nascendi* from the fructose from which the strain of mannitol bacteria studied by Gayon and Dubourg yielded mannitol.

More recently Willstätter and Lowry[9] have recorded observations on the behaviour of a saccharose fermenting yeast which, according to these writers, support the view that a direct fermentation of disaccharides is possible without preliminary hydrolysis. Willstätter and Lowry found that a certain saccharose fermenting yeast would retain from 70–80 per cent. of its fermenting properties unimpaired under conditions which reduced the action of its saccharase by 95 per cent. It is not shown, however, that this remaining 5 per cent. of saccharase is insufficient to maintain the somewhat reduced fermentative activity of the yeast in question, or that sufficient enzymes, as suggested by von Euler,[10] may not be produced during the actual fermentation to ensure this reduced rate of fermentation. This view is held by Cohn,[11] who points out that the performance of an enzyme is not a simple function of its quantity, and that a retardation of the fermentation of saccharose occurs on the partial inactivation of the saccharase of the yeast employed for its fermentation.

There are thus at present no grounds, as Cohn rightly asserts, for assuming a direct fermentation of saccharose.

In recording the available information on the action of micro-organisms on the natural tetra-, tri-, and disaccharides there is at present little justification for not inquiring in the first instance into the hydrolysing actions taking place before proceeding to discuss the chemical changes to which monoses are subjected by micro-organisms for the liberation of the energy accumulated in these substances.

HYDROLYSIS OF TETRASACCHARIDES

Stachyose, a tetrasaccharide present in a number of plants, was first discovered by von Planta and Schulze[12] in the tubers of *Stachys tuberifera*. On partial hydrolysis it yields one molecule of fructose and one molecule of mannotriose, the latter yielding glucose and galactose on decomposition.

The information available as to the action of micro-organisms on stachyose, as well as on other tetra-, tri-, and disaccharides, will show that microbiological action runs parallel if it is not identical with the action of other hydrolysing agents. To demonstrate this is the chief justification for including in the present pages the often very fragmentary information available on the subject.

The hydrolysis of stachyose by *Aspergillus niger* was studied by Tanret,[13] who found that the tetrasaccharide was first broken down to fructose and mannotriose, the latter subsequently being slowly decomposed. He was unable to decide whether the action on mannotriose was due to the saccharase produced by the fungus or to some other enzyme. Vintilesco,[14] who reinvestigated the action of *Aspergillus niger* on stachyose, came to the conclusion that saccharase had no action on mannotriose, but that in the presence of saccharase and emulsin-containing β-glucosidic enzymes stachyose breaks down into its component monoses, fructose, glucose, and galactose. More recently Neuberg and Lachmann[15] have studied the action of the enzyme mixture of kephir on stachyose and have found that it liberates fructose. They ascribe this action to the lactase contained in the enzyme mixture and mention that yeast maltase contained in the enzyme mixture has a similar action on stachyose. The latter statement undoubtedly requires verification, since maltase hydrolyses α-glucosides only, while lactase decomposes β-glucosidic carbohydrates.

It is noteworthy that lactase should have been unable to attack mannotriose in Neuberg and Lachmann's investigations since emulsin, according to them, has a slight hydrolysing action on the trisaccharides.

HYDROLYSIS OF TRISACCHARIDES

Gentianose. Meyer[16] gave the first description of gentianose, which he obtained from the rhizomes of *Gentiana lutea*. The carbohydrate was shown by Bourquelot and Hérissey[17] to be a trisaccharide.

On subjecting gentianose to the action of the enzyme mixture produced by *Aspergillus niger*, Bourquelot[18] observed a complete hydrolysis of the trisaccharide into its component monoses, fructose and glucose. That this action was due to more than one enzyme he concluded from the fact that saccharase obtained from yeast liberated fructose but left unattacked a disaccharide, gentiobiose, composed of two glucose molecules, and regarded by Berlin[19] as identical with Fischer's isomaltose. In a later paper Bourquelot and Hérissey[20] state that the complete hydrolysis of gentianose by *Aspergillus niger* occurs in two stages, the liberation of fructose by the saccharase of the fungus and the subsequent hydrolysis of the gentiobiose by an enzyme either identical with, or contained in, emulsin.

Gentianose has a limited practical use in mountainous countries where *Gentiana* species occur in abundance. Here the roots are used for the preparation of an alcoholic beverage, the making of which was investigated by Guyot.[21]

Raffinose or **Melitriose** occurs as a normal constituent of the carbohydrates in sugar beet. It is therefore of considerable practical interest. It was first isolated by Loiseau[22] from beet molasses and has shown to yield fructose, galactose, and glucose on hydrolysis.

Neuberg[23] maintains, probably rightly, that the hydrolysis of raffinose by bacteria and fungi follows the lines of the decomposition of this carbohydrate by yeast. For *Aspergillus niger* Bourquelot[24] has shown this to be the case, since the hydrolysis proceeds in two stages, resulting first in the liberation of fructose and the formation of melibiose, and subsequently in the hydrolysis of melibiose to glucose and galactose. Gillot[25] confirms the formation of the three monoses by raffinose as the result of the action of *Aspergillus niger* on the polysaccharide. Whether in the case of bacteria and fungi an action is possible such as that observed by Neuberg in the case of emulsin, that is, with the liberation of galactose and *saccharose*, was not definitely established by Neuberg and remains to be determined.

A fermentation of raffinose by *Bact. lactiarabinosum* was observed by Fred, Peterson, and Anderson,[26] by *Bact. Friedländer* by Frankland, Stanley, and Frew,[27] and by *Monilia sitophila* by Went.[28]

The enzyme responsible for the hydrolysis of raffinose, according to Willstätter and Kuhn,[29] is not to be regarded as identical with saccharase.

Melezitose. Melezitose was first isolated by Villiers[30] from the manna of *Alhagi camelorum*, and has been referred to by von Schrenk[31] as contained in the droplets of liquid which exude from the sporophores of various *Polyporaceae*, types of wood destroying higher fungi. The trisaccharide was shown by Alekhine[32] to be decomposable by dilute acids into glucose and a disaccharide turanose, which in turn, and under the same influence, yielded one further molecule of glucose and one molecule of fructose. It might be thought therefore that melezitose was a dehydration product of one molecule of glucose and one molecule of saccharose. This, however, does not appear to be so since the saccharase produced by yeast is unable to decompose it (Alekhine). Attempts have been made by Kuhn and von Grundherr[33] to explain the mode of combination of saccharose with glucose in melezitose, but it must be concluded with Bridel and Aagaard[34] that there is at present no experimental evidence to show how this combination has been brought about.

The information available on the microbiological decomposition of melezitose is very scanty indeed. That melezitose is unfermentable, presumably by yeast, was the conclusion arrived at by Alekhine.

Bourquelot and Hérissey[35] found that the enzyme of *Aspergillus niger* hydrolyses melezitose to glucose and turanose, while Kayser[36] showed that a lactic acid producing bacterium isolated by him from 'sauerkraut' was capable of fermenting and, presumably, of hydrolysing it. Perhaps this type of lactic acid bacterium was related to the *Bact. lactiarabinosum* of Fred, Peterson, and Anderson,[26] which is claimed to be a vigorous melezitose fermenting type.

HYDROLYSIS OF DISACCHARIDES

Trehalose. Trehalose, a diglucose not reducing Fehling, was first isolated by Bourquelot.[37] He found it to be widely distributed among fungi, where it is produced in the sporophores on commencement of spore formation. During the ripening of the spores the carbohydrate disappears, a specific enzyme, trehalase, being responsible for its conversion into glucose. This enzyme was found by Bourquelot to be different from saccharase, amylase, and emulsin. Ivanov[38] draws attention to the presence of trehalose in *Myxomycetes*, organisms which at certain stages of their development produce also the corresponding hydrolytic enzyme trehalase.

Where the enzyme is absent, for instance in the stipe of the sporophore of many higher fungi, trehalose accumulates in such quantities that these tissues may be used as a raw material for the isolation of the carbohydrate.

Among the lower fungi Bourquelot found the enzyme trehalase present in the mycelium of *Aspergillus niger*. He showed that it was different from the maltase produced by the same fungus, since the two enzymes withstood high temperature to a varying extent.

Fischer[39] found that yeast is capable of hydrolysing trehalose, and that an aqueous suspension of dried pure yeast converted about 20 per cent. of any trehalose present into reducing sugars. An aqueous extract of living yeast, however, had no action on the carbohydrate. Bourquelot[37] had previously shown that yeast saccharase had no action on trehalose.

According to Went,[28] trehalase is produced by *Monilia sitophila* when trehalose is added to the culture medium in which the fungus is grown.

An attempt to utilize trehalose for diagnostic purposes was made by Koser,[40] who found that *Bact. paratyphosum*, *Bact. Schottmülleri*, and *Bact. enteritidis* fermented it with the evolution of gas and production of acid, while *Bact. suipestifer* was unable to hydrolyse it. Kayser[36] in his investigations on lactic acid bacteria found one of his strains capable of fermenting trehalose. Trehalose, according to Frouin and Guillaumie,[41] would appear also to be a carbohydrate suitable for maintaining the growth of the tubercle bacterium.

Saccharose. The observation that yeast produces alcohol from saccharose long ago caused chemists and biologists to take an interest in the reactions involved in this conversion. Quevenne[42] reports that before 1832, and independently of each other, Baudrimont and Dubrunfaut had established that saccharose becomes converted into non-crystallizable sugars when left in contact with yeast. Berthelot[43] records that Pasteur endeavoured to correlate this reaction with the presence of a 'soluble ferment' in the yeast cell but failed to do so, and therefore concluded that the appearance of the copper-reducing sugars was the result of a side reaction during fermentation, due to the action on saccharose of the succinic acid formed by yeast during fermentation. In 1860 Berthelot undertook to test this hypothesis experimentally. For the purpose he allowed succinic acid to act on a saccharose solution under conditions which in the presence of yeast would have resulted in the hydrolysis of the disaccharide. The experiment showed that no inversion of the saccharose took place. He obtained further proof that the hydrolysis was independent of the presence of succinic acid by fermenting saccharose at alkaline reactions under conditions which excluded succinic acid from exercising a hydrolytic action. As reducing sugars nevertheless were formed under these conditions, Berthelot concluded that the inversion must be more intimately connected with the activity of the yeast than Pasteur had assumed. He therefore attempted to isolate the substances responsible for the conversion of saccharose into reducing sugars. He succeeded in showing that an aqueous extract of yeast was capable of hydrolysing saccharose and that the reactive substance could be precipitated from the extract by addition of alcohol. This convinced Berthelot that the living yeast cell was not itself the ferment, but that it produced one, capable of acting independently of the life functions of the cell.

More than twenty years later Gayon[44] confirmed Berthelot's experiments, and again showed that succinic acid has no hydrolysing action on saccharose at ordinary temperatures.

The substance saccharase which Berthelot isolated from yeast is frequently described under the name invertase. The enzyme is widely distributed among micro-organisms, particularly among fungi, where most of the higher fungi as well as many lower fungi, particularly the *Aspergilli* and the *Penicillia*, hydrolyse cane sugar. Among the *Mucoraceae* the enzyme saccharase is less widely distributed, and only one species, *Mucor racemosus*, has so far been shown to produce the enzyme. Even within this one species Kostytschew and Eliasberg[45] have found that only the minus strain is able to hydrolyse the carbohydrate.

Among bacteria saccharase is undoubtedly less frequently found. Nevertheless the few saccharose hydrolysing types mentioned by Fermi[46] and Fermi and Montesano[47] by no means exhaust the number of saccharose hydrolysing bacteria.

Certain types of coliform bacteria studied by Burri[48] and by Thaysen[49] are of particular interest. On first being isolated from their natural habitat these types do not decompose saccharose, but apparently acquire the property of doing so on being cultivated on media containing cane sugar. Types acting similarly towards lactose had been investigated previously by Neisser,[50] Massini,[51] Burri,[48] and others.

In the case of bacteria saccharase does not appear to have been isolated in substance. Fermi and his collaborators used cultures of the test organisms grown in broth for about fourteen days as solutions of the enzyme, a method which seems to have been adopted by all subsequent investigators.

A similar procedure of utilizing a solution of the enzyme secreted into the culture medium or into water has usually been adopted, except in the case of yeast saccharase and takadiastase saccharase. Some authors have preferred to work with the juice pressed or triturated from the mycelium of the fungus. This was noticeably the case in Fischer and Lindner's[52] experiments, carried out to ascertain the stage in the life-cycle of *Monilia candida* at which saccharase was being formed by the fungus. Fischer and Lindner disintegrated fresh cells of *Monilia candida* in a mortar after mixing them with glass powder and found that the resultant paste hydrolysed saccharose as effectively as did cells of the fungus, thus showing that saccharase, as had been assumed, was not produced only on the drying out of the cells. In exceptional cases only has saccharase been separated from such solutions.

The information available on the nature and properties of saccharase has in most cases been derived from a study of the enzyme obtainable from yeast. The review of the properties of saccharase given in the following pages refers to this enzyme therefore where not otherwise stated.

Before proceeding to discuss these properties it should be mentioned that in none of the experiments of Fermi and his collaborators were actinomycetes found capable of hydrolysing saccharose. Subsequent work by Waksman[53] has shown that some actinomycetes are able to do so, and to develop moderately well on media containing saccharose as sole source of carbon. Generally speaking, however, saccharose cannot be regarded as a carbohydrate favouring the growth of actinomycetes.

Though available as a solid, the substance known until recently as saccharase was a very heterogeneous compound containing a large percentage of mineral matter, of gum (hemicelluloses), and pectin. Great efforts were made to establish the connexion of these substances with the enzyme and the part played by them in the action of saccharase on cane sugar. The existing literature contains a large number of publications dealing with this question, which now has no more than historical interest. von Euler[54] and his collaborators and Willstätter[55] in their publications have been able not only to increase the efficiency of their saccharase solution by elaborate methods of purification, but the latter investigator has shown that the purified saccharase prepared by him contains no mineral matter, carbohydrates, or protein.

E

It is not within the scope of this volume to give a detailed description of the modern methods by which saccharase of high purity can be prepared, but a broad outline of the principles adopted may perhaps be included.

The yeast used can be extracted while still living or after destruction through drying, disintegration, or autolysis. In the former case, and when very cold water is used, a less active enzyme solution is obtained (Salkowski[56]) than when the extraction is carried out at temperatures between 30 and 40° C. When dried or autolysed yeast is used, the enzyme solution contains a large percentage of impurities.

The most efficient way of removing these impurities is at present that adopted by Willstätter and his collaborators. This consists in treatment of the crude enzyme with kaolin followed by precipitation of the purified saccharase with tannin at 0° C. In this way Willstätter, Schneider, and Wenzel[57] have prepared an enzyme of even greater purity than their earlier preparations, which had been entirely free from gum and proteins.

The existing very extensive literature dealing with the physical and chemical properties of saccharase has been largely based on data collected with less highly purified enzyme preparations than Willstätter's. This can hardly have failed to affect the results obtained. In interpreting the available information on the chemical and physical properties of saccharase, it is advisable to bear this in mind.

In his studies on saccharase von Euler[10] expresses the view that yeast does not secrete the enzyme but synthesizes it during the actual fermentation with energy derived from the breakdown of carbohydrates. This statement postulates that yeast grown on media in the absence of carbohydrates should contain no saccharase. How far this is the case does not appear to have been confirmed experimentally. Kertesz,[58] however, maintains that *Penicillium glaucum* when grown on a medium containing 5 per cent. of glycerol or of invert sugar as the only source of carbon produces no saccharase.

On the other hand the presence of carbohydrates undoubtedly favours the production of saccharase. Thus von Euler and Cramer[59] increased the saccharase content of yeast by 20 per cent. by adding mannose to the culture medium. Willstätter, Lowry, and Schneider[60] found a similar though slighter effect when using maltose, but none where lactose or glycerin was added to the medium. In the case of *Aspergillus niger*, Grezes[61] increased the saccharase content of the fungus by cultivating it in a medium containing cane sugar. A suitable incubation temperature also appears to favour saccharase production. Thus Svanberg[62] records that yeast cultivated between 25° C. and 28° C. showed a higher saccharase content than cultures grown outside this optimum. At the optimum temperature the production of saccharase by a non-multiplying culture of yeast was found by von Euler and Svanberg[63] to remain constant throughout the period of investigation. The optimum coincided with the optimum hydrogen ion concentration of the enzyme (pH values 4·0 to 5·0 in von Euler and Laurin's[64] experiments). Willstätter, Lowry, and Schneider[60] record a somewhat wider optimum range, between pH values of 4·5 and 7·0.

In the case of the mycelium of *Penicillium glaucum* grown at or below 16° C. von Euler[65] found that the largest amount of saccharase was produced on the fourth day after inoculation. It amounted to only one-tenth of that produced under optimum conditions by a bottom yeast or one-sixth of that of a top yeast. The conidia of the *Penicillium* species studied contained but one-third of the saccharase found in the mycelium. In a species of *Fusarium* investigated in 1887 by Wasserzug[66] copper-reducing carbohydrates were not observed in a saccharose solution acted upon by the fungus until the fifth day after inoculation. Here, therefore, the production of saccharase had been even slower than in the case of *Penicillium glaucum*.

A reduction in saccharase production was observed by Fermi and Montesano in the case of their test-organisms when grown beyond their optimum temperatures. This may have been due to a general lowering of the vitality of the organisms since the recovery of enzyme production did not take place for a number of generations. At 35° C. von Euler and Svanberg[67] were unable to detect saccharase production by their yeast strain.

The action of saccharase was thought by Brown[68] to lead in the first instance to a compound being formed between the enzyme and the hydrolyte, cane sugar. This view became discredited, but has recently been accepted as correct by Colin and Chaudun.[69] It is also supported by Fermi and Montesano's observation that saccharase shows greater resistance to high temperatures in the presence of cane sugar than in the absence of the carbohydrate. According to H. E. and E. F. Armstrong[70] saccharase extends its influence over the whole of the saccharose molecule, and differs in this respect from other disaccharide hydrolysing enzymes such as maltase, which affects only one part of the hydrolyte.

From O'Sullivan and Thompson's[71] investigations in 1890 to Ingersoll's[72] observations in 1926, the subject of the rate of hydrolysis of saccharose by its specific enzyme has received considerable attention. Under favourable conditions, and in solutions containing up to 5 per cent. of saccharose, the rate will increase proportionally to the amount of hydrolyte present. Beyond this the rate remains stationary until a 20 per cent. concentration of saccharose is reached (von Euler and Myrbäck[73]), when a decrease in rate sets in. The reason for this decrease has not been satisfactorily explained so far. Colin and Chaudun[74] associate it with the greater viscosity of high concentrations, pointing out that glycerin, as was first observed by Michaelis and Pechstein[75] and by Bourquelot,[76] produces a similar inhibition. But increased viscosity apparently (Ingersoll[72]) is not an important factor. Perhaps the saccharose itself, as Ingersoll suggests, may be the factor governing the retardation.

Another type of inhibition in the rate of hydrolysis is that caused by the two products of reaction, glucose and fructose, even at favourable concentrations of saccharose. It is usually observed that saccharase from yeast is inhibited by fructose and that *Aspergillus* saccharase is similarly affected by the addition of glucose. For this reason the former enzyme has been regarded as different from the latter, possessing a specific affinity for the fructose half of the saccharose molecule as against the specificity of the *Aspergillus* saccharase for the glucose half of saccharose. The terms fructo- and gluco-saccharase respectively have sometimes been applied to the two enzymes (Kuhn and Münch[77]). The study of the action of glucose, fructose, and methylglucoside on the rate of hydrolysis of saccharose is at present being actively pursued. Contributions to this study have been made by Nelson and Anderson,[78] Nelson and Post,[79] Josephson,[80] von Euler and Josephson,[81] and by Weidenhagen,[82] so far, however, without any definite conclusions being reached as to the significance of the various observations made.

An accelerating action of various acids on the activity of saccharase was observed by Bertrand and Rosenblatt.[83] They found that the saccharase of *Aspergillus niger* usually was less markedly affected in its action by acids than yeast saccharase, though the effect differed with the nature of the acid. In the case of propionic acid the concentration inducing the most rapid acceleration of the reaction was found to be the same for both enzymes. Formic, phosphoric, and nitric acids, on the other hand, acted at lower concentrations on *Aspergillus* saccharase than on yeast saccharase. The effect of the acid on saccharase therefore was dependent both on its kations and anions. An increased action of saccharase was noticed by H. E. and E. F. Armstrong[70] on adding glycine to the reacting enzyme solution.

Unlike maltase, saccharase, according to Michaelis and Rona,[84] remains soluble at all hydrogen ion concentrations.

Unexplained so far is the inhibition caused by sodium chloride on the action of koji saccharase (Kellner, Moi, and Nagaoka[85]). Fales and Nelson[86] studied this action in greater detail, and showed it to depend on the prevailing hydrogen ion concentration of the saccharose solution. They do not explain, however, why the action of sodium chloride should be negligible at the optimum hydrogen ion concentration of saccharase and increase with increasing deviations from this optimum.

The effect of magnesia on the action of saccharase was studied by Tribot,[87] who found that less cane sugar is hydrolysed by saccharase in a given time when magnesia is present, provided the time taken is sufficiently short. Giving a longer time for the reaction the effect apparently is the opposite, the magnesia inducing the enzyme to greater activity except at temperatures above 40° C., when the activity of the enzyme becomes independent of the presence of magnesia.

The action of silver nitrate and mercury bichloride was studied by von Euler and Svanberg.[88] Both salts were found to have a very marked effect on the enzyme, the former in proportion to its concentration. The action depends also on the concentration of the enzyme solution and on its reaction. It is interesting to note that the elimination of the metal from the poisoned enzyme resulted in regeneration of the enzyme.

The question of the regeneration of saccharase acquired renewed interest some time ago by the investigations of Durieux,[89] who found that, after being heated to boiling point, the enzyme would recover as much as 10 per cent. of its former hydrolysing power. If heated only to 70° C. to 80° C. it was completely inactivated. Durieux's explanation of this behaviour of saccharase is not entirely convincing. He assumes that the proteins present in the saccharase solution become coagulated on being heated to 70° C. to 80° C. and that on precipitating they carried with them the saccharase held in suspension, thus removing the enzyme from the solution. A further increase of the temperature, Durieux suggests, causes the saccharase to become water soluble, and therefore to return into solution. Only when the temperature rises considerably above the boiling point of water is the enzyme finally destroyed. A reinvestigation of Durieux's observation with the saccharase preparation of Willstätter would be of great interest, since this preparation contains no protein, at least no traces of coagulable protein.

Durieux's actual observations on the action of heat on saccharase have been confirmed by Bertrand and Rosenblatt.[90] These writers remark that the property of regeneration is not possessed by the maltase of yeast. In this fact they see additional support for the view that the two enzymes are different.

Saccharase, according to Bourquelot and Bridel,[91] also has a hydrolysing action on the three carbohydrates—raffinose, gentianose, and stachyose—at a rate decreasing in the order named. In each case fructose is liberated, showing that saccharose constitutes a part of the molecule of each of these sugars. Bourquelot and Bridel find that the remainder of the hydrolysed carbohydrate exercises an inhibitory action not only on the inversion of these sugars but also, as already mentioned, on that of saccharose.

The question of the reversibility of the action of saccharase, and consequently of the biological synthesis of saccharose, is still open. Visser,[92] who published some very interesting data on this subject, came to the conclusion that a reversibility does exist, while both Blagowestschenski[93] and Hudson and Paine[94] deny that this is the case. Hudson and Paine attribute the decline in rotatory power of a solution of fructose and glucose on addition of saccharase—a decline which Visser interpreted as support for his contention—to the action of the hydrogen ions present on the rotation of fructose. In future investigations on this subject Bourquelot and Bridel's[95] researches on the activity of saccharase in high concentrations of ethyl alcohol should not be overlooked. They found that the hydrolysing properties of saccharase remained practically unaffected by dissolving the enzyme in ethyl alcohol even of 90 per cent. strength, that is, under conditions which should facilitate the elimination of any cane sugar synthesized from glucose and fructose owing to its low solubility in this strength of alcohol.

Maltose. The production by micro-organisms of an enzyme capable of hydrolysing maltose was first suggested by Bourquelot[96] in 1886. As he was unable to trace the presence of glucose in the maltose-containing medium in which yeast developed, and since apparently he did not feel justified in assuming that the maltose was being assimilated directly, he concluded that a specific maltose hydrolysing enzyme would be necessary and suggested that it was being produced by the yeast cell within the cell wall.

The conception of maltase as a specific enzyme was not shared by all investigators, and as late as 1894 Emil Fischer[97] suggested that the maltose hydrolysing enzyme might be identical with saccharase. The observation made by Röhmann[98] that commercial saccharase does not act on maltose was explained by Fischer on the assumption that the treatment with alcohol to which commercial saccharase is subjected rendered it incapable of acting on maltose. Subsequent research has proved Fischer's views to be incorrect. In addition to Röhmann's discovery that maltase is destroyed by alcohol, a chemical to which saccharase is very resistant, Lintner and Kröber[99] have brought forward evidence to show that the optimum temperatures of the two enzymes differ materially, that of maltase being 40° C. and that of saccharase 52°–53° C.

The optimum hydrogen ion concentration of maltase was shown by Michaelis and Rona[100] to be covered by the pH values of 6·1 to 6·8, a range considerably less acid than the optimum usually attributed to saccharases. At a pH value of 4·5 maltase was found to be quite inactive. Michaelis and Rona point out that maltase is active only as an anion, while the uncharged molecule of saccharase is capable of hydrolysing cane sugar. They also found that, while maltase is precipitated at its isoelectric point, saccharase remains in solution at all hydrogen ion concentrations. A further difference between the two enzymes noted by them was that maltase is absorbed by kaolin, while saccharase is not.

Nevertheless a certain similarity between the two enzymes

appears to exist. When discussing the action of acids on saccharase it was mentioned that this action depended as much on the anion of the acid as on its kation. According to Kopaczewsky[101] this is the case also with maltase where the optimum hydrogen ion concentration, when trichloracetic acid is used to establish it, is equal to a pH value of 2·8, but using acetic acid it amounts to a pH value of 6·97.

It has been suggested that maltase might be capable of hydrolysing α-glucosides, seeing that maltase itself is an α-glucoside. This, however, does not appear to be the case. Aubry[102], for instance, found that the enzyme mixture extracted from *Aspergillus niger*, though hydrolysing maltose, had no action on α-methylglucoside. Among yeasts Aubry found some types which did not produce α-methyl glucosidase though all of them produced maltase.

Maltase is produced by a large number of micro-organisms other than yeast. In fact, judging from the observation of Bokorny[103] that maltose is a highly suitable carbohydrate for a wide range of organisms, it is to be concluded that the production of maltase is common among micro-organisms.

In his study of the production of maltase by *Monilia sitophila* Went made several interesting observations. He found that not only maltose but several other carbohydrates were capable of inducing the secretion of maltase, among them raffinose, trehalose, starch, cellulose, and xylose. That this action cannot have been in the nature of a trigger action, as observed in the case of *Microspira agarliquefaciens* by Gray and Chalmers[104], is clear from the fact that maltase production in the case of *Monilia sitophila* increased proportionally with the increase in carbohydrate concentration until a maximum had been reached. Exceeding this point an inhibition set in which according to Went was not caused by the increase in osmotic pressure.

Since Bourquelot's investigations it has generally been accepted that the diffusion of maltase through the cell wall of yeast cells is impossible. Some years ago, however, Willstätter, Oppenheimer, and Steibelt[105] came to the conclusion that a diffusion did occur but that the maltase as it left the cell was destroyed by the acid produced during fermentation.

Gentiobiose. Bourquelot and Hérissey[106] obtained this disaccharide from gentianose and showed that the enzyme mixture of *Aspergillus niger* was capable of hydrolysing it. A later investigation[107] indicated that yeast enzymes were unable to attack it.

Cellobiose. This disaccharide contains two glucose residues. It can be obtained by hydrolysis of cellulose acetate or by the action of micro-organisms on cellulose.

The property of hydrolysing cellobiose is probably widespread among micro-organisms, but so far only two groups of bacteria, *Bact. coli commune* and *Bact. lactis aerogenes*, appear to have been tested for their fermentative action on cellobiose. Both Jones and Wise[108] and Koser[109] have found that cellobiose is fermented by *Bact. lactis aerogenes* while the typical *Bact. coli commune* does not do so. They see in this fact a means of differentiating the two types. Possessing a β-glucosidic constitution emulsin has been regarded as the enzyme responsible for the hydrolysis of cellobiose (Fischer and Zemplén[110]). Bertrand and Compton[111] have shown, however, that this is not the case and that a specific cellobiose or cellase occurs in nature. The cellobiase isolated from *Aspergillus niger* was found by them to be most active at a pH value of about 6·0, while the optimum activity of emulsin was found to be nearer the alkaline side of the neutral point. That the sugar resulting from the hydrolysis of cellobiose by *Aspergilli* is glucose was shown by Bertrand and Holderer.[112]

Lactose. The association of lactose hydrolysing enzymes with the activity of lactose fermenting micro-organisms was first suggested by Naegeli (see Oppenheimer[113]). Seven years later, in 1889, Beijerinck[114] turned his attention to lactose fermenting yeasts and came to the conclusion that their fermentative power was intimately connected with the production by them of a lactose hydrolysing enzyme which he termed lactase. Subsequently Emil Fischer[115] obtained a lactase from kephir granules, a material from which he found the enzyme easier to extract than from yeast. Fischer also suggested that the lactase of yeast might be different from that of kephir since the latter is more resistant towards alcohol than the former.

The presence of lactase in fungi other than yeast has occasionally been reported, both in the case of higher fungi (*Polyporus sulphureus* by Bourquelot and Hérissey[116]) and in that of lower types such as *Aspergillus niger* (Pottevin[117]; Bierry and Coupin[118]), certain *Rhizopus* species (Nakazawa[119]; Hauzawa[120]), and *Mucor Rouxii* (Wehmer[121]).

Its presence in actinomycetes, organisms which are sometimes reported (Bergey[122]) to produce acid in milk, has not been demonstrated.

In many types of bacteria which ferment lactose it is to be assumed that lactase is present. But except for those types which with yeast constitute the kephir granules, the presence of the enzyme has not been demonstrated. And even here the lactase may have been derived from the yeast and not from the bacteria.

The isolation of lactase in substance has never progressed beyond Beijerinck's[114] attempts at precipitating it from a yeast culture with 85 per cent. alcohol, and Barendrecht's[123] method of adsorbing it on kieselguhr added to a culture of kephir yeast grown in whey for 48 hours.

Information on the nature and the properties of lactase is limited to a few indirect observations on its temperature range and hydrogen ion concentration.

From Wehmer's[121] observation that *Mucor Rouxii* ferments lactose more readily at 80° C. than at 15° C. it may be concluded that the optimum temperature for the activity of lactase is to be found nearer the former than the latter temperature. And from Bokorny's[124] demonstration that lactase is highly resistant even to high concentrations of lactic acid it follows that its optimum temperature is to be sought well on the acid side of the neutral point.

Though Beijerinck and Barendrecht obtained their lactase

preparations from the medium in which kephir yeast had developed without first destroying and disintegrating the cells, the opinion is frequently expressed (Pottevin[117]; Bierry and Coupin[118]; and Coupin[125]) that lactase is an endoenzyme. This view is supported by Fischer's statement that it is necessary to disintegrate the cells before lactase can be extracted from kephir yeast.

Before leaving the subject of lactase reference must be made to certain bacteria of the coli-paratyphosum group, first observed by Neisser and subsequently studied by Massini[51], Burri[48], and others. These types possess the faculty of acquiring fermentative powers towards lactose or saccharose when grown for some days in a medium containing lactose and saccharose respectively.

When first observed, the acquisition by these bacteria of fermentative power towards lactose and saccharose appeared to be spontaneous, occurring in a few cells of a colony or a culture. The acquisition was for that reason described as a mutation. This interpretation of the change, however, was shown by Burri[48] and by Pringsheim[126] to be misleading and has now been abandoned in favour of an explanation which allocates to each cell of the culture a latent power of fermenting lactose or saccharose, when either of these sugars is provided in the absence of other suitable carbohydrates. The nature of the enzymes thus activated has not been studied.

Melibiose is a product of hydrolysis of raffinose or melitriose. It was first observed and isolated by von Lippman[127] from the stalks of certain *Malvaceae*. Very little is known of the extent to which micro-organisms are capable of hydrolysing melibiose. That many types of yeast, notably bottom yeast, are capable of doing so was noted by Fischer and Lindner.[52]

LITERATURE

1. H. Pringsheim, *Die Polysaccharide*, 2nd edition, 1923 (Julius Springer, Berlin).
2. E. Abderhalden, *Lehrbuch d. Physiolog. Chemie*, 5th edition, 1923 (Urban and Schwarzenberg, Berlin).
3. L. Rose, *Wochenschrift f. Brauerei*, vol. 27, p. 525, 1910.
4. P. Lindner and K. Saito, *Wochenschrift f. Brauerei*, vol. 27, p. 509, 1910; vol. 28, p. 561, 1911.
5. A. J. Kluyver, *Biochem. Zeits.*, vol. 52, p. 486, 1913.
6. H. Pringsheim and G. Zemplén, *Z. f. physiol. Chem.*, vol. 62, p. 374, 1909.
7. H. Violle, *Ann. Inst. Pasteur*, vol. 35, p. 218, 1921.
8. U. Gayon and E. Dubourg, *Ann. Inst. Pasteur*, vol. 8, p. 108, 1894.
9. R. Willstätter and C. D. Lowry, *Z. physiol. Chem.*, vol. 150, p. 287, 1925.
10. H. von Euler, *Biochem. Zeits.*, vol. 85, p. 406, 1918.
11. R. Cohn, *Z. physiol. Chem.*, vol. 168, p. 92, 1927.
12. A. von Planta and Schulze, *Berichte*, vol. 23, p. 1692, 1890; vol. 24, p. 2705, 1891.
13. C. Tanret, *Bull. de la Soc. chim.*, vol. 27, p. 947, 1902; vol. 29, p. 888, 1903.
14. J. Vintilesco, *J. de Pharm. et Chim.* (6), vol. 30, p. 167, 1909.
15. C. Neuberg and S. Lachmann, *Biochem. Zeits.*, vol. 24, p. 171, 1910.
16. A. Meyer, *Z. physiol. Chem.*, vol. 6, p. 135, 1882.
17. E. Bourquelot and H. Hérissey, *Comptes rend.*, vol. 132, p. 571, 1901.
18. E. Bourquelot, *Comptes rend.*, vol. 126, p. 1045, 1898.
19. H. Berlin, *J. Amer. Chem. Soc.*, vol. 48, p. 1107, 1926.
20. E. Bourquelot and H. Hérissey, *Comptes rend.*, vol. 132, p. 571, 1901; vol. 135, p. 399, 1902.
21. H. Guyot, *Bull. de la Société botanique*, Genève, vol. 8, p. 283, 1916.
22. D. Loiseau, *Comptes rend.*, vol. 82, p. 1058, 1876.
23. C. Neuberg, *Biochem. Zeits.*, vol. 3, p. 519, 1907.
24. E. Bourquelot, *J. de Pharmacie et Chimie* (6), vol. 3, p. 390, 1896.
25. H. Gillot, *Chem. Zentrbl.*, 5th Series, vol. 3, p. 129, 1899.
26. E. B. Fred, W. H. Peterson, and J. A. Anderson, *J. Biol. Chem.*, vol. 48, p. 385, 1921.
27. P. F. Frankland, A. Stanley, and W. Frew, *Trans. Chem. Soc.*, vol. 59, p. 253, 1891.
28. F. A. F. C. Went, *Jahrb. d. wissenschaftl. Bot.*, vol. 36, p. 611, 1901.
29. R. Willstätter and R. Kuhn, *Z. f. physiol. Chem.*, vol. 115, p. 180, 1921.
30. A. Villiers, *Comptes rend.*, vol. 84, p. 35, 1877.
31. H. von Schrenk, *Agric. Bureau of Plant Ind. Bull.*, 25, 1900 (Washington).
32. A. Alekhine, *Ann. de Chim. et Physique* (6), vol. 18, p. 532, 1889.
33. R. Kuhn and G. E. Grundherr, *Berichte*, vol. 59, p. 1655, 1926.
34. M. Bridel and Th. Aagaard, *Comptes rend.*, vol. 185, p. 147, 1927.

35. E. Bourquelot and H. Hérissey, *J. de Pharm. et Chim.*, vol. 4, p. 385, 1896.

36. E. Kayser, *Ann. Inst. Pasteur*, vol. 8, p. 737, 1894.

37. E. Bourquelot, *Comptes rend.*, vol. 116, pp. 826 and 1143, 1893.

38. N. N. Ivanov, *Biochem. Zeits.*, vol. 162, p. 454, 1925.

39. E. Fischer, *Berichte*, vol. 28, II, p. 1429, 1895.

40. S. A. Koser, *J. Infect. Diseases*, vol. 29, p. 67, 1921.

41. A. Frouin and M. Guillaumie, *Bull. Soc. chim. biol.*, vol. 8, p. 1178, 1926.

42. —. Quevenne, *J. praktisch. Chemie*, vol. 14, p. 334, 1838.

43. M. P. E. Berthelot, *Comptes rend.*, vol. 50, p. 980, 1860.

44. M. Gayon, *Bull. Soc. Chim.*, vol. 35, p. 501, 1881.

45. S. Kostytschew and P. Eliasberg, *Z. f. physiol. Chem.*, vol. 118, p. 233, 1922.

46. Cl. Fermi, *Zentrbl. f. Bakt.*, vol. 12, p. 713, 1892.

47. Cl. Fermi and G. Montesano, *Zentrbl. f. Bakt.*, Abt. II, vol. 1, p. 482, 1895.

48. R. Burri, *Zentrbl. f. Bakt.*, Abt. II, vol. 28, p. 321, 1910.

49. A. C. Thaysen, *Zentrbl. f. Bakt.*, Abt. I, Orig., vol. 67, p. 1, 1912.

50. M. Neisser, *Zentrbl. f. Bakt.*, Abt. I, Ref., vol. 38, p. 98, 1906.

51. R. Massini, *Arch. f. Hyg.*, vol. 61, p. 250, 1907.

52. E. Fischer and P. Lindner, *Berichte*, vol. 28, p. 3034, 1895.

53. S. A. Waksman, *Soil Science*, vol. 8, p. 71, 1919.

54. H. von Euler and O. Svanberg, *Z. f. physiol. Chem.*, vol. 107, p. 269, 1919.

    H. von Euler and O. Svanberg, *Z. f. physiol. Chem.*, vol. 110, p. 175, 1920.

    H. von Euler, A. Hedelius, and O. Svanberg, *Z. f. physiol. Chem.*, vol. 110, p. 190, 1920.

55. R. Willstätter and W. Wassermann, *Z. f. physiol. Chem.*, vol. 123, p. 181, 1922.

56. E. Salkowski, *Z. f. physiol. Chem.*, vol. 61, p. 124, 1909.

57. R. Willstätter, K. Schneider, and E. Wenzel, *Z. f. physiol. Chem.*, vol. 151, p. 1, 1926.

58. Z. I. Kertesz, *Fermentforschung*, vol. 9, p. 300, 1928.

59. H. von Euler and H. Cramer, *Biochem. Zeits.*, vol. 58, p. 467, 1914.

60. R. Willstätter, C. D. Lowry jr., and K. Schneider, *Z. f. physiol. Chem.*, vol. 146, p. 158, 1925.

61. G. Grezes, *Ann. Inst. Pasteur*, vol. 26, p. 556, 1912.

62. O. Svanberg, *Z. f. physiol. Chem.*, vol. 120, p. 65, 1920.

63. H. von Euler and O. Svanberg, *Z. f. technische Biologie*, vol. 7, p. 165, 1919.

64. H. von Euler and T. Laurin, *Z. f. physiol. Chem.*, vol. 108, p. 64, 1919.

65. H. von Euler, *Fermentforschung*, vol. 4, p. 242, 1920–1.

66. E. Wasserzug, *Ann. Inst. Pasteur*, vol. 1, p. 525, 1887.

67. H. von Euler and O. Svanberg, *Z. f. physiol. Chem.*, vol. 106, p. 201, 1919.

68. A. J. Brown, *J. Chem. Soc.*, vol. 81, p. 373, 1902.
69. H. Colin and A. Chaudun, *Comptes rend.*, vol. 167, p. 338, 1918.
70. H. E. Armstrong and E. F. Armstrong, *Proc. Royal Soc.*, Series B, vol. 79, p. 360, 1907.
71. C. O'Sullivan and F. W. Thompson, *J. Chem. Soc.*, vol. 57, p. 834, 1890.
72. C. D. Ingersoll, *Bull. Soc. chim. biol.*, vol. 8, p. 264, 1926.
73. H. von Euler and K. Myrbäck, *Z. f. physiol. Chem.*, vol. 124, p. 159, 1922.
74. H. Colin and A. Chaudun, *Bull. Inst. Past.*, vol. 20, p. 463, 1922.
75. L. Michaelis and H. Pechstein, *Biochem. Zeits.*, vol. 60, p. 79, 1914.
76. E. Bourquelot, *Comptes rend.*, vol. 165, p. 567, 1917.
77. R. Kuhn and H. Münch, *Z. physiol. Chem.*, vol. 163, p. 1, 1927.
78. J. M. Nelson and R. S. Anderson, *J. Biol. Chem.*, vol. 69, p. 443, 1926.
79. J. M. Nelson and C. Irwin Post, *J. Biol. Chem.*, vol. 68, p. 265, 1926.
80. K. Josephson, *Arch. f. Kem. Mineralog. o. Geolog.*, vol. 9, p. 1, 1926.
81. H. von Euler and K. Josephson, *Z. physiol. Chem.*, vol. 155, p. 1, 1926.
82. R. Weidenhagen, *Z. Ver. d. deutsch. Zuckerind.*, Tech. Teil, vol. 78, p. 406, 1928.
83. G. Bertrand and M. et Mme Rosenblatt, *Ann. Inst. Pasteur*, vol. 26, p. 932, 1912; ibid., vol. 27, p. 366, 1913.
84. L. Michaelis and P. Rona, *Biochem. Zeits.*, vol. 57, p. 70, 1913.
85. O. Kellner, Y. Moi, and M. Nagaoka, *Z. physiol. Chem.*, vol. 14, p. 297, 1890.
86. H. A. Fales and G. M. Nelson, *J. Amer. Chem. Soc.*, vol. 37, p. 2769, 1915.
87. G. Tribot, *Comptes rend.*, vol. 148, p. 788, 1909.
88. H. von Euler and O. Svanberg, *Fermentforschung*, vol. 3, p. 330, 1920.
89. O. Durieux, *Bull. Soc. chim. Belgique*, vol. 28, p. 99, 1914.
90. G. Bertrand and M. Rosenblatt, *Comptes rend.*, vol. 158, p. 1455, 1914.
91. E. Bourquelot and M. Bridel, *J. de Pharm. et Chim.* (7), vol. 3, p. 569, 1911.
92. A. W. Vissier, *Z. physiol. Chem.*, vol. 52, p. 257, 1905.
93. A. Blagowestschenski, *Biochem. Zeits.*, vol. 61, p. 446, 1914.
94. C. S. Hudson and H. S. Paine, *J. Amer. Chem. Soc.*, vol. 36, p. 1571, 1914.
95. E. Bourquelot and M. Bridel, *J. Pharm. et Chim.* (7), vol. 9, p. 321, 1914.
96. E. Bourquelot, *J. de l'Anatomie et de la Physiologie*, vol. 22, p. 162, 1886.
97. E. Fischer, *Berichte*, vol. 27, p. 3479, 1894.
98. F. Röhmann, *Berichte*, vol. 27, p. 3251, 1894.
99. C. J. Lintner and E. Kröber, *Berichte*, vol. 28, p. 1050, 1895.
100. L. Michaelis and P. Rona, *Biochem. Zeits.*, vol. 57, p. 70, 1913.
101. W. Kopaczewsky, *Comptes rend.*, vol. 158, p. 640, 1914.
102. A. Aubry, *J. Pharm. et Chim.* (7), vol. 10, p. 23, 1914.
103. Th. Bokorny, *Zentrbl. f. Bakt.*, Abt. II, vol. 47, p. 191, 1917.
104. P. H. H. Gray and C. H. Chalmers, *Ann. App. Biol.*, vol. 11, p. 324, 1924.

105. R. Willstätter, T. Oppenheimer, and W. Steibelt, *Z. physiol. Chem.*, vol. 110, p. 232, 1920.

106. E. Bourquelot and H. Hérissey, *J. Pharm. et Chim.* (6), vol. 7, p. 369, 1898.

107. E. Bourquelot and H. Hérissey, *Comptes rend.*, vol. 132, p. 571, 1901.

108. H. N. Jones and L. E. Wise, *J. Bacteriol.*, vol. 11, p. 359, 1926.

109. A. Koser, *J. Infect. Dis.*, vol. 38, p. 506, 1926.

110. E. Fischer and G. Zemplén, *Ann. der Chem.*, vol. 365, p. 1, 1909.

111. G. Bertrand and A. Compton, *Bull. Soc. chim.* (4), vol. 7, p. 995, 1910.

112. G. Bertrand and M. Holderer, *Comptes rend.*, vol. 149, p. 1385, 1909.

113. C. Oppenheimer, *Die Fermente*, 5th edition, vol. 1, p. 627, 1924 (Gustav Fischer, Jena).

114. M. W. Beijerinck, *Zentrbl. f. Bakt.*, vol. 6, p. 44, 1889.

115. E. Fischer, *Berichte*, vol. 27, p. 3479, 1894.

116. E. Bourquelot and H. Hérissey, *Comptes rend.*, vol. 137, p. 56, 1903.

117. H. Pottevin, *Ann. Inst. Pasteur*, vol. 17, p. 31, 1903.

118. H. Bierry and F. Coupin, *Comptes rend.*, vol. 157, p. 246, 1913.

119. R. Nakazawa, *Zentrbl. f. Bakt.*, Abt. II, vol. 24, p. 482, 1909.

120. J. Hauzawa, *Mykologisches Zentrbl.*, vol. 1, p. 76, 1912.

121. C. Wehmer, *Zentrbl. f. Bakt.*, Abt. II, vol. 6, p. 353, 1900.

122. D. H. Bergey, *Manual of Determinative Bacteriology*, 2nd edition, 1928 (Baillière, Tindal & Cox, London).

123. H. P. Barendrecht, *Zeitschr. f. physikal. Chem.*, vol. 54, p. 357, 1906.

124. Th. Bokorny, *Chem. Zentrbl.*, vol. 74, p. 1334, 1903.

125. F. Coupin, *J. de Physiol. Path. gen.*, vol. 16, p. 419, 1914.

126. H. Pringsheim, *Die Variabilität niederer Organismen*, 1910 (Julius Springer, Berlin).

127. E. O. von Lippmann, *Berichte*, vol. 53, p. 2069, 1920.

CHAPTER IV

HYDROLYSIS OF GLUCOSIDES

IN spite of the great interest which attaches to the micro-biological decomposition of glucosides, both from a pharmacological and from a physiological point of view, little has been done to study the problem even in the case of such important glucosides as digitalin, digitoxin, and strophanthin. Judging from the available literature, interest appears to have been limited almost entirely to ascertaining whether micro-organisms do or do not hydrolyse glucosides. Only in the case of the industrially important glucoside indican and the equally important glucosidic substance tannin has an attempt been made to investigate in greater detail the hydrolysis and the subsequent decomposition.

In general it may be claimed that many bacteria and fungi possess the property of hydrolysing glucosides. Among actinomycetes, however, the property is rare.

Bourquelot[1] found that amygdalin, sambucin, coniferin, aesculin, and salicin were hydrolysed by many wood-destroying fungi. Kohnstamm[2] added to the list of glucosides arbutin and helicin. Among the lower fungi Bourquelot and Hérissey[3] found that the enzyme mixture of *Aspergillus niger* hydrolysed amygdalin, salicin, coniferin, arbutin, aesculin, helicin, populin, and phloridzin. *Penicillium glaucum* was tested by Gerard[4] on amygdalin and on salicin and was found to hydrolyse both.

The readiness with which a fungus hydrolyses a glucoside was studied by Brunstein[5] and was found by him to vary considerably. Amygdalin and coniferin were most easily decomposed. Arbutin, helicin, and salicin were less so, owing, he suggests, to the inhibitory action exercised on the growth of the fungus by the products of hydrolysis. Nevertheless, Castellani's[6] investigations on certain bacteria indicate that salicin is far more frequently hydrolysed than amygdalin.

F

As a general rule Brunstein found that a well-nourished mycelium acted more quickly and more completely on glucosides than did a starved mycelium. For that reason he recommended the use of a starved fungus for the study of the progress of the hydrolysis, since the slower rate of conversion of the glucoside by such a mycelium made it possible to follow the intermediate stages of the breakdown and to show that the carbohydrate liberated during hydrolysis becomes subsequently assimilated by the fungus.

This liberation of a carbohydrate indicates that glucosides are capable of serving as a food-substance for the organisms hydrolysing them, a view which is supported by Puriewitsch's[7] observation that spores of *Aspergillus niger*, *Aspergillus glaucus*, and *Penicillium glaucum* germinate and form a mycelium in an aqueous solution of helicin.

That glucoside hydrolysing enzymes are present in the mycelium of a fungus from the time of the germination of its spore was shown by Javillier and Tschernoroutzky.[8] In their experiments Javillier and Tschernoroutzky also observed that the presence of a zinc salt in the culture medium was favourable to the secretion of glucosidase. Studying *Aspergillus* and *Penicillium* species these workers established that less enzyme diffuses into the surrounding medium from young cultures than from older ones, and that the rate of diffusion may vary according to the nature of the enzyme. The optimum hydrogen ion concentration for the activity of amygdalase by the species mentioned was determined by Javillier and Tschernoroutzky to be equal to a pH value of about 3·8 to 4·0.

Among bacteria the glucoside hydrolysing properties of the coli-typhosum group have been studied by Twort,[9] after Inghilleri[10] had shown that *Bact. coli commune* decomposes amygdalin while *Bact. typhosum* does not. Twort examined the behaviour of a large number of strains of the coli-typhosum group towards no less than forty-nine different glucosides, with a view to discovering differences in the behaviour of these strains, applicable to their classification. He found that as a rule the strains which hydrolysed lactose attacked glucosides fairly readily. But he was unable to base any system of classification on their behaviour towards glucosides since two types of one sub-group might differ in this respect while two members of different sub-groups might show an identical behaviour towards glucosides.

A year before Twort's publication van der Leck[11] had emphasized the value of the use of glucosides as a means of differentiating bacteria and had shown that *Bact. coli commune* and *Bact. lactis aerogenes* are both capable of hydrolysing indican and aesculin. Van der Leck based his technique on the method introduced by Molisch,[12] who tested bacteria for glucoside hydrolysing properties by cultivating them on an agar prepared by the addition of the required percentage of the gel to an extract of *Indigofera* leaves. Molisch found that types of bacteria capable of hydrolysing indican produced a blue growth on this medium.

The action of bacteria on glucosides was also studied by Fermi and Montesano,[13] who showed that amygdalin is hydrolysed by *Micrococcus pyogenes tenuis* and usually by *Vibrio Metchnikoff*, at least when freshly isolated strains are employed. *Bact. coli commune*, on the other hand, sometimes gave negative results, an observation which is not altogether surprising considering the wide range of variation represented. The findings of Fermi and Montesano were confirmed some years later by Twort's observations referred to above.

In Fermi and Montesano's experiments *Bac. Megatherium, Sarcina aurantiaca*, and *Corynebacterium diphtheriae* were sometimes found capable of hydrolysing amygdalin. This is of considerable interest, particularly as regards the last-named type, since none of the typical actinomycetes tested by Fermi and Montesano were found capable of hydrolysing glucosides.

On the subject of the physical properties of glucosidases secreted by bacteria and fungi, information is limited to the observations of Bourquelot and Aubrey[14] and of Fischer[15] that these enzymes are highly sensitive to acids. In Bourquelot and Aubrey's experiments even 'very small' quantities of acetic acid destroyed the β-glucosidase of fungi.

The hydrolysis of glucosides by micro-organisms has acquired practical importance in two directions, in the production of natural indigo and in the fermentation of tannin. In both cases the hydrolysis of a glucoside, or at least of a compound related to the glucosides, is an essential part of the industrial process involved.

MANUFACTURE OF INDIGO

Like retting, the preparation of natural indigo is an agricultural process traceable to remote antiquity. And even more than retting has indigo preparation been allowed to proceed on old established lines without any serious attempt to apply the result of scientific investigation, despite the pressure of competition brought about by the introduction of synthetic indigo.

Indigo can be prepared from plants which produce the glucoside indican. The process, in brief outline, consists in an extraction of the indican-containing tissues, usually the leaves, with eight to ten parts of water at ordinary temperatures, followed by an oxidation of the extract in a process termed the beating process, during which the indoxyl in the extract is converted into indigotin. The extraction, usually known as the fermentation, is allowed to proceed as a rule for 12 to 14 hours, and is the stage during which microbiological activity predominates. Though investigators agree that a varied and vigorous microflora exists in the extraction vats during fermentation, the part it takes in the hydrolysis of indican to indoxyl and glucose has been very differently estimated. Some investigators, notably Bréaudat[16] and Beijerinck,[17] have expressed the view that the conversion of the indican to indoxyl is due solely to the action of a specific enzyme secreted by the plant tissues. Others, Molisch[12] for instance, while not denying that micro-organisms are capable of converting indican to indigotin and admitting (Bergtheil[18]) that the microflora may exercise some slight action, still see the chief hydrolysing agency in a specific enzyme produced by the plant tissues, or regard the conversion as a purely chemical reaction (Molisch[12]). Alvarez,[19] and more recently Davis[20], maintain that the microflora present in the steeping vats is the chief hydrolysing agent and regard the action of any indican hydrolysing enzyme produced by the plant tissues as of secondary importance if not actually detrimental. As early as 1887 Alvarez isolated a bacterium in pure culture from the content of steeping vats, a bacterium which he found capable of hydrolysing indican and therefore termed *Bact. indigogenum*. He described it as a short rod with rounded ends, often occurring in pairs or short chains.

Davis[20] accepts Alvarez's claim that micro-organisms constitute the normal agency for the conversion of indican into indoxyl, and supplies data supporting this, showing also that in actual practice the yield of indigotin depends on the presence of an adequate number of suitable bacteria in the tanks used for extraction, a number which may be supplied naturally with the steeping water or introduced artificially as pure cultures.

Using a medium consisting of an indigo leaf extract and the requisite percentage of agar, Hutchinson (see Davis[20]) was able to sub-divide these indican hydrolysing micro-organisms into two groups, an active group producing intensely blue colonies and a poor type giving pale blue or colourless colonies. Where the former type predominated good yields of indoxyl could always be relied upon, while a large number of faintly staining types gave rise to destructive changes with resulting loss in yield of quality of indigo.

Though he gives but few details on the fermentation process, it is clear from Davis's papers that considerable quantities of carbon dioxide are produced during the decomposition of the glucose liberated through the hydrolysis of indican. In fact this carbon dioxide is claimed to be almost entirely responsible for the very marked acidity which, if not checked, may cause considerable loss in yield and quality of the resulting dye. On the other hand, a certain acidity of the water used for extraction is stated to be essential, since the indican cannot diffuse out into the water surrounding the leaves under neutral or alkaline conditions. Davis observed that the extraction of the glucoside and the development of acidity proceeded almost concurrently. Both increased during the earlier stages in direct proportion to time. An accumulation of indican in the extract did not occur, the glucoside being hydrolysed into indoxyl and glucose as rapidly as it passed into solution.

The liquor from the steeping or fermentation vats is usually of a pale yellow colour with a greenish fluorescence. Immediately on being drawn from the vat it is subjected to an oxidation through which the comparatively unstable indoxyl is converted into indigotin. The efficiency of this conversion was found by Davis to depend on several factors, principally on the acidity developed during steeping. Where the fermentation had given rise to a high acidity, owing to the accumulation of acid forming micro-organisms, the efficiency of the oxidation was low. Neutralizing the acidity resulted in improved yields. Davis regards the conversion of indoxyl into indigo brown, a substance which does not oxidize to indigotin under normal conditions, as due to an excessive initial acidity in the steeping liquor. He sees a further sign of the serious effects of a high acidity in the solution of plant proteins and their subsequent precipitation during beating. These are the proteins which are described in indigo technology as indigo gluten. Not infrequently this indigo gluten represents as much as 20 per cent. of an ordinary cake of indigo.

The varied microflora which must be introduced into the steeping vats with fresh leaves no doubt contains many types capable of producing volatile and non-volatile acids from the glucose liberated during the hydrolysis of the indican. It is noteworthy that this flora should be unable to form these acids under the conditions prevailing in the steeping vats. Davis specifically mentions that volatile acids such as formic, acetic, and butyric acids are not met with in appreciable quantities during normal fermentations, and that lactic, citric, and tartaric acids usually were absent. This apparent anomaly renders a further study of the physiology of the true indican hydrolysing bacteria most desirable.

The oxidation process completed, the indigotin is allowed to settle, and, together with admixed indigo brown, indigo gluten, and other impurities, is collected in paste form. The paste is usually heated to a temperature sufficient to prevent further microbiological activity and is then allowed to dry under neutral conditions.

THE PRODUCTION OF GALLIC ACID THROUGH THE FERMENTATION OF TANNIN

The conversion of tannin into gallic acid must have been one of the earliest biological reactions to be seriously investigated. As early as 1785 Scheele[21] expressed the view that gallic acid exists in gall apples but cannot be extracted directly owing to its being protected by other substances which only a decay of the apples can remove. This view was not accepted by subsequent investigators. A clear conception of the formation of gallic acid was not obtained until nearly a century later when van Tieghem[22] showed that gallic acid is formed by the decomposition of tannin present in gall apples. Since then interest has become centred on the question of the agent responsible for the conversion of tannin. Various fungi developing on gall apples during their decay, i.e. their fermentation, were usually thought to be associated with the conversion, though Robiquet[23] maintained that a plant enzyme, a pectase, was the responsible agent. Van Tieghem ascribed the conversion to the activity of an enzyme secreted by the fungi present, but failed to prove this. When Duclaux[24] succeeded in doing so a fairly accurate impression was obtained of the reaction taking place.

Duclaux gives the following description of the preparation of gallic acid from gall apples. Gall apples which normally contain from 40 to 60 per cent. of tannin are made damp and incubated at 25° C. to 30° C. for a month under moist conditions. The apples swell and, through the action of the fungi developing on them, undergo a 'fermentation' in which no appreciable evolution of gas occurs except where yeast is added to remove the glucose liberated by the hydrolysis of the tannin. The progress of the fermentation is followed by determining the decrease in glucose present. When complete, a yield of 30 to 50 per cent. of gallic acid should have accumulated. In practice, however, the yield is often as low as 20 per cent. The reason for this was shown by Knudson[25] to be due to various causes, primarily to the absence of suitable fungi, and secondly to lack of a certain percentage of an additional food other than tannin. In his experiments *Penicillium rugulosum* and *Aspergillus niger* were the only fungi studied which developed normally at tannin concentrations higher than 10 per cent. This growth was found most rapid in concentrations of about 15 per cent. of tannin and under aerobic conditions. But to ensure an economic conversion of the tannin into gallic acid he found it necessary to add 10 per cent. of cane sugar. This prevented the fungi from breaking down the liberated gallic acid. In his investigations 1 mg. of mycelium of *Aspergillus niger*, the more active of the two fungi, was found sufficient to hydrolyse 2·70 mg. of tannin in 10 days.

LITERATURE

1. E. Bourquelot, *Comptes rend.*, vol. 117, p. 383, 1893.
2. Ph. Kohnstamm, *Beihefte botan. Zentrbl.*, vol. 10, p. 90, 1901.
3. E. Bourquelot and H. Hérissey, *Comptes rend.*, vol. 121, p. 693, 1895.
4. E. Gerard, *Comptes rend. Soc. biol.*, vol. 5 (9), p. 651, 1893.
5. A. Brunstein, *Beihefte botan. Zentrbl.*, vol. 10, p. 1, 1901.
6. A. Castellani, *Zentrbl. f. Bakt.*, Abt. I, vol. 62, p. 262, 1912.
7. K. Puriewitsch, *Ber. deut. botan. Gesell.*, vol. 16, p. 368, 1898.
8. M. Javillier and H. Tschernoroutzky, *Ann. Inst. Pasteur*, vol. 27, *Bull. Sci. Pharm.*, vol. 20, p. 132, 1913.
9. F. W. Twort, *Proc. Royal Soc.*, Series B, vol. 79, p. 329, 1907.
10. —. Inghilleri, *Zentrbl. f. Bakt.*, vol. 15, p. 821, 1894.
11. G. van der Leck, *Zentrbl. f. Bakt.*, Abt. II, vol. 17, p. 366, 1906.

12. H. Molisch, *Sitzber. Akad. Wiss. Wien, Math.-Naturwiss. Kl.*, vol. 107, p. 758, 1898.

13. C. Fermi and G. Montesano, *Zentrbl. f. Bakt.*, vol. 15, p. 722, 1894.

14. E. Bourquelot and A. Aubrey, *Comptes rend.*, vol. 116, p. 742, 1915.

15. E. Fischer, *Z. physiol. Chem.*, vol. 107, p. 176, 1919.

16. L. Bréaudat, *Comptes rend.*, vol. 127, p. 769, 1898.

17. M. W. Beijerinck, *Proc. Kon. Akad. van Wetenschap*, Amsterdam, Section Science, vol. 3, p. 101, 1900–1.

18. C. Bergtheil, *Trans. Chem. Soc.*, vol. 85, p. 870, 1904.

19. E. Alvarez, *Comptes rend.*, vol. 105, p. 286, 1887.

20. W. A. Davis, *Publication of the Agricultural Research Institute*, Pusa. Indigo publication, No. 9, 1921; No. 11, 1922.

21. K. W. Scheele, *Opuscula*, vol. 2, p. 229, 1785.

22. Ph. van Tieghem, *Arch. d. Sciences naturelles* bot. (5), vol. 8, p. 240, 1867.

23. E. Robiquet, *Ann. Chim. Phys.* (3), vol. 39, p. 453, 1853.

24. E. Duclaux, *Frémy's Encyclopédie chimique*, vol. 9, p. 1, p. 226, 1883. (Durod, Paris.)

25. L. Knudson, *J. Biol. Chem.*, vol. 14, pp. 159 and 285, 1913.

PART TWO

CHAPTER V

THE FERMENTATION OF MONOSES

THE hydrolytic processes by which polysaccharides are converted by micro-organisms into their component monoses results in the liberation of very little energy, far from sufficient to cover the requirements of the cells responsible for the hydrolysis. To satisfy these requirements the liberated monoses must undergo decomposition.

The fact that numerous products result from this decomposition has been regarded as an indication that micro-organisms possess a large number of enzymes, each of them responsible for a specific change of the monose molecule. Recent investigations, however, indicate that these changes are the result of comparatively few and simple reactions, catalysed in some manner hitherto not definitely ascertained. To explain these reactions Oppenheimer and Neuberg[1] suggest the functioning of a single group of enzymes which they term 'desmolases'.

Quastel[2] favours the assumption of the presence of powerful electrical fields on the surface of the bacterial cell membrane. But it may well be that some other explanation will in time be found to be a more suitable working theory.

Until about the second decade of the present century it was customary to speak of the carbohydrate decomposing activities of micro-organisms as oxidation processes by which food substances such as monoses became decomposed, either in the presence of atmospheric oxygen (aerobic respiration), or of oxygen contained as an integral part of the molecule of one of the substances which were being decomposed (anaerobic respiration, fermentation).

With the accumulation of experimental evidence in support of Wieland's[3] theory on the chemistry of respiration this view had to be abandoned in favour of the assumption that hydrogen atoms, contained in the decomposing molecule, became 'activated' before oxygen entered the field of reaction. Through their activation the hydrogen atoms were rendered capable of combining with oxygen—or with any other substances capable of combining with activated hydrogen. The molecule containing the activated hydrogen atoms is termed the hydrogen donator, the oxygen, or any other hydrogen absorbing molecule or molecule radical, the hydrogen acceptor. Such substances as methylene blue, litmus, and nitrates can function as hydrogen acceptors.

Very interesting work on the activating properties of certain facultative anaerobic and obligatory aerobic microorganisms has been carried out by Quastel and his collaborators;[4] work which has demonstrated experimentally that these organisms activate the molecules of the substances to be dehydrogenated (oxidized) before a fermentation takes place. This activation involves in some cases the hydrogen donator only, in others both the hydrogen donator and the hydrogen acceptor. It is clear from Quastel's work that the activation of the hydrogen donator is essential in all cases, but that certain hydrogen acceptors, methylene blue for instance, are able to function without preliminary activation.

Atmospheric oxygen possibly belongs to those hydrogen acceptors which function without preliminary activation. Some authorities, however, among them Hopkins,[5] Rapkine and Wurmster,[6] Oppenheimer,[7] von Scent-Györgyi,[8] and Kluyver and Donker,[9] favour the view that an activation is essential before oxygen becomes capable of combining with activated hydrogen.

As a result of the transfer of hydrogen to the acceptor, the energy necessary for growth is liberated and substances are formed which, according to Quastel and Stephenson,[10] serve as the basis for the synthetic processes of the microorganisms responsible for the activation.

Thus the essential feature of respiration—and of fermentation—as viewed in the light of Wieland's theory, is an action of the living plasma, or of enzymes produced by the plasma, or of electrical fields functioning on the surface of the cell membrane (on the actual agency opinions still differ), on certain molecules of the medium in which the plasma is suspended. A transfer of hydrogen thereby becomes possible. The function of oxygen has been reduced to that of an acceptor for hydrogen, a function which it shares with a good many other substances, which in the case of anaerobic respiration at least are more suitable than oxygen itself.

The principle of this more recent conception of respiration and fermentation is an interaction between hydrogen donator and hydrogen acceptor, through what Oppenheimer[11] describes as oxidation-reductions.

Why oxygen should be of less value than other acceptors is not yet clearly explained. It is conceivably connected with the inability of anaerobic organisms to produce catalase, an enzyme responsible for the destruction of the peroxide of hydrogen formed as the final product of reaction between activated hydrogen and oxygen.

In these and subsequent pages the above conception has been adopted to explain the manifold and apparently unconnected data which in the course of time have been collected on the subject of the action of micro-organisms on monoses. This conception is an indispensable part of the only existing working theory which makes it possible to reduce the various known data on bacterial fermentations to something like order, and which makes it feasible to co-ordinate this subject into a comprehensible system—a system which already shows signs of being capable of withstanding criticism based on experimental evidence.

In order to appreciate the system adopted for the grouping of the various types of bacterial fermentation an outline must be given of the working theory on which it is based.

It is generally accepted that a monose must be esterified into monosephosphoric esters before it can be decomposed by yeast, or by any other living cell or cell extract, into compounds containing chains of less than six carbon atoms. The exact nature of these esters has not yet been clearly defined. They may be identical with the hexosediphosphoric ester first isolated by Harden and Young;[12] or with the hexose-monophosphoric ester of Robison;[13] or they may perhaps be represented by specially labile esters which on stabilization yield either hexosediphosphoric or hexosemonophosphoric esters (Kluyver and Struyk[14]).

Following the formation of these phosphoric esters it is possible to conceive the conversion of monoses into any or all of the known fermentation products on the assumption of the occurrence of progressive oxidation-reduction reactions, activated by the responsible micro-organisms. Instead of a multitude of specific enzymes the working theory adopted in these pages requires the presence of two catalytic agencies only, one responsible for the esterification of a monose into monose phosphoric esters and another activating the hydro-gen transfer from a hydrogen donator to a hydrogen acceptor. The diversity of the final fermentation products is conceived to be the result, of variations in the functions of the activating agency, in the faculty of a specific organism to utilize certain substances as hydrogen acceptor, and conceivably also in the possession by the organism of protective powers against the accumulation of certain substances—hydrogen peroxide for instance—which in higher concentrations might destroy the cell.

As early as 1907 Meyer[15] suspected that methylglyoxal, $CH_3-CO-C\diagdown_H^O$, might be an intermediate fermentation product of glucose when acted upon by yeast. This view was further developed by Neuberg and Kerb,[16] who assume that glucose when fermented by yeast is first converted into two molecules of methylglyoxal, each of which is further dis-integrated until alcohol and carbon dioxide results. In the course of time numerous attempts have been made to ascer-tain the behaviour of a large number of micro-organisms towards methylglyoxal, sometimes with positive results showing that this substance is decomposable into the normal fermentation products of the test organism, and some-times with negative results. Through these investigations it came to be widely accepted that methylglyoxal is the first intermediate decomposition product in all those fermentations in which a rupture of the monose chain occurs. Recently, however, work by Lambie[17] and by Kermack, Lambie, and Slater[18] on the function of methylglyoxal in insulin hypoglycaemia has thrown doubt on the soundness of this view. It would appear that methylglyoxal cannot replace glucose in the alleviation of insulin hypoglycaemia, while dihydroxyacetone, $CH_2OH.CO.CH_2OH$, another compound possessing a three carbon chain, is even better suited to do so than glucose itself. Methylglyoxal, therefore, cannot be a physiological intermediary of glucose, at least not in the form in which it was tested by Lambie. If a substance is to function as an antidote against insulin hypoglycaemia, it must be affected by insulin in the same way as glucose is affected and for that reason must be either glucose itself or a physiological derivative of glucose.

It may be, therefore, that dihydroxyacetone and not methylglyoxal is the first detectable intermediate decomposition product of hexose. This was suspected many years ago by Bertrand[19] and by Boysen-Jensen.[20]

However this may be, there is considerable experimental evidence in support of the assumption that on saponification of a monosephosphoric ester by micro-organisms, the liberated hexose is converted into two molecules possessing three carbon chains.

Kluyver and Donker,[9] who are the authors of the working theory adopted in these pages for the purpose of grouping the various microbiological fermentations, explain the conversion of glucosephosphoric esters into methylglyoxal by the following scheme:

(1) $CH_2OH.CH.CH^*OH.CHOH.CHOH.CHO \rightarrow$

$$\begin{array}{c} | \\ O \\ | \\ PO_3R_2 \end{array}$$

(2) $CH_2OH.CH.CHO + CH_2OH.CHOH.CHO \rightarrow$

$$\begin{array}{c} | \\ O \\ | \\ PO_3R_2 \end{array} \qquad \text{glyceraldehyde}$$

(3) $CH_2OH.CH.CHO + H_2O \rightarrow CH_2OH.CHOH.CHO$
$$\begin{array}{c} | \\ O \\ | \\ PO_3R_2 \end{array} \qquad\qquad\qquad + PO_4R_2H$$

glyceraldehyde phosphoric   glyceraldehyde + phosphoric
          ester   ester

(4) $CH_2.CH^*OH.C{\Large\langle}^H_{OH} \rightarrow CH_3.COH.C{\Large\langle}^H_{OH} \rightarrow$
$$\underset{O}{\diagdown\diagup}\qquad\qquad H\quad O\;\;OH$$

glyceraldehyde anhydride

$$CH_3.C{\Large\langle}^{OH}_{OH} - \overset{H}{\underset{}{C}} - OH \rightarrow CH_3.CO.C{\Large\langle}^O_H$$
$$\qquad\qquad\qquad\qquad\quad {\diagdown}OH$$

methylglyoxal

The activating properties of the organism attacking the
monose are assumed to affect, in the first instance, the hydrogen atom bound to the fourth carbon atom. This is indicated
above by an asterisk placed against this atom. Through the
activation, the third carbon atom becomes capable of functioning as a hydrogen acceptor, with the result that the
activated hydrogen wanders to this carbon atom. Thereby
the six carbon chain is broken up into one glyceraldehyde
molecule and one glyceraldehyde phosphoric ester molecule.
The latter becomes hydrolysed, yielding one additional molecule of glyceraldehyde and one molecule of phosphoric acid,
the latter combining with a fresh monose molecule so long as
the esterifying agency continues to function.

Under the influence of the fermenting organism the hydrogen of the second carbon atom in the glyceraldehyde anhydride molecule is activated and transferred to the third. The

introduction of a molecule of water gives rise to the formation of methylglyoxal.

The assumption of the occurrence of dihydroxyacetone as the first detectable intermediate product of fermentation postulates a slightly different conception of this initial stage of fermentation. In this case the activated hydrogen of the second carbon atom would be transferred to the first carbon atom thus:

$$(1)\quad CH_2.CHOH.C{\overset{\textstyle OH}{\underset{\textstyle\ \ O}{\diagup}}}\diagdown\underset{H}{}\ \to\ CH_2.COH.\overset{OH}{\underset{O}{C}}-H\diagdown H$$

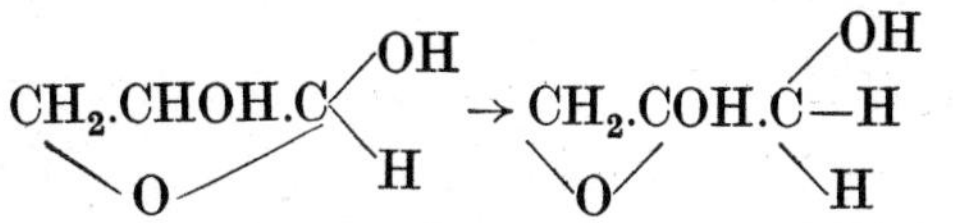

     glyceraldehyde anhydride

On introduction of one molecule of water dihydroxyacetone would result

$$(2)\quad CH_2.COH.CH_2OH\ \to\ CH_2OH.\overset{OH}{\underset{OH}{C}}-CH_2OH\to$$

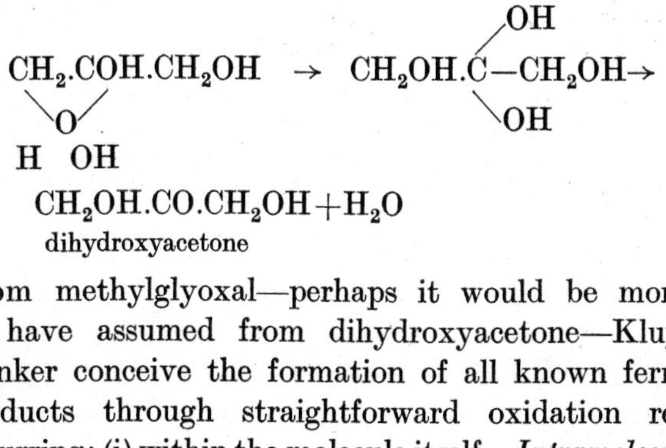

   H   OH

     $CH_2OH.CO.CH_2OH + H_2O$

       dihydroxyacetone

From methylglyoxal—perhaps it would be more correct to have assumed from dihydroxyacetone—Kluyver and Donker conceive the formation of all known fermentation products through straightforward oxidation reductions, occurring: (i) within the molecule itself—*Intramolecular oxidation reductions*; (ii) between two molecules of intermediate products—*Intermolecular oxidation reductions*; or (iii) through *Condensations*, that is, through oxidation reductions resulting in the coupling of the hydrogen donator with the hydrogen acceptor.

As instances of intramolecular oxidation reductions of methylglyoxal the following reactions may be mentioned:

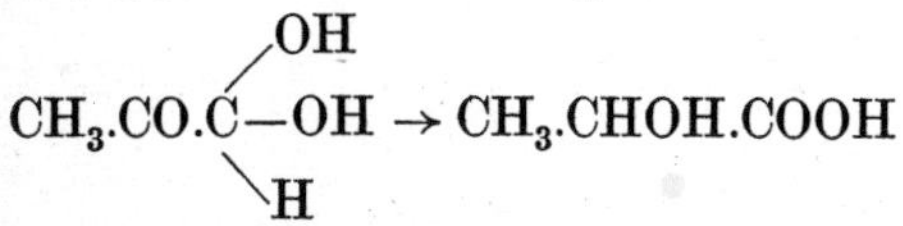

$$CH_3.CO.\overset{OH}{\underset{H}{C}}-OH \to CH_3.CHOH.COOH$$

   methylglyoxal hydrate   lactic acid

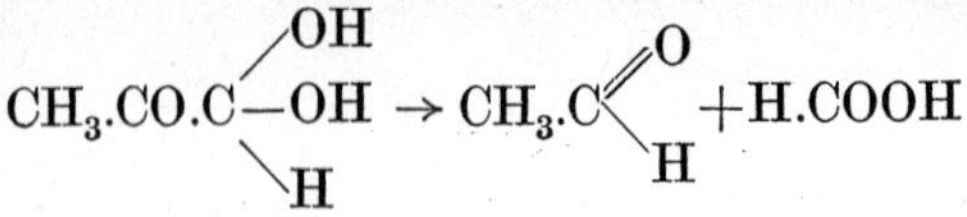

$$CH_3.CO.C\begin{smallmatrix}OH\\-OH\\H\end{smallmatrix} \rightarrow CH_3.C\begin{smallmatrix}O\\\\H\end{smallmatrix} + H.COOH$$

methylglyoxal hydrate   acetaldehyde   formic acid

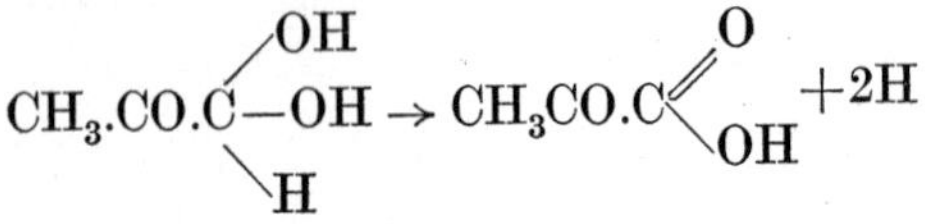

$$CH_3.CO.C\begin{smallmatrix}OH\\-OH\\H\end{smallmatrix} \rightarrow CH_3CO.C\begin{smallmatrix}O\\\\OH\end{smallmatrix} + 2H$$

methylglyoxal hydrate   pyruvic acid

$$H.COOH \qquad \rightarrow \qquad CO_2 + 2H$$

formic acid

Instances of intermolecular oxidation reductions would comprise the following reactions:

$$CH_3.CHO + 2H \quad \rightarrow \quad CH_3CH_2OH$$

acetaldehyde   ethyl alcohol

$$CH_3.CO.CHOH.CH_3 + 2H \rightarrow CH_3CHOH.CHOH.CH_3$$

acetylmethylcarbinol   2:3 butyleneglycol

$$CH_3CH_2CH_2COOH + 4H - CH_3CH_2CH_2CH_2OH + H_2O$$

n-butyric acid   n-butyl alcohol

$$C_6H_{12}O_6 + 2H \qquad \rightarrow \qquad C_6H_{14}O_6$$

fructose   mannitol

$$CH_3.CH(OH)_2 \quad \rightarrow \quad CH_3.COOH + 2H$$

acetaldehyde hydrate   acetic acid

Condensations would be represented by the following reactions:

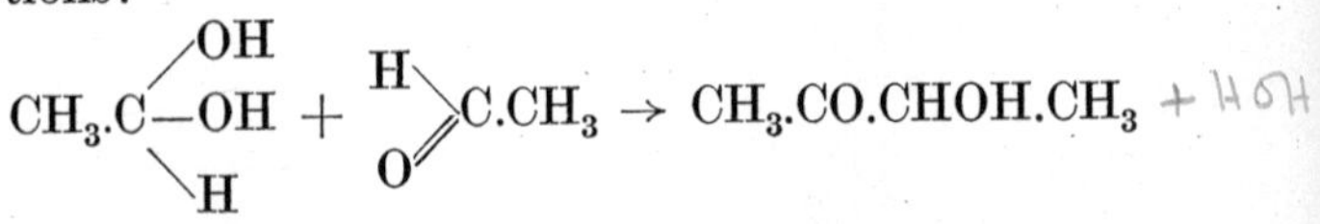

$$CH_3.C\begin{smallmatrix}OH\\-OH\\H\end{smallmatrix} + \begin{smallmatrix}H\\\\O\end{smallmatrix}\rangle C.CH_3 \rightarrow CH_3.CO.CHOH.CH_3 + HOH$$

acetaldehyde hydrate   acetaldehyde   acetylmethylcarbinol

$$CH_3.C\begin{smallmatrix}O\\\\H\end{smallmatrix} + H-C\begin{smallmatrix}H\\\\H\end{smallmatrix}-C\begin{smallmatrix}OH\\-OH\\H\end{smallmatrix} \rightarrow CH_3.CHOH.CH_2.C\begin{smallmatrix}OH\\-OH\\H\end{smallmatrix} \rightarrow$$

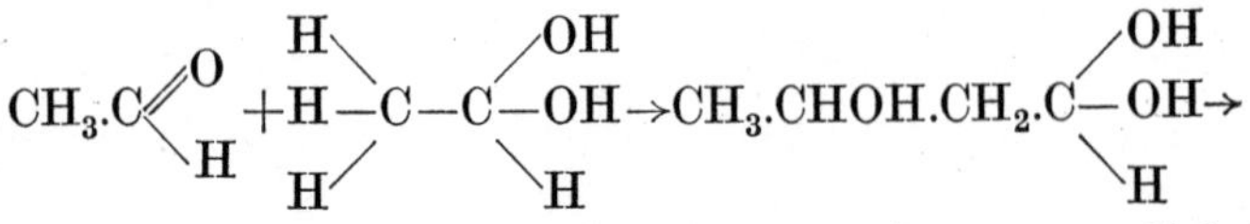

acetaldehyde   acetaldehyde   β-hydroxybutaldehyde
hydrate

$$CH_3.CH_2.CH_2.COOH + H_2O$$

n-butyric acid

$$CH_3C\diagdown_{OH}^{O} +H-\overset{H}{\underset{H}{C}}-COOH \rightarrow CH_3.CO.CH_2.COOH \rightarrow$$

acetic acid   acetic acid   acetoacetic acid

$$CH_3.CO.CH_3+CO_2$$
acetone

To illustrate Kluyver and Donker's conception by a concrete example the behaviour of *Bact. coli commune* may be chosen. The fermenting properties of this bacterium have frequently been investigated. It has been established by various investigators that it produces from glucose lactic, formic, and acetic acids as well as ethyl alcohol, carbon dioxide, and hydrogen. All of these substances can be visualized as derived from glucose through oxidation reductions with glucose phosphoric esters, glyceraldehyde, and methylglyoxal (or perhaps dihydroxyacetone) as intermediate fermentation products.

$$2C_6H_{12}O_6 \rightarrow 2C_6H_{10}O_5.R_2PO_4 \rightarrow$$
glucose   glucose phosphoric ester

$$4C_3H_6O_3 \nearrow 4CH_3.CO.C\diagdown_H^O$$
methylglyoxal

$$\searrow or\ 4CH_2OH.CO.CH_2OH \rightarrow$$

glyceraldehyde   dihydroxyacetone

$$2CH_3.CHOH.COOH+2CH_3.C\diagdown_H^O + 2H.COOH$$

lactic acid   acetaldehyde   formic acid

$$CH_3.C\diagdown_{OH}^{O} \quad CH_3.CH_2OH \quad 2H \quad 2CO_2 \quad H_2$$

acetic acid   ethyl alcohol   activated hydrogen

However, in the case of the fermentation of glucose by *Bact. coli commune* there are not sufficiently definite data available on the actual yields of the various fermentation products from which support could be derived for the assumption that the conversion of glucose to the final fermentation products had actually followed the lines suggested above. Nor have all of the fermentation products of this bacterium been definitely established.

A carefully determined list of all the fermentation products, other than those synthesised into plasma and plasma content is available, however, for another organism, *Bac. acetoethylicus*, which Donker[21] studied for this purpose.

In columns 1 and 2 of Table II a list is given of these fermentation products and of the percentage of each of them obtained from glucose when fermented by *Bac. acetoethylicus*.

TABLE II

Bac. acetoethylicus *grown in yeast-water containing 2 per cent. of glucose and 1 per cent. of calcium carbonate.*

Fermentation product.	Percentage of fermentation product calculated on glucose fermented.	Number of gramme molecules produced per 50 gramme molecules of glucose fermented.		
		Carbon dioxide.	Hydrogen.	Acetaldehyde.
Carbon dioxide	52·6	+107·6	—	—
Hydrogen	1·52	—	+68·4	—
Formic acid	2·6	+ 5·1	+ 5·1	—
Acetic acid	5·2	—	— 7·8	+ 7·8
Ethyl alcohol	31·2	—	+61·0	+61·0
Acetone	9·1	—14·1	—28·2	+28·2
Acetymethylcarbinol	traces	—	—	—
2:3 Butyleneglycol	0·6	—	+ 0·6	+ 1·2
Total		98·6	99·1	98·2

Assuming the fermentation of the glucose to have proceeded in this case *via* methylglyoxal to acetaldehyde and formic acid, and the formic acid to have been partly converted into carbon dioxide and hydrogen, and postulating also that the whole of the various fermentation products, as recorded in columns 1 and 2 of Table II, were derived by oxidation reductions from this acetaldehyde and formic acid, it is clear not only that equimolecular quantities of acetaldehyde and formic acid—or of hydrogen and carbon dioxide—must have been produced from the glucose, but that the sum total of all the fermentation products, when expressed as gramme molecules of acetaldehyde and formic acid (carbon dioxide and hydrogen respectively), must have been exactly double that of the number of gramme molecules of glucose fermented.

The following equation of the fermentation of glucose by *Bac. acetoethylicus* will illustrate the necessity for this assumption.

$$C_6H_{12}O_6 \rightarrow 2CH_3.CO.C{\Large\diagup}{\!}^{O}_{H} \rightarrow 2CH_3C{\Large\diagup}{\!}^{O}_{H} + 2H.COOH \rightarrow$$

glucose   methylglyoxal   acetaldehyde   formic acid

$$2CH_3.C{\Large\diagup}{\!}^{O}_{H} + 2H_2 + 2CO_2$$

acetaldehyde   hydrogen   carbon dioxide

The actual yield therefore of each of the final fermentation products as recorded in column 2 of Table II must have been a definite fraction of this total number of gramme molecules of acetaldehyde and formic acid (or carbon dioxide and hydrogen), and their total when expressed as gramme molecules of acetaldehyde, hydrogen, and carbon dioxide must have been double that of the gramme molecules of glucose fermented.

That this is actually the case is clear from Table II. In the last three columns of this table the numbers of gramme molecules of each of the fermentation products obtained from 50 gr. molecules of glucose fermented have been entered. These figures were arrived at on the basis of the reasoning given below. It will be seen from these figures that the total number of gramme molecules of acetaldehyde, hydrogen, and carbon dioxide are very nearly double that of the gramme molecules of glucose fermented by *Bac. acetoethylicus*.

These figures were arrived at in the following manner. Ethyl alcohol was produced by the organism to the extent of 31·2 per cent. calculated on the glucose fermented. This amount is equal to 61·04 gr. molecules of ethyl alcohol per 50 gr. molecules of glucose since

$$46^* \times X = \frac{50 \times 180^* \times 31\cdot2}{100} \ ; \ X = 61\cdot04.$$

This alcohol was assumed to have been formed from acetaldehyde by hydrogenation on the lines shown below:

$$CH_3.C\overset{\displaystyle O}{\underset{\displaystyle H}{\diagup}} + 2H \rightarrow CH_3CH_2OH.$$

It is to be concluded, therefore, that there must have been available 61·04 gr. molecules of acetaldehyde and 61·04 gr. molecules of hydrogen for this purpose. Both of these quantities are entered in their respective columns of Table II, preceded by a — sign.

In the case of the acetic acid produced by *Bac. acetoethylicus* 5·2 per cent. was obtained from the sugar fermented. This amount is equivalent to 7·8 gr. molecules per 50 gr. molecules of glucose, since

$$60^* \times X = \frac{50 \times 180^* \times 5\cdot2}{100} \ ; \ X = 7\cdot8.$$

The acetic acid was derived from acetaldehyde by dehydrogenation according to the following formula:

$$CH_3.C\overset{\displaystyle OH}{\underset{\displaystyle H}{\diagdown}}OH \rightarrow CH_3.C\overset{\displaystyle OH}{\underset{\displaystyle O}{\diagup}} + 2H$$

acetaldehyde   acetic acid.
hydrate

The 7·8 gr. molecules of acetic acid therefore must have required the presence of 7·8 gr. molecules of acetaldehyde

* indicates molecular weight.

hydrate less 7·8 gr. molecules of hydrogen. These amounts have been entered in their respective columns of Table II as —7·8 gr. molecules of acetaldehyde and —7·8 gr. molecules of hydrogen.

For the purpose of calculation the yields of the remaining fermentation products have been similarly converted. Together they give the totals recorded in Table II.

Similar evidence in support of Kluyver and Donker's theory of fermentation has been obtained by the last-named writer in the case of a number of other glucose-fermenting bacteria. It is to be hoped that the scope of this work will be extended to embody all other types of fermentation in order that it may be ascertained to what extent Kluyver and Donker's efforts to co-ordinate and to simplify the conception of bacterial fermentations are justifiable experimentally.

The conception that the fermentative activity of micro-organisms is a function of their hydrogen activating properties admits of a sub-division of these activities into aerobic, facultative anaerobic, and obligatory anaerobic fermentations, depending on the faculty of a given organism to utilize oxygen as a hydrogen acceptor. But a grouping of this order would be wholly inadequate to account for the great diversity of ways in which carbohydrates are decomposed by micro-organisms.

A further though still incomplete grouping is undoubtedly possible on the above assumption and has been attempted by Kluyver and Donker.[9] These writers reduced the fermentative activities of micro-organisms to seven types as occurring:

    I. among the organisms producing gluconic acid;
    II. among the aerobic spore forming bacteria;
    III. in yeast fermentations;
    IV. in the group of *Bact. coli commune—Bact. typhosum*;
    V. among the true lactic acid bacteria;
    VI. among the propionic acid bacteria; and
    VII. among the butyric acid—butyl alcohol bacilli.

In broad outline Kluyver and Donker's subdivision has been adhered to in the following pages, but attention has been paid also to the property of micro-organisms of utilizing oxygen as hydrogen acceptor.

The information available on the fermentation of pentoses has been included in a separate chapter—Chapter XIII—not because this type of fermentation shows a marked difference from that of hexoses, but because of lack of information on this type of fermentation. A separate chapter has been devoted also to the mucus fermentations in which a synthesis of hexoses to hexosans occurs.

Among the obligatory aerobic micro-organisms two distinct modes of hexose fermentation are clearly discernible. In the first group the carbohydrate is subjected to direct dehydrogenation, frequently without the rupture of the six carbon chain. This group comprises the acetic acid bacteria and certain fungi. It is dealt with in Chapter VI.

In the second group of aerobic fermentations a preliminary disintegration of the six carbon chain occurs. To this group belong the obligatory aerobic soil bacilli, dealt with in Chapter VII.

Among the facultative anaerobic micro-organisms two main types of fermentations are possible, both of them involving a preliminary cleavage of the hexose chain.

The first, dealt with in Chapter VIII, does not give rise to lactic acid formation under normal conditions. In this group must be placed such types as *Bact. fluorescens liquefaciens*, *Bact. prodigiosum*, *Bac. ethaceticus* and *Bac. acetoethylicus*.

The second involves the production of lactic acid in smaller or larger quantities. This mode of fermentation must be divided up into two sub-groups, the first comprising micro-organisms which, in addition to lactic acid, produce a number of other important fermentation products; the second composed of the true lactic acid bacteria which convert the bulk of the glucose into lactic acid. These facultative anaerobic, lactic acid producing types are discussed in detail in Chapters IX and X.

Among the facultative anaerobic micro-organisms with decided preference for anaerobiosis and among the obligatory anaerobes lactic acid production is not an important final fermentation product. It may be produced as an intermediate, however, as in the case of the propionic acid bacteria dealt with in Chapter XI and by the butyric acid and butyl alcohol bacteria discussed in Chapter XII.

LITERATURE

1. C. Oppenheimer and C. Neuberg, *Biochem. Zeits.*, vol. 166, p. 250, 1925.
2. J. H. Quastel, *Biochem. J.*, vol. 20, p. 166, 1926.
3. C. Wieland, *Oppenheimer's Handbuch der Biochemie*, 2nd edition, vol. 2, p. 252. Gustav Fischer, Jena, 1923.
4. J. H. Quastel, M. Stephenson, and M. D. Whetham, *Biochem. J.*, vol. 19 pp. 304, 520, 645, 652, 1925.
5. R. Hopkins, *Opening address to the International Congress of Physiologists in Stockholm*, 1926.
6. L. Rapkine and R. Wurmster, *Proc. Roy. Soc.*, vol. 102 (B), p. 128, 1927.
7. C. Oppenheimer, *Chem. Ztg.*, vol. 52, p. 709, 1928.
8. A. von Scent-Györgyi, *Biochem. Zeits.*, vol. 150, p. 195, 1924.
9. A. J. Kluyver and H. J. L. Donker, *Zeits. d. Zelle und Gewebe*, vol. 13, p. 134, 1926.
10. J. H. Quastel and M. Stephenson, *Biochem. J.*, vol. 19, p. 660, 1925.
11. C. Oppenheimer, *Die Fermente und ihre Wirkungen*, 5th edition, G. Thieme, Leipzig, 1924–6.
12. A. Harden and W. J. Young, *Proc. Roy. Soc.*, B., vol. 82, p. 321, 1910.
13. R. Robison, *Biochem. J.*, vol. 16, p. 809, 1922.
14. A. J. Kluyver and A. P. Struyk, *Proc. Kon. Akad. van Wetenschap*, Amsterdam, vol. 30, p. 871, 1927; vol. 31, p. 882, 1928.
15. P. Mayer, *Biochem. Zeits.*, vol. 2, 435, 1907.
16. C. Neuberg and J. Kerb, *Biochem. Zeits.*, vol. 58, p. 158, 1913.
17. C. G. Lambie, *J. Soc. Chem. Ind.*, vol. 46, p. 300 T., 1927.
18. W. O. Kermack, C. G. Lambie, and R. H. Slater, *Biochem. J.*, vol. 21, p. 40, 1927.
19. G. Bertrand, *Ann. Chim. Phys.* (8), vol. 3, p. 181, 1904.
20. P. Boysen-Jensen, *Biochem. Zeits.*, vol. 58, p. 451, 1914.
21. H. J. L. Donker, *Bijdrage tot de Kennis der Boterzuur-Butyl alcoholen Acetonegistingen*. Dissertation, W. D. Meinema, Delft, 1926.

CHAPTER VI

THE DEHYDROGENATION OF HEXOSES RESULTING IN THE PRODUCTION OF GLUCONIC, SACCHARIC, SUCCINIC, FUMARIC, OXALIC, AND CITRIC ACIDS.

THE grouping of the substances dealt with in this chapter as products of one single type of fermentation indicates the existence of an intimate connexion between their various modes of formation by micro-organisms. This can hardly be substantiated experimentally at present, since the observations made on the production of gluconic, saccharic, succinic, fumaric, citric, and oxalic acids by micro-organisms have done little beyond establishing their actual occurrence as definite hexose fermentation products. A relationship between these substances is indicated, nevertheless, by the fact that one and the same type of organism, or group of organisms, can produce one or more, or sometimes all of the compounds mentioned, being governed in this respect by external conditions such as the reaction of the culture medium and the presence or absence of certain food-substances and powerful hydrogen acceptors.

A discussion of the available, somewhat extensive literature will indicate the present position of knowledge on the subject and will show how far the suggested grouping is justifiable.

PRODUCTION OF GLUCONIC ACID

One of the most interesting observations which has been made was that recorded recently by Müller,[1, 2] that a press juice can be prepared from the mycelium of species of *Aspergillus* and *Penicillium* which, when acting on glucose, converts the carbohydrate into an acid which can be identified as gluconic acid. The conversion takes place only in the presence of an abundance of oxygen, within a temperature range of 0° C. to 30° C. and at a definite hydrogen ion concentration equal to a pH value of 5·5 to 6·5. Particularly noteworthy is Müller's observation that phosphates fail to accelerate the action of the press juice. This can only be interpreted as indicating that the conversion of the glucose to gluconic acid proceeds without the intervention of phosphoric esters and supports Kluyver and Donker's[3] contention that the glucose molecule as such is dehydrogenated without the preliminary formation of intermediates containing shorter carbon chains. The conversion of glucose to gluconic acid therefore may be visualized as a dehydrogenation of the enolic form of glucose in the presence of a powerful hydrogen acceptor such as oxygen or, according to Hoyer,[4] methylene blue, litmus or indigotin.

$$CH_2OH.CHOH.CHOH.CHOH.CHOH.C{\overset{\displaystyle H}{\underset{\displaystyle OH}{-}}}OH \rightarrow$$

$$CH_2OH.CHOH.CHOH.CHOH.CHOH.C{\overset{\displaystyle O}{\underset{\displaystyle OH}{}}} + 2H.$$

The formation of gluconic acid by micro-organisms was first observed by Boutroux[5] in 1878, who at the time was under the impression that the acid which he had obtained was lactic acid. At Pasteur's suggestion he had undertaken to investigate the behaviour of an organism, closely related to Pasteur's *Mycoderma aceti* (*Bact. Pasteurianum*) towards glucose. He came to the conclusion that his organism was identical with Pasteur's lactic acid 'ferment' since it produced a colourless, tasteless, viscous, and non-crystalline acid from glucose. Subsequently Boutroux[6] corrected this view and showed that the acid which he had obtained and in 1880[7] had termed zymogluconic acid was identical with the gluconic acid obtainable from glucose by oxidation with bromine. The formation of gluconic acid by *Bact. Pasteurianum* was confirmed by Brown[8] in 1886. Since then several writers, notably Henneberg,[9] have reported on the production of gluconic acid by acetic acid bacteria. From these observations it may be concluded that the direct dehydrogenation of glucose to gluconic acid is a special feature of the activity of the acetic acid bacteria.

Acids have been observed to be produced by acetic acid bacteria also from fructose and from various di- and trisaccharides such as saccharose, maltose, lactose, and raffinose. The nature of these acids, however, has but rarely been ascertained. In Hoyer's[4] experiments the action of *Bact. xylinum* on saccharose was definitely shown to result in the production of gluconic acid, but Hermann's[10] observations that *Bact. gluconicum* produces acetic acid from maltose and from fructose leaves it an open question whether the types studied by Henneberg[11] and by Zeidler[12] produced gluconic or acetic acid from carbohydrates other than glucose. It is felt by the writers of these pages that a renewed investigation of the action of acetic acid bacteria on carbohydrates would be of considerable theoretical interest, particularly in view of the observations made by Neuberg and Simon[13] that *Bact. ascendens*, when allowed to act on glucose under anaerobic conditions, produces ethyl alcohol in considerable quantities. The acetic acid bacteria apparently have at their command, in addition to their direct dehydrogenating powers, other means of attacking hexoses, resembling those of yeasts and certain alcohol producing bacteria.

The action of acetic acid bacteria on saccharose is utilized in China for the preparation of a drink known as 'Kombucha'. According to Hermann[10] this drink is prepared by allowing acetic acid bacteria, in the form of a mucous covering, to develop on sweetened tea, thereby converting any saccharose present into gluconic acid. This is the only case known to the writers in which practical use has been made of the acidic properties of gluconic acid. There are many reasons, notably an increased nutritive value over acetic acid, why gluconic acid, as suggested by Herzfeld and Lanart,[14] should be more extensively used in the preparation of foods if a cheap and efficient method for its production could be devised. The utilization of micro-organisms for this purpose might be worthy of consideration.

The direct dehydrogenating properties of acetic acid bacteria are evident in their behaviour towards glycerol, which is converted by them into dihydroxyacetone when conditions are favourable, that is, when a powerful hydrogen acceptor is available. The reaction may be visualized by the following formula:

$$(1)\ CH_2OH.CHOH.CH_2OH \rightarrow CH_2OH.CO.CH_2OH + 2H$$
$$\text{glycerol} \qquad\qquad \text{dihydroxyacetone}$$

where the available CHOH group, the only group in the glycerol molecule which, according to Bertrand,[15] can be oxidized (dehydrogenated), has had its H atoms activated.

The production of dihydroxyacetone by micro-organisms was first observed by Bertrand in his study of an organism which he described as the sorbose bacterium but which has since been identified with *Bact. xylinum*. The sorbose bacterium was given its name by Bertrand because it was found to be able to convert sorbitol, present in the juice of mountain ash berries, into the corresponding carbohydrate sorbose.

Virtanen and Bärlund[16] have studied the conditions favouring the formation of dihydroxyacetone and find that a suitable hydrogen ion concentration is essential for the conversion. The reaction, according to them, proceeds best at an acidity in the culture medium equal to a pH value of 5·0. The method has been considerably elaborated by the German chemical industries, who have secured patents[17] protecting the conversion of glycerol to dihydroxyacetone in the presence of food material such as hay infusions and distillery waste extracts. To this mixture of food solutions and glycerol the requisite bacteria are added. *Bact. xylinum* and *Bact. suboxidans* would appear to be particularly suitable for the purpose.

A reference was made above to work by Müller on the extraction of an enzyme from species of *Aspergillus* and *Penicillium*, which converted glucose into gluconic acid.

Production of gluconic acid by fungi was first recorded in 1922 by Molliard.[18] Subsequent work by Falck and Kapur,[19] Falck and van Beyma thoe Kingma,[20] Butkewitsch,[21] Wehmer,[22] May, Herrick, Thom and Church,[23] Herrick and May,[24] and notably by Bernhauer,[25] has demonstrated that the production of this acid by species of *Aspergillus* and by some *Penicillia* is extremely common, at least when certain physiological conditions prevail. It is clear from the publications quoted that the presence of an abundant supply of oxygen is essential for the smooth conversion of glucose to gluconic acid. It has been established also that the production proceeds best at a reaction approaching neutrality, that is, in the presence of calcium carbonate, and in the absence of excessive amounts of nitrogen. An optimum temperature for the conversion would appear to exist, 30° C. to 35° C. being quoted by Bernhauer[25] and by Molliard,[26] 22° C. by Falck and Kapur, presumably depending on the particular strain of fungus used.

Under the most favourable conditions May and his collaborators succeeded in converting 80 per cent. of the available glucose into gluconic acid in the course of 12 days, and under such conditions gluconic acid was found to be the only dehydrogenation product formed, at least when *Penicillium luteum purpurogenum* was used as the activating organism.

Both in the case of fungi and in that of bacteria the action on the carbohydrate may take a different course and various other dehydrogenation products may be formed either in addition to gluconic acid or in its place.

Of such Boutroux[27] recorded the production from glucose and gluconic acid of *oxygluconic acid*, $CH_2OH.CO.CHOH$ $.CHOH.CHOH.C \overset{O}{\underset{OH}{<}}$ by a coccus isolated by him and claimed to be similar to a previously isolated gluconic acid producing type.

Grüss[28] isolated a species of yeast *Amphiernia rubra* which carried the dehydrogenation of glucose still farther, producing saccharic acid, $COOH.CHOH.CHOH.CHOH.CHOH.COOH$, an acid which was detected also by Challenger, Subramanian and Walker[29] as a dehydrogenation product when glucose was acted upon by *Aspergillus niger*. There are at present no observations available to indicate the conditions required for the production of these higher oxidation products of glucose, but seeing that their formation does not involve a disruption of the glucose molecule, it may be permitted perhaps to assume that the agency and the conditions governing the production of gluconic acid may suffice—possibly if further intensified—to convert glucose to oxygluconic and saccharic acid.

Far more difficult is the interpretation of the formation of the various other substances which have been obtained as dehydrogenation products of glucose when acted upon by micro-organisms discussed here, notably by acetic acid bacteria and various species of *Aspergillus and Penicillium*. These substances comprise succinic acid, fumaric acid, oxalic acid, and citric acid.

The first two of these acids possess a four carbon chain, the oxalic acid a two carbon chain, while citric acid has six carbon atoms in its molecule. As these six carbon atoms do not form a straight chain, it must be assumed that citric acid, like the other acids referred to, has been derived from the glucose molecule after preliminary disruption of the six carbon chain of the carbohydrate. There is at present nothing to indicate how this disruption can have taken place. Preliminary conversion of the glucose into glucosephosphoric esters does not appear to occur, since the addition of phosphoric acid, according to Bernhauer and Wolf,[30] does not increase the rate of production of citric acid any more than other acids capable of establishing a suitable hydrogen ion concentration. It is noticeable also that Bernhauer and Schön,[31] who detected the presence of acetaldehyde in saccharose-containing cultures of *Aspergillus niger*, emphasize that acetaldehyde is in no way connected with the production of citric acid by this fungus.

Raistrick and Clark's[32] suggestion that the glucose molecule is first split into a two and a four carbon molecule, and that the production of citric acid results from the union of one molecule of acetic acid—derived from the two carbon molecule—and one molecule of oxalacetic acid—resulting from the four carbon molecule—is purely speculative, and is based solely on the observation of these workers that *Aspergillus niger*, which produces citric acid, develops well on four carbon dibasic acids such as succinic and fumaric which, as already mentioned, are produced from glucose by this and other fungi.

The only other proposal which has been advanced to throw light on the theoretical aspect of the conversion of glucose into organic acids is that of Bernhauer,[34] who suggests that the formation of citric acid—and perhaps also of the other acids involved—is preceded by the disruption of the six carbon chains into two three-carbon chains. This, however, is equally unfounded experimentally. As indications of the changes taking place, there remain the empirically established facts that one and the same type of fungus or two systematically closely related fungi can produce from glucose and from certain other hexoses, gluconic acid, succinic acid, fumaric acid, citric acid, and oxalic acid, according to the conditions prevailing during the action of the organisms on the carbohydrate.

It is not to be understood that any one of these acids can be normally produced to the complete exclusion of all the others. Most writers on the subject agree that gluconic acid is produced first and under all conditions, and that this acid is present therefore at one stage or another of the conversion of glucose by fungi.

Succinic and fumaric acids mixed with gluconic acid (Wehmer[33]) are formed, for instance, by *Aspergillus fumaricus*, while the most typical citric acid producing types are capable of producing gluconic acid (Bernhauer[34]), and probably do so during the early stages of their action on glucose. This might appear to indicate that gluconic acid is the first intermediate product in the conversion of glucose to the various acidic compounds dealt with, a view which has been widely held, but which is strongly disputed by Bernhauer.[35] The fact remains nevertheless that gluconic acid can be converted into citric acid by various fungi such as *Aspergillus fumaricus* (Schreyer[36]). There is another significant observation which throws light on the important part played by gluconic acid in the action of fungi and glucose. Both Wehmer[37] and Schreyer[38] have observed that the typical fumaric acid producing fungus *Aspergillus fumaricus* loses the power of producing its characteristic acid when cultivated on artificial media for a prolonged time and then produces chiefly gluconic acid.

Oxalic acid has been shown to be formed both by acetic acid bacteria and by fungi not only from glucose but from gluconic acid, succinic acid, and fumaric acid (Raistrick and Clark[32]), and from citric acid (Banning[39]). It might be thought therefore that this acid represents a further dehydrogenation product of the various acids mentioned, and that succinic, fumaric, and citric acids are intermediaries between gluconic and oxalic acid. This may be the case, but it has not yet been confirmed experimentally. In accepting this view it should be noted, however, that recent work by Kostytschev and Tschesnokov[40] and by Chrzaszcz and Tinkow[41] indicates that the formation of oxalic acid is dependent on outside influences, particularly on the presence of a sufficient alkalinity in the culture medium, and that it is not an essential stage in the dehydrogenation of glucose by the micro-organism dealt with in this chapter.

PRODUCTION OF SUCCINIC ACID

The conversion of glucose to succinic acid $COOH.CH_2.$ $CH_2.COOH$ has been demonstrated only in the case of two species of *Mucoraceae*, *Mucor Rouxii* and *Mucor stolonifer*. Using the former as inoculant, Goupil[42] obtained succinic acid as the main fermentation product when the fungus developed on glucose containing media under aerobic conditions. In Butkewitsch and Fedoroff's[43] experiments *Mucor stolonifer* yielded mainly fumaric acid COOH.CH.CH.COOH, but 10 per cent. of the sugar converted could be identified as succinic acid.

Presence of alkali, or at least of calcium carbonate, and oxygen would appear to be essential for the conversion. No work has been done to ascertain the effect of varying the concentration of the hydrogen acceptor present on the proportional yields of fumaric and succinic acids obtained. As fumaric acid must be a dehydrogenation product of succinic acid, it is to be expected that a restricted supply of hydrogen acceptors—oxygen for instance—must affect the conversion of glucose by *Mucor stolonifer* in favour of the formation of increased amounts of succinic acid.

PRODUCTION OF FUMARIC ACID

Fumaric acid has been shown to be formed both by species of *Mucor* [*Mucor stolonifer*] and of *Aspergillus* [*Aspergillus fumaricus*]. Ehrlich[44] first recorded its formation by the former, Wehmer[45] by the latter. Shortage of nitrogen in the culture medium, a hydrogen ion concentration approaching neutrality, restricted supply of hydrogen acceptors (oxygen), and a temperature between 21 and 23° C. are conditions favouring the production of fumaric acid by *Aspergillus fumaricus*. But even with these conditions assured the organism loses its power of forming fumaric acid on prolonged artificial cultivation (Schreyer[38]) and then reverts to a strain giving essentially gluconic and citric acids (Wehmer[37]).

The subject of fumaric acid production by fungi is at present of theoretical interest only. The proposal has been advanced by Bailey and Potter,[46] however, that fumaric acid might be used for the synthesis of indigo. Should this method be found industrially important the microbiological conversion of sugars to fumaric acid might become of practical interest.

PRODUCTION OF OXALIC ACID

In the presence of carbohydrates and various other carbon compounds, and of an abundance of oxygen as well as of calcium carbonate, both acetic acid bacteria (Zopf[47]) and the species of lower fungi discussed in this chapter—*Aspergillus niger* for instance—will produce greater or smaller quantities of oxalic acid.

The occurrence of oxalic acid as a product of micro-biological activity militated seriously against the first attempt at utilizing fungi for the production of citric acid on an industrial scale. Wehmer[48] in his early work found it difficult if not impossible to prevent the formation of oxalic acid in his cultures owing, it may now be asserted, to his carrying through the citric acid fermentation in the presence of calcium carbonate at reactions particularly favourable for the production of oxalic acid.

PRODUCTION OF CITRIC ACID

It was Wehmer[48] who first drew attention to this interesting fermentation process, which he attributed to the action of a specific type of fungus, *Citromyces*. In his description of this fungus Wehmer[49] referred to two different species, *Citromyces Pfefferianus* and *Citromyces glaber*. They differ, he declared, from *Penicillium* in the absence of branching of the conidiophores and in the formation of a vesicle; from *Aspergillus* in the absence of marked foot cells, in the rudimentary development of the vesicle, and in the successive formation of the sterigmata. Sartory and Bainier[50] gave the following characteristics of the three types.

In *Penicillium* species the sterigmata are formed at the top of the undifferentiated hypha.

In *Citromyces* an aerial hypha gives rise to a single, usually a terminal sterigma, which becomes separated from the hypha by a wall. Subsequently other sterigmata arise at the base of the first, and the end of the conidiophore swells to form a vesicle.

In *Aspergillus* the sterigmata are formed simultaneously in smaller or larger numbers over the whole surface of the vesicle, which has been formed previously at the top of the conidiophore. In recent text-books, notably in that of Thom and Church,[51] this classification of *Citromyces* as a distinct genus has been abandoned, since it has been possible to show experimentally that all species of *Aspergilli* and some *Pencillia* are capable of forming citric acid, and that the characteristics of *Citromyces* as defined by Sartory and Bainier are insufficient to distinguish it from the *Aspergilli*.

Apart from the *Aspergilli*, various other fungi, such as *Penicillium glaucum* (Butkewitsch[52]), *Penicillium luteum* (Wehmer[53]), *Penicillium citrinum* and *Penicillium divaricatum* (May and collaborators[23]), as well as *Mucor piriformis* (Wehmer[53]), have been shown to produce citric acid from hexoses.

The *Aspergilli* giving the highest yields of citric acid— over 25 per cent. calculated on the carbohydrates decomposed —were claimed by Falck and van Beyma thoe Kingma[20] to be those producing black, brown, or fawn pigments. The moderately active types, giving from 10 to 20 per cent. of acid, were those producing a yellowish-green pigment; the inferior types, with less than 10 per cent. yields, were those with slight pigmentation or none at all.

After the first unsuccessful attempt by Wehmer the industrial application of fungi for the production of citric acid was allowed to lapse. Recently, and noticeably since Currie's[54] investigations of the reaction, renewed interest has been taken in the matter and patents have been secured for the protection of what are claimed to be reliable and economic methods for the production of citric acid (Fernbach and Yuill[55]).

The outstanding feature of Currie's investigations is his observation that the formation of citric acid proceeds far more readily at distinctly acid reactions than at the hydrogen ion concentrations prevailing when calcium carbonate is added to the food solution. Currie recommends an initial hydrogen ion concentration of the pH value 3·4 to 3·5. He secures this by adding hydrochloric acid to the food solution, which is composed of the following substances:

Ammonium nitrate . . .	0·2 to 0·25	per cent.
Potassium dihydrogen phosphate	0·075 to 0·1	,, ,,
Magnesium sulphate (crystalline)	0·02 to 0·025	,, ,,
Saccharose	12·5 to 15	,, ,,
Tap water to a total of . .	100	,, ,,

During the first two or three days after inoculation little production of citric acid occurs as during this period the fungus spreads and covers the surface of the liquid. When this has been effected, after the third to the eighth day, the rise in acidity is very rapid, corresponding to a daily production of 2 per cent. of citric acid.

When the hydrogen ion concentration of the solution has reached a pH value of 1·4, fungus development has become practically impossible, and the solution therefore is effectively protected against the growth of infecting fungi. This is important, since Wehmer's early attempts failed partly owing to the mashes becoming infected by undesirable types of fungi. It will be noticed that Currie recommends the use of saccharose and not of glucose as carbohydrate. In this respect he is following the usage of earlier investigators, and even of Wehmer himself, who found saccharose as suitable as glucose for the production of citric acid; this incidentally confirms the view already expressed in this chapter that the dehydrogenation of the hexose molecule by acetic acid bacteria and by the fungi discussed in these pages proceeds via the enolic form of the carbohydrate.

Citric acid production has been shown by Butkewitsch[56] and by Bernhauer[57] to be favoured by the presence of an abundance of nitrogen in the food solution. The optimum temperature for the conversion would appear (Bernhauer[57]) to depend to some extent on the prevailing nitrogen concentration, 30° C. being most favourable in the presence of abundant nitrogen, 35° C. at lower nitrogen concentrations.

A restriction of the oxygen supply available in the culture medium favours citric acid production (Buchner and Wüstenfeld,[58] and Bernhauer[57]).

LITERATURE

1. D. Müller, *Biochem. Zeits.*, vol. 199, p. 136, 1928.
2. D. Müller, *Biochem. Zeits.*, vol. 205, p. 111, 1929.
3. A. J. Kluyver and H. J. L. Donker, *Zeits. f. Chem. d. Zelle und Gewebe*, vol. 13, p. 134, 1926.
4. D. P. Hoyer, *Die deutsche Essigindustrie*, vol. 3, p. 1, 1899.
5. L. Boutroux, *Comptes rend.*, vol. 86, p. 605, 1878.
6. L. Boutroux, *Comptes rend.*, vol. 104, p. 369, 1887.
7. L. Boutroux, *Comptes rend.*, vol. 91, p. 236, 1880.
8. A. J. Brown, *J. Chem. Soc.*, vol. 49, p. 172, 1886.
9. W. Henneberg, *Die deutsche Essigindustrie*, vol. 2, p. 145, 1898.
10. T. S. Hermann, *Biochem. Zeits.*, vol. 192, pp. 176 and 188, 1928.
11. W. Henneberg, *Zentrbl. f. Bakt.*, Abt. II, vol. 4, p. 14, 1898.
12. A. Zeidler, *Zentrbl. f. Bakt.*, Abt. II, vol. 2, p. 729, 1896.
13. C. Neuberg and E. Simon, *Biochem. Zeits.*, vol. 197, p. 259, 1928.
14. A. Herzfeld and G. Lanart, *Zeits. Verein d. deutsch. Zuckerindustrie*, Tech. Teil, vol. 69, p. 122, 1919.
15. G. Bertrand, *Comptes rend.*, vol. 122, p. 900, 1895; vol. 127, p. 842, 1898. *Ann. Chim. Phys.* (8), vol. 3, p. 181, 1904.
16. A. I. Virtanen and B. Bärlund, *Biochem. Zeits.*, vol. 169, p. 169, 1926.
17. I. G. Farbenindustrie, *B. Pat.*, 269, 950, 1928.
18. M. Molliard, *Comptes rend.*, vol. 174, p. 881, 1922.
19. R. Falck and S. N. Kapur, *Berichte*, vol. 57, p. 920, 1924.
20. R. Falck and van Beyma thoe Kingma, *Berichte*, vol. 57, p. 915, 1924.
21. W. Butkewitsch, *Biochem. Zeits.*, vol. 154, p. 177, 1924.
22. C. Wehmer, *Berichte*, vol. 58, p. 2616, 1925.
23. O. E. May, H. T. Herrick, C. Thom and M. B. Church, *J. Biol. Chem.*, vol. 75, p. 417, 1928.
24. H. T. Herrick and O. E. May, *J. Biol. Chem.*, vol. 77, p. 185, 1928.
25. i. K. Bernhauer, *Biochem. Zeits.*, vol. 153, p. 517, 1924.
    ii. K. Bernhauer, *Biochem. Zeits.*, vol. 172, p. 313, 1926.
    iii. K. Bernhauer, *Z. physiol. Chem.*, vol. 177, p. 86, 1928.
26. M. Molliard, *Comptes rend.*, vol. 178, p. 161, 1924.
27. L. Boutroux, *Comptes rend.*, vol. 127, p. 1224, 1898.
28. J. Grüss, *Jahrb. f. wiss. Bot.*, vol. 66, p. 109, 1926.
29. F. Challenger, V. Subramanian and T. K. Walker, *Nature*, vol. 119, p. 674, 1927.
30. K. Bernhauer and H. Wolf, *Z. physiol. Chem.*, vol. 177, p. 270, 1928.
31. K. Bernhauer and K. Schön, *Biochem. Zeits.*, vol. 202, p. 164, 1928.
32. H. Raistrick and A. B. Clark, *Biochem. J.*, vol. 13, p. 329, 1919.
33. C. Wehmer, *Biochem. Zeits.*, vol. 197, p. 418, 1912.
34. K. Bernhauer, *Biochem. Zeits.*, vol. 197, p. 278, 1928.
35. K. Bernhauer, *Biochem. Zeits.*, vol. 197, p. 1164, 1928.
36. R. Schreyer, *Berichte*, vol. 58, p. 2647, 1925.
37. C. Wehmer, *Biochem. Zeits.*, vol. 197, p. 418, 1928.

38. R. Schreyer, *Biochem. Zeits.*, vol. 202, p. 131, 1928.
39. F. Banning, *Zentrbl. f. Bakt.*, Abt. II, vol. 8, p. 395, 1902.
40. S. Kostytschev and V. Tschesnokov, *Botan. Centrbl.*, vol. 154, p. 158, 1928.
41. T. Chrzaszcz and D. Tinkow, *Biochem. Zeits.*, vol. 204, p. 106, 1929.
42. R. Goupil, *Comptes rend.*, vol. 153, p. 1172, 1912.
43. W. S. Butkewitsch and M. W. Fedoroff, *Biochem. Zeits.*, vol. 206, p. 440, 1929.
44. F. Ehrlich, *Berichte*, vol. 44, p. 3737, 1911.
45. C. Wehmer, *Berichte*, vol. 51, p. 1663, 1918.
46. G. C. Barley and R. S. Potter, *J. Amer. Chem. Soc.*, vol. 44, p. 215, 1922.
47. W. Zopf, *Ber. d. deutsch. bot. Gesell.*, vol. 18, p. 32, 1900.
48. C. Wehmer, *Botan. Zeitg.*, vol. 9, p. 163, 1891. *Ber. d. deutsch. botan. Gesell.*, vol. 11, p. 333, 1893.
49. C. Wehmer, *F. Lafar's Handbuch d. technischen Mykologie*, vol. 4, p. 234, 1905/7. Gustav Fischer, Jena.
50. A. Sartory and S. Bainier, *Comptes rend. Soc. Biol.*, vol. 70, p. 873, 1911.
51. C. Thom and M. B. Church, *The Aspergilli*, Williams & Wilkins, Baltimore, 1926.
52. W. Butkewitsch, *Biochem. Zeits.*, vol. 129, p. 464, 1922.
53. C. Wehmer, *Chem. Zeitg.*, vol. 21, p. 1022, 1897.
54. J. N. Currie, *J. Biol. Chem.*, vol. 31, p. 15, 1917.
55. A. Fernbach, J. L. Yuill and Messrs. Rowntree & Co., *B. Pat.*, No. 266414, 1925.
56. W. Butkewitsch, *Biochem. Zeits.*, vol. 131, p. 338, 1922.
57. K. Bernhauer, *Biochem. Zeits.*, vol. 172, p. 324, 1926.
58. E. Buchner and H. Wüstenfeld, *Biochem. Zeits.*, vol. 17, p. 397, 1909.

CHAPTER VII

THE AEROBIC DEHYDROGENATION OF HEXOSES, RESULTING IN THE FORMATION OF ACETIC AND FORMIC ACIDS, ACETYLMETHYLCARBINOL AND 2:3 BUTYLENEGLYCOL

A FAIRLY clear conception of this mode of hexose dehydro-genation has been gained in recent years by the study of certain obligatory aerobic bacilli.

The earliest efforts to establish the action of these micro-organisms on hexoses were made by Péré,[1] who reported finding glyceraldehyde $CH_2OH.CHOH.C\diagup^O_{\diagdown H}$ and formalde-hyde $H.CHO$ in his glucose containing cultures.

Subsequent investigations by Desmots[2] on the behaviour of *Bac. mesentericus vulgatus*, *Bac. mesentericus niger*, and *Bac. mesentericus ruber*; by Fernbach[3] on *Bac. tenuis* (*Tyro-thrix tenuis*), and by Lemoigne[4] on certain types claimed by him to be *Bac. subtilis* and *Bac. mesentericus*, showed that the substance characterized by Péré as glyceraldehyde was acetylmethylcarbinol $CH_3.CO.CHOH.CH_3$. In addition to this product Desmots found acetic and valeric acids as well as traces of ethyl alcohol.

Péré's observation on the formation of formaldehyde was confirmed by Fernbach[3] in the case of *Bac. tenuis*. Fernbach also reported the presence in cultures of this organism on glycerine of methylglyoxal $CH_3.CO.C\diagup^O_{\diagdown H}$, dihydroxyacetone $CH_2OH.CO.CH_2OH$, and acetic acid. In addition Aubel[5] detected pyruvic acid $CH_3.CO.COOH$ in glycerine cultures of *Bac. subtilis*, while 2:3 butyleneglycol $CH_3.CHOH.CHOH.CH_3$ was detected by Lemoigne[4] as a decomposition product of glucose by the strains described by him as *Bac. subtilis* and *Bac. mesentericus*—strains which produced considerable quantities of carbon dioxide from the carbohydrate. With macerations of an organism related to *Bac. Megatherium* Lemoigne[6] observed the formation of β-hydroxybutyric acid, $CH_3.CHOH.CH_2.COOH$.

The absence of lactic acid as a product of decomposition of glucose in these cases is noteworthy. That it is not likely to have been overlooked is supported both by theoretical consideration and by experimental evidence. In their study on facultative anaerobiosis Quastel and his collaborators[7] found that only those organisms which were capable of activating nitrates to function as hydrogen acceptors could be expected to utilize lactic acid for growth. The aerobic bacilli do not belong to the nitrate reducing types. This was shown by Quastel in the case of *Bac. subtilis*. It had been demonstrated previously by Lemoigne[8] that the growth of his strain of *Bac. subtilis*, which is claimed to produce carbon dioxide, was extremely slow in a medium containing calcium lactate as sole source of carbon.

The various observations referred to above indicate that a direct dehydrogenation of glucose to gluconic acid does not occur. The first fermentation product is invariably a substance with less than six carbon atoms. It is probable therefore that the first stage in the action of the aerobic bacilli on glucose is the formation of hexose phosphoric esters.

A relationship to the group of the acetic acid bacteria is discernible nevertheless in the property of the aerobic bacilli of dehydrogenating glycerine to dihydroxyacetone, a reaction which, it may be recalled, was shown by Bertrand[9] to occur when *Bact. xylinum* acted on glycerine.

Dehydrogenation of methylglyoxal would result in the formation of pyruvic acid, the presence of which was reported by Aubel[5] as an intermediate. The functions of pyruvic acid may be assumed with Cambier and Aubel[10] and with Quastel[11] to be connected, partly at least, with the synthetic processes of the cell plasma. Through intramolecular hydrogen transfer methylglyoxal might give rise to acetaldehyde and formic acid (Kluyver and Donker[12]), of which the latter was detected by Péré as a fermentation product of some of the micro-organisms discussed in this chapter.

Acetaldehyde has not to the writers' knowledge been discovered as an intermediate fermentation product of the aerobic bacilli. There is every reason to assume, however, that acetaldehyde is produced, since ethyl alcohol, acetyl-methylcarbinol, 2:3 butyleneglycol, and β-hydroxybutyric acid have been found. It is true that Lemoigne[4] suggests a different origin for acetylmethylcarbinol and butyleneglycol. He states that the glucose molecule becomes dislocated through the action of the bacteria and that 2:3 butyleneglycol is thereby produced with evolution of carbon dioxide. The acetylmethylcarbinol is regarded by him as formed from 2:3 butyleneglycol by subsequent oxidation. But this is hardly a correct interpretation. The work of Neuberg and Rein-furth,[13] and of Kluyver, Donker, and Visser't Hooft[14] on the formation of acetylmethylcarbinol by yeast, shows that acetaldehyde is the mother substance of this compound and that it is produced from acetaldehyde in the presence of hydrogen acceptors, notably of oxygen.

The formation of the β-hydroxybutyric acid, detected by Lemoigne, might result from the coupling of one molecule of acetaldehyde with one molecule of acetic acid.

$$CH_3.C\!\!\begin{array}{c}O\\\\H\end{array} + H\!-\!\overset{H}{\underset{H}{C}}\!-\!C\!\!\begin{array}{c}O\\\\OH\end{array} \rightarrow CH_3.CHOH.CH_2.C\!\!\begin{array}{c}O\\\\OH\end{array}$$

acetaldehyde   acetic acid β-hydroxybutyric acid.

The origin of the valeric acid observed by Péré has not been traced by subsequent investigators; in fact it seems problematic whether this substance was really derived from carbohydrates.

The presence of formic acid as a fermentation product of the aerobic bacteria has not been reported—though formalde-hyde, as already mentioned, was found by Péré[1] and by Fernbach.[3]

Reviewing the above observations, it is to be assumed that

the hexose molecule in the mode of fermentation dealt with in this chapter is converted first into hexosephosphoric esters. On saponification of these glyceraldehyde results, followed by methylglyoxal, pyruvic acid, acetaldehyde, and formic acid, with side reactions leading to 2:3 butyleneglycol, acetylmethylcarbinol, acetic acid, and β-hydroxybutyric acid.

In the ordinary bacteriological methods of diagnosis these changes would be indicated only by the production of acid in litmus glucose broth, coupled perhaps with a reduction of litmus. Where the test organism produced lactose hydrolysing enzymes, acid production, and possibly discoloration or coagulation, would occur in litmus milk.

The formation of acetylmethylcarbinol in the presence of peptone would give rise to a positive Voges and Proskauer[15] reaction—a fluorescent discoloration of the upper part of the culture, similar to that of a dilute alcoholic solution of eosin, on addition of potash to the glucose broth culture and 24 hours' standing of the culture at room temperature.

Harden[16] showed that this reaction was due to the presence of acetylmethylcarbinol. The reaction is now no longer used for the identification of acetylmethylcarbinol, but has been replaced by that devised by Lemoigne[17] or its modification recommended by Kluyver, Donker, and Visser't Hooft,[14] both of which allows of a quantative estimation of both acetylmethylcarbinol and 2:3 butyleneglycol.

Some very early investigations of the action of *Bac. subtilis* on glucose, carried out by Vandevelde[18] in 1884, differ materially from the view set out above. Vandevelde obtained from glucose lactic acid, butyric acid, caproic acid, and two alcohols, one of which boiled below 100° C., and the other above. It is probably justifiable to assume with Lemoigne[4] that the organism studied by Vandevelde was not *Bac. subtilis*, particularly as it is stated to have produced a gas, consisting of carbon dioxide, hydrogen, nitrogen, and an undetermined residue.

It is much to be regretted that a list of the various microorganisms acting on glucose in a manner similar to that of the aerobic bacilli cannot be compiled. Here, as in the case of most other fermentations, the study of the action of the organisms on carbohydrates has been far too superficial to make such compilations possible or even desirable at present.

LITERATURE

1. A. Péré, *Ann. Inst. Pasteur*, vol. 10, p. 417, 1896.
2. H. Desmots, *Comptes rend.*, vol. 138, p. 581, 1904.
3. A. Fernbach, *Comptes rend.*, vol. 151, p. 1004, 1910.
4. M. Lemoigne, *Comptes rend.*, vol. 152, p. 1873, 1911; vol. 155, p. 792, 1912. *Ann. Inst. Pasteur*, vol. 27, p. 856, 1913.
5. E. Aubel, *Comptes rend. Soc. Biol.*, vol. 84, p. 574, 1921.
6. M. Lemoigne, *Comptes rend.*, vol. 176, p. 1761, 1923.
7. J. H. Quastel, M. Stephenson and M. D. Whetham, *Biochem. J.*, vol. 19, p. 304, 1925.
8. M. Lemoigne, *Comptes rend.*, vol. 177, p. 652, 1923.
9. G. Bertrand, *Comptes rend.*, vol. 122, p. 900, 1895.
10. R. Cambier and E. Aubel, *Comptes rend.*, vol. 175, p. 71, 1922.
11. J. H. Quastel, *Biochem. J.*, vol. 19, p. 641, 1925.
12. A. J. Kluyver and H. J. L. Donker, *Zeits. f. Chem. d. Zelle und Gewebe*, vol. 13, p. 134, 1926.
13. C. Neuberg and E. Reinfurth, *Biochem. Zeits.*, vol. 143, p. 553, 1923.
14. A. J. Kluyver, H. J. L. Donker, and F. Visser't Hooft, *Biochem. Zeits.*, vol. 161, p. 361, 1925.
15. O. Voges and B. Proskauer, *Z. f. Hygiene*, vol. 28, p. 20, 1898.
16. A. Harden, *Proc. Roy. Soc.*, Series B, vol. 77, p. 424, 1926.
17. M. Lemoigne, *Comptes rend.*, vol. 170, p. 131, 1920.
18. G. Vandevelde, *Z. physiol. Chem.*, vol. 8, p. 367, 1884.

CHAPTER VIII

THE FACULTATIVE ANAEROBIC DEHYDROGENATION OF HEXOSES RESULTING IN THE PRODUCTION OF ACETIC ACID, FORMIC ACID, ETHYL ALCOHOL, ACETYLMETHYLCARBINOL AND 2:3 BUTYLENEGLYCOL

THERE appear to be three methods by which hexoses can be fermented by facultative anaerobic micro-organisms without the formation of lactic acid. These three modes of fermentation are dealt with in the present chapter as one group.

The first is represented by the action of *Bact. vulgare*, the second by that of *Bact. fluorescens liquefaciens* and *Bact. prodigiosum*, and the third by that of *Bact. pneumoniae* and *Bac. acetoethylicus*.

The action of *Bact. vulgare* on glucose was studied by Smith[1] from the point of view of gas production. He obtained a mixture of gaseous products consisting of 33 per cent. of carbon dioxide and 66 per cent. of hydrogen. Lemoigne[2] showed that *Bact. vulgare* produced both acetylmethylcarbinol $CH_3.CO.CHOH.CH_3$ and 2:3 butyleneglycol, $CH_3.CHOH.CHOH.CH_3$. Quastel and Wooldridge[3] found that *Bact. vulgare* activated no other hexoses than glucose and fructose. A slight activation of fumarates and malates was also noted. Nitrates were the only markedly activated hydrogen acceptors.

The formation of acetylmethylcarbinol by *Bact. vulgare* must be taken as an indication that acetaldehyde and acetic acid are formed as intermediate decomposition products, if it is assumed with Kluyver and Donker[4] that the fermentation of hexoses proceeds along lines of comparatively simple hydrogenations, dehydrogenations, and condensations. On the same assumption the formation of acetaldehyde would indicate the occurrence of methylglyoxal $CH_3.CO.CHO$, or

perhaps of dihydroxyacetone $CH_2.OH.CO.CH_2OH$, glyceraldehyde $CH_2OH.CHOH.CHO$, and hexosephosphoric esters
as precursors. The formation of these intermediaries has
still to be proved experimentally, however.

On being converted into acetaldehyde, methylglyoxal
would yield one molecule of formic acid for every molecule
of acetaldehyde. The formic acid on being dehydrogenated
would yield carbon dioxide and hydrogen in equal proportions, part of the latter being used for the hydrogenation of
acetylmethylcarbinol to 2:3 butyleneglycol. Smith's yields
referred to above do not agree with the quantities to be
expected under the above scheme.

The fermentation of hexoses by *Bact. fluorescens liquefaciens*, *Bact. pyocyaneum*, and *Bact. prodigiosum* has been
studied by Lemoigne,[5] Aubel,[6] Quastel and Whetham,[7] and
Quastel and Wooldridge.[8] According to Quastel and his
collaborators the activating properties of both species are
much more marked than those of *Bact. vulgare*.

Lemoigne[5] found that a species which he terms *Bact.
prodigiosum*, but which is more likely to have been *Bact.
ruber indicum*, a type capable of fermenting saccharose
(Hefferan[9]), produced traces of acetaldehyde and ethyl
alcohol, acetylmethylcarbinol, and 2:3 butyleneglycol. Evolution of carbon dioxide by *Bact. prodigiosum* was observed by
Schottelius[10] and by Hefferan.[9]

When acting on glucose *Bact. pyocyaneum* was found by
Aubel[6] to yield formic acid and acetic acid in the proportions
of 1:2. Ethyl alcohol was also detected by him. An evolution
of carbon dioxide or of hydrogen from hexoses by *Bact.
pyocyaneum* or *Bact. fluorescens liquefaciens* has not been
reported, nor have acetylmethylcarbinol and 2:3 butyleneglycol been found.

In spite of these differences, which on further investigation
may be shown to be less marked than appears to be the case,
a similarity in the action of *Bact. fluorescens liquefaciens*,
Bact. pyocyaneum, and *Bact. prodigiosum* has undoubtedly
been established. It is noteworthy, for instance, that in none

of the cases does the breakdown of glucose lead to the formation of lactic acid. Gas evolution is restricted in both cases
and never leads to the evolution of molecular hydrogen. And
ethyl alcohol is formed as a fermentation product by both
types.

It is probable that the fermentation proceeds in both cases
via hexosephosphoric esters, methylglyoxal—or dihydroxyacetone—to pyruvic acid, $CH_3.CO.COOH$, with side reactions
to acetaldehyde and formic acid, acetic acid, ethyl alcohol,
acetylmethylcarbinol, and 2:3 butyleneglycol. The scheme of
fermentation suggested by Aubel[6] supports this assumption.

The third method of facultative anaerobic glucose fermentation not involving the production of lactic acid is represented
by the action of *Bact. pneumoniae*, *Bac. ethaceticus*, and *Bac.
acetoethylicus*.

The most exhaustive investigation of this mode of fermentation was carried out by Frankland and his collaborators[11] in
the case of *Bact. pneumoniae* and *Bac. ethaceticus*, and by
Northrop, Ashe and Senior,[12] and Donker[13] in the case of *Bac.
acetoethylicus*.

The principal glucose fermentation products of *Bact.
pneumoniae* and *Bac. ethaceticus* were shown by Frankland
to be acetic acid, formic acid, and ethyl alcohol, in equal
molecular proportions, as well as traces of succinic acid.
Hydrogen and carbon dioxide were given off under anaerobic
conditions in equal proportions. Calcium lactate was fermented, yielding the same fermentation products as glucose
but in different molecular proportions, four molecules of
acetic acid being formed to one molecule of ethyl alcohol.
The observation of Grimbert[14] that *l*-lactic acid is also produced has not been confirmed.

As fermentation products of *Bac. acetoethylicus*, Northrop,
Ashe and Senior detected formic and acetic acids, ethyl
alcohol, acetone, carbon dioxide, and hydrogen. Traces of
propyl and butyl alcohols were also reported present by them.
Neither acetylmethylcarbinol nor 2:3 butyleneglycol was

found. Details of the experimental data obtained by Donker in his study of the fermentation of glucose by this organism were given in Chapter V, page 86. Donker does not confirm the presence of propyl or butyl alcohol, but records finding traces of ethylmethylcarbinol and measurable quantities of 2:3 butyleneglycol.

Of particular interest is the appearance of succinic acid as a fermentation product of *Bac. pneumoniae* and *Bac. ethaceticus* and of acetone in the case of *Bac. acetoethylicus*.

Succinic acid, $COOH.CH_2.CH_2.COOH$, was found by Grey[15] to be a fermentation product of *Bact. coli commune*. Grey concluded from his observations that the precursor of succinic acid in the case of *Bact. coli commune* was identical with that of acetic acid and ethyl alcohol—that is, with methylglyoxal or dihydroxyacetone. If this view must be taken as correct, the production of succinic acid would follow a different course to that taken in the formation of succinic acid by the micro-organisms dealt with in Chapter VI.

Experimental evidence on the formation of acetone from acetic acid by microbiological activity was brought forward by Desborough[16] in the case of an obligatory anaerobic bacillus, *Bac. acetonigenus (Clostridium acetonigenum)*, Donker.[13] Its formation from the same intermediate in the case of *Bac. acetoethylicus* has not been proved, but if likely to occur would result in two molecules of acetic acid combining to form one molecule of acetone and one molecule of carbon dioxide.

In the case of *Bac. ethaceticus* and *Bac. acetoethylicus*, the final fermentation products again indicate the preliminary conversion of the hexose molecule into phosphoric esters, followed by the production of glyceraldehyde, methylglyoxal (or perhaps dihydroxyacetone), acetaldehyde, and formic acid, with various side reactions giving rise to the other fermentation products which have been identified. Of the chief intermediate fermentation products of *Bac. acetoethylicus* acetaldehyde has actually been isolated by Peterson and Fred.[17]

LITERATURE

1. Th. Smith (see K. B. Lehmann and R. O. Neumann, *Bakteriol. Diagnostik*, 5th edition). Lehmann, München, 1912.
2. M. Lemoigne, *Comptes rend. Soc. biol.*, vol. 88, p. 498, 1923.
3. J. H. Quastel and W. R. Wooldridge, *Biochem. J.*, vol. 19, p. 652, 1925.
4. A. J. Kluyver and H. J. L. Donker, *Z. f. Chem. d. Zelle und Gewebe*, vol. 13, p. 134, 1926.
5. M. Lemoigne, *Comptes rend. Soc. biol.*, vol. 82, p. 234, 1919.
6. E. Aubel, *Comptes rend.*, vol. 173, p. 1493, 1921.
7. J. H. Quastel and M. D. Whetham, *Biochem. J.*, vol. 18, p. 519, 1924.
8. J. H. Quastel and W. R. Wooldridge, *Biochem. J.*, vol. 19, p. 652, 1925.
9. M. Hefferan, *Zentrbl. f. Bakt.*, Abt. II, vol. 11, p. 311, 1904.
10. M. Schottelius, *Zentrbl. f. Bakt.*, vol. 2, p. 439, 1887.
11. { P. F. Frankland, A. Stanley and W. Frew, *J. Chem. Soc.*, vol. 59, p. 253, 1891.
    P. F. Frankland, G. Frankland and J. Fox, *Chem. News*, vol. 60, p. 181, 1889.
    P. F. Frankland and J. S. Lumsden, *J. Chem. Soc.*, vol. 61, p. 432, 1892.
12. J. H. Northrop, L. H. Ashe and J. K. Senior, *J. Biol. Chem.*, vol. 39, p. 1, 1919.
13. H. J. L. Donker, *Bijdrage tot de Kennis der Boterzuur-Butyl alcoholen Acetonegistingen*, W. D. Meinema, Delft, 1926.
14. L. Grimbert, *Comptes rend.*, vol. 132, p. 706, 1901.
15. E. C. Grey, *Proc. Roy. Soc.*, Sec. B, vol. 90, p. 75, 1917.
16. A. P. H. Desborough, *Eng. Pat.*, 128403, 1918.
17. W. H. Peterson and E. B. Fred, *J. Biol. Chem.*, vol. 44, p. 29, 1929.

CHAPTER IX

THE FACULTATIVE ANAEROBIC DEHYDROGENATION OF HEXOSES INVOLVING THE FORMATION OF LACTIC ACID AS AN ESSENTIAL DECOMPOSITION PRODUCT

I. THE GROUPS OF BACT. COLI COMMUNE AND BACT. LACTIS AEROGENES

THE mode of fermentation represented by this group is undoubtedly extremely common among micro-organisms. It was investigated in considerable detail by Harden[1] in the case of *Bact. typhosum* and *Bact. coli commune*, organisms which he found capable of converting approximately 50 per cent. of any available hexoses into lactic acid, the remainder yielding ethyl alcohol and acetic acid in approximately equal molecular proportions, with formic acid, carbon dioxide, and hydrogen in lesser proportions. Succinic acid $COOH.CH_2$. $CH_2.COOH$ was also detected by Harden as a fermentation product of *Bact. coli commune*. Observations made by him in collaboration with Penfold[2] on specially treated strains of *Bact. coli commune* convinced Harden that the fermentation of hexoses by this organism is performed by three independent enzymes, one leading to the production of lactic acid, one to ethyl alcohol, acetic acid and formic acid, and one to carbon dioxide and hydrogen. The view that three independent stages occur has been confirmed and elaborated by subsequent investigators, notably by Grey,[3] Aubel,[4] and Aubel and Salabartan.[5] Formic acid production and evolution of carbon dioxide and hydrogen are regarded by them as the result of the activity of one enzyme, the formation of acetic acid, ethyl alcohol, and succinic acid as that of another, and lactic acid production as the result of the function of a third and entirely independent enzyme.

It is questionable whether this conception is correct. Recent work by Quastel and collaborators[6] indicates that the governing factor in these reactions is more likely to be found in the hydrogen activating properties of the organisms than in the existence of several specific enzymes.

Formation of formic acid, carbon dioxide, hydrogen, acetic acid, ethyl alcohol, and succinic acid at least are closely connected with these properties. This is particularly noticeable in the case of the conversion of formic acid to carbon dioxide and hydrogen, a reaction which is readily performed under normal conditions by *Bact. coli commune* when once formic acid has been activated to function as hydrogen donator.

Grey, who realized the connexion between production of formic acid and the evolution of carbon dioxide and hydrogen, pointed to the close relationship of these reactions with the formation of ethyl alcohol, and suggested that the rate at which ethyl alcohol, acetic acid, and succinic acid are produced depends upon the availability of hydrogen liberated by the breakdown of formic acid. Where an excess of hydrogen was available Grey observed an increase in alcohol production from the acetaldehyde which Neuberg and Nord[7] detected as an intermediate fermentation product of *Bact. coli commune*, while a scarcity of active hydrogen resulted in an increased production of succinic acid. To obtain activated hydrogen Grey added formates to a glucose containing culture of *Bact. coli commune*.

This observation that formates break down with the liberation of nascent hydrogen under the influence of micro-organisms is of very great importance, and, as Grey himself suggests, should have an important bearing on the study of other fermentation processes in which the production of activated hydrogen is aimed at. Grey's experiments lead him to conclude that the formation of lactic acid is independent of the other reactions performed by *Bact. coli commune*.

It is clear from the work of Grey, as well as from that of Stephenson and Whetham,[8] that the formation of lactic acid by *Bact. coli commune*—and presumably by all other micro-organisms producing this acid—is intimately connected with the growth of the cells. Grey found that practically no lactic acid was formed by *Bact. coli commune* during the period characterized by rapid death of the cells—the latter part of the fermentation—while 70 per cent. of the hexoses consumed were converted into lactic acid during the period following immediately upon the rapid multiplication of the cells—the early part of fermentation.

The period of destruction of the cells was characterized by the transformation of hexoses into alcohol, acetic acid, formic acid, and succinic acid.

The limitation of lactic acid production to the period of growth of the cells justifies Stephenson and Whetham's assumption that its formation is intimately connected with the liberation of the energy required for the synthetic activities of the cells.

The question of the precursors of lactic acid has engaged the attention of Neuberg and his pupils,[9] of Aubel, and of several other writers. That the precursor is likely to be methylglyoxal, $CH_3.CO.CHO$, had been suggested by Nef.[10] Dakin and Dudley[11] have since proved that lactic acid is produced by animal cells and tissues from this intermediate. Neuberg, Aubel, and de Graaf and le Fèvre[12] found that *Bact. coli commune* decomposed methylglyoxal, and, according to Neuberg and Gorr,[9] with a theoretical yield of lactic acid. Aubel accepts methylglyoxal as the precursor of lactic acid. As mother substance of methylglyoxal, Kluyver and Donker[13] suggest glyceraldehyde, $CH_2OH.CHOH.CHO$, which de Graaf and le Fèvre found readily decomposed by *Bact. coli commune* and its related types, though not with the production of methylglyoxal or lactic acid, but with formation of carbon dioxide, acetic acid, and traces of ethyl alcohol.

Neither acetylmethylcarbinol, $CH_3.CO.CHOH.CH_3$, nor 2:3 butyleneglycol, $CH_3.CHOH.CHOH.CH_3$, appears to be a normal fermentation product of *Bact. typhosum*, *Bact. paratyphosum* or *Bact. coli commune*, though de Graaf and le Fèvre report the presence of traces of the former in cultures of *Bact. coli commune* containing glyceraldehyde and dihydroxyacetone, $CH_2OH.CO.CH_2OH$.

As a further decomposition product of glucose Aubel[14] detected pyruvic acid, $CH_3.CO.COOH$, which both Quastel[15] and Cambier and Aubel[16] regard as the basic substance used in the synthetic processes of this and other carbohydrate decomposing micro-organisms. Kluyver and Donker consider that the pyruvic acid is derived from methylglyoxal, and this in turn from glyceraldehyde. Aubel[4] does not agree that methylglyoxal can be the precursor of pyruvic acid, since he found *Bact. coli commune* unable to decompose methylglyoxal. He must have been unaware of de Graaf and le Fèvre's observations, however, that certain strains of *Bact. coli commune* do so, and must have been studying types of the organism incapable of activating methylglyoxal to function as hydrogen donator. That such strains exist is emphasized by de Graaf and le Fèvre. The reactions giving rise to the formation of succinic acid are not yet clear. Its formation from glutamic acid by yeast was reported by Ehrlich;[17] from ketoglutamic acid by Neuberg and Ringer.[18] Virtanen[19] regards it as the product of a side reaction of carbohydrate decomposition, during which no phosphoric esters are formed —that is presumably a production similar to that occurring among the species of *Aspergillus* and *Mucor* discussed in Chapter VI.

Summarizing the observations discussed in the preceding pages, the following scheme for the fermentation of hexoses by *Bact. coli commune* may be suggested.

Hexose→glyceraldehyde→methylglyoxal→
(or perhaps dihydroxyacetone)

→ { lactic acid
    pyruvic acid

→ { acetaldehyde+formic acid
    ↓   ↓
    ethyl alcohol   carbon dioxide
    ↓   +
    acetic acid   hydrogen

This scheme differs somewhat from that suggested by Neuberg and Nord,[20] who assume that the pyruvic acid is converted into acetaldehyde and carbon dioxide, and the acetaldehyde to ethyl alcohol and acetic acid by a Cannizzaro reaction. In the scheme advanced by these workers, the molecular hydrogen is thought to have been derived from the conversion of glucose to pyruvic acid.

In the mode of fermentation outlined above lactic acid is regarded as a final fermentation product. It should not be concluded, however, that this acid cannot be further decomposed by the organism. Both Quastel and Aubel have shown that lactic acid can enter the fermentation when suitable hydrogen acceptors—for instance nitrates—are available. It is then utilized for the production of pyruvic acid.

The fermentation of hexoses by *Bact. typhosum* would follow lines similar to those of *Bact. coli commune*. But since *Bact. typhosum* does not possess activating powers towards formic acid, carbon dioxide and hydrogen are not evolved by this organism.

The fermentation of hexoses by *Bact. paratyphosum* and by its numerous related types occurring in the soil, on plants and in water, follows a middle course between those of the two previous types, formic acid being activated in some cases, with a resulting evolution of carbon dioxide and hydrogen.

Parallel with its analytic functions, or perhaps preceding them, Grey[21] thought he observed a marked synthetic activity in *Bact. coli commune*. This action is stated to be particularly noticeable during the early stages of the fermentation of glucose and is claimed to result in the production of starch. Further work would appear to be desirable before the observations of Grey can be accepted as correct.

The fermentation of hexoses by *Bact. lactis aerogenes* differs markedly in certain respects from that by the *Bact. typhosum-Bact. coli* group, though in this case also the formation of lactic acid is an important stage in the reaction. Harden and Walpole,[22] who subjected the fermentative activity of *Bact. lactis aerogenes* to exhaustive investigation, state that ethyl alcohol, acetic acid, succinic acid, formic acid, carbon dioxide and lactic acid are produced. The evolution of gas was found to be greater than in the case of *Bact. coli commune*. The proportion of carbon dioxide in the mixture was considerably greater than that of hydrogen in Harden and Walpole's experiments, indicating, they suggest, that the former is derived from a source additional to formic acid. It has still to be shown, however, that the excess of carbon dioxide over hydrogen cannot have been due to a consumption of part of the hydrogen derived from formic acid in intermediate reactions.

In this connexion it is perhaps worth recording that the presence of methane—7 per cent. of the gas mixture of *Bact. lactis aerogenes*—was recorded by Baginsky.[23]

Of the fermentation products mentioned above ethyl alcohol accounted for 17·1 to 18·2 per cent. of the hexoses fermented, as against 12·85 per cent. in the case of *Bact. coli commune*; acetic acid represented 4·2 to 8·6 per cent. as against 18·84 per cent. in the case of *Bact. coli commune*; succinic acid 2·4 to 4·5 per cent. as against 5·2 per cent.; lactic acid 4·7 to 9·1 per cent., as against 31·9 per cent.; formic acid 0·75 to 1·7 per cent.; carbon dioxide 35·2 to 38 per cent.

Altogether these products represented no more than 66 per cent. of the carbon of the glucose fermented. A search for the remaining 33 per cent. revealed the presence in the cultures of acetylmethylcarbinol and 2:3 butyleneglycol. The former of these substances was shown by Harden[24] to be responsible for the Voges-Proskauer reaction.[25]

Harden and Walpole suggest that both the acetylmethylcarbinol and the 2:3 butyleneglycol are formed at the expense of those intermediate fermentation products which, in the case of *Bact. coli commune*, lead to acetic acid and lactic acid, and Walpole[26] subsequently asserted that the 2:3 butyleneglycol was the mother substance of the acetylmethylcarbinol, the latter being formed from the former through oxidation. The work of Neuberg and Reinfurth[27] and of Kluyver, Donker and Visser't Hooft[28] on the formation of acetylmethylcarbinol and 2:3 butyleneglycol by yeasts, indicates a different origin, however. Both Neuberg and Kluyver found that the addition of acetaldehyde to a culture of a fermenting yeast led to the production of acetylmethylcarbinol, and Kluyver and his collaborators showed that in the absence of sufficient oxygen the acetylmethylcarbinol could be made to function as hydrogen acceptor, thereby becoming reduced to 2:3 butyleneglycol. Moreover, where methylene blue or sulphur was added to a culture of yeast containing glucose, added acetaldehyde could be recovered by Kluyver, not as acetylmethylcarbinol, but as 2:3 butyleneglycol.

A similar course is probably followed in the case of *Bact. lactis aerogenes*, where acetylmethylcarbinol and 2:3 butyleneglycol are produced, the mother substance of both, acetaldehyde, being first converted into acetylmethylcarbinol, and this subsequently reduced to 2:3 butyleneglycol.

That lactic acid, as suggested by Harden and Walpole, should be an intermediate of acetylmethylcarbinol and its product of hydrogenation does not appear likely in view of the fact that lactic acid when it is fermented by *Bact. coli commune* yields pyruvic acid.

Though the intermediate stages in the fermentation of hexoses by *Bact. lactis aerogenes* have by no means been fully explored, it does not appear unreasonable to suggest the following scheme for the reactions taking place during this fermentation:

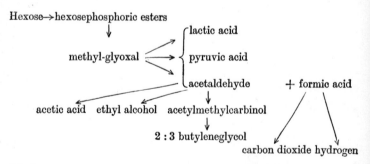

Of these reactions the conversion of methylglyoxal to lactic acid by *Bact. lactis aerogenes* has been experimentally confirmed by Neuberg and Gorr.[29]

An entirely different conception of the fermentation of hexoses by *Bact. lactis aerogenes* has been advanced by Virtanen[19] and by Myrbäck and von Euler.[30] Studying various aspects of the functions of enzymes Virtanen came to the conclusion that *Bact. lactis aerogenes* carried out the fermentation of glucose without the aid of a co-enzyme, and that consequently the initial stages of the fermentation differed from that of yeast and of lactic acid bacteria, which produce co-enzymes and form hexose phosphoric esters as preliminary fermentation products.

The assumed absence of these esters in the breakdown of glucose by *Bact. lactis aerogenes* suggested to Virtanen the possibility that the glucose molecule might in the first instance be converted into a two carbon and a four carbon intermediate. In other words, that the fermentation might proceed on lines similar to those suggested by Raistrick and Clark[31] for *Aspergillus niger*, giving rise in the first instance to the production of succinic acid and acetaldehyde.

$$C_6H_{12}O_6 \rightarrow COOH.CH_2.CH_2.COOH + CH_3.C\overset{O}{\underset{H}{\diagup}} + H_2O$$

succinic acid   acetaldehyde.

Myrbäck and von Euler see in acetaldehyde the mother substance of the acetic acid and formic acid which have been detected as additional fermentation products of *Bact. lactis aerogenes*.

In referring to this conception of the fermentation of glucose by *Bact. lactis aerogenes*, the writers desire to emphasize that they cannot accept it without additional and more convincing evidence than has so far been supplied.

LITERATURE

1. A. Harden, *J. Chem. Soc.*, vol. 79, p. 612, 1901.

2. A. Harden and W. J. Penfold, *Proc. Roy. Soc.*, Ser. B, vol. 85, B, p. 415, 1912.

3. E. C. Grey, *Proc. Roy. Soc.*, Ser. B, vol. 87, p. 461, 1914; Ser. B, vol. 90, p. 75, 1917; Ser. B, vol. 90, p. 92, 1917; Ser. B, vol. 91, p. 294, 1920.

4. E. Aubel, *Comptes rend.*, vol. 181, p. 571, 1925; vol. 183, p. 572, 1926.

5. E. Aubel and J. Salabartan, *Comptes rend.*, vol. 180, p. 1183, 1925; vol. 180, p. 1784, 1925.

6. J. H. Quastel, M. Stephenson and M. D. Whetham, *Biochem. J.*, vol. 19, p. 304, 1925.
   J. H. Quastel and M. D. Whetham, *Biochem. J.*, vol. 19, p. 520, 1925.
   J. H. Quastel and M. D. Whetham, *Biochem. J.*, vol. 19, p. 645, 1925.
   J. H. Quastel and W. R. Wooldridge, *Biochem. J.*, vol. 19, p. 625, 1925.
   J. H. Quastel and M. Stephenson, *Biochem. J.*, vol. 19, p. 660, 1925.

7. C. Neuberg and F. T. Nord, *Biochem. Zeits.*, vol. 96, p. 133, 1919.

8. M. Stephenson and M. D. Whetham, *Biochem. J.*, vol. 18, p. 498, 1924.

9. C. Neuberg and G. Gorr, *Biochem. Zeits.*, vol. 162, p. 490, 1925.

10. J. U. Nef, *Annalen*, vol. 335, p. 279, 1904.

11. H. D. Dakin and H. W. Dudley, *J. Biol. Chem.*, vol. 14, p. 155, 1913.

12. W. C. de Graaf and A. J. le Fèvre, *Biochem. Zeits.*, vol. 155, p. 313, 1925.

13. A. J. Kluyver and H. J. L. Donker, *Zeits. f. Chem. d. Zelle und Gewebe*, vol. 13, p. 134, 1926.

14. E. Aubel, *Comptes rend.*, vol. 181, p. 571, 1925.

15. J. H. Quastel, *Biochem. J.*, vol. 19, p. 641, 1925.

16. R. Cambier and E. Aubel, *Comptes rend.*, vol. 175, p. 71, 1922.

17. F. Ehrlich, *Biochem. Zeits.*, vol. 18, p. 391, 1909.

18. C. Neuberg and M. Ringer, *Biochem. Zeits.*, vol. 71, p. 226, 1915.

19. A. I. Virtanen, *Ann. Acad. Sci. Fennicae*, vol. 29, p. 15, 1927.

20. C. Neuberg and F. T. Nord, *Biochem. Zeits.*, vol. 96, p. 130, 1919.

21. E. C. Grey, *Biochem. J.*, vol. 18, p. 712, 1924.

22. A. Harden and G. S. Walpole, *Proc. Roy. Soc.*, Ser. B, vol. 77, p. 399, 1906.

23. A. Baginsky, *Z. f. physiol. Chem.*, vol. 12, p. 434, 1888.

24. A. Harden, *Proc. Roy. Soc.*, Ser. B, vol. 77, p. 424, 1906.

25. O. Voges and B. Proskauer, *Z. f. Hygiene*, vol. 28, p. 20, 1898.

26. G. S. Walpole, *Proc. Roy. Soc.*, Ser. B, vol. 83, p. 272, 1911.

27. C. Neuberg and E. Reinfurth, *Biochem. Zeits.*, vol. 143, p. 553, 1923.

28. A. J. Kluyver, H. J. L. Donker and F. Visser't Hooft, *Biochem. Zeits.*, vol. 161, p. 361, 1925.

29. C. Neuberg and G. Gorr, *Biochem. Zeits.*, vol. 166, p. 482, 1925.

30. K. Myrbäck and H. von Euler, *Berichte*, Ser. B, vol. 57, p. 1073, 1924.

31. H. Raistrick and A. B. Clark, *Biochem. J.*, vol. 13, p. 329, 1919.

CHAPTER X

THE FACULTATIVE ANAEROBIC DEHYDROGENA-TION OF HEXOSES INVOLVING THE FORMA-TION OF LACTIC ACID AS AN ESSENTIAL DECOM-POSITION PRODUCT

II. THE GROUP OF THE LACTIC ACID BACTERIA

THE earliest investigations on the action of lactic acid bacteria on sugars indicated that other fermentation products than lactic acid, notably acetic acid, were frequently formed.

Subsequently, and owing primarily to the researches of Kayser,[1] it became customary to subdivide the lactic acid bacteria into two main groups, one which in addition to lactic acid produced volatile acids in appreciable, though varying, quantities, and another, the true lactic acid bacteria, which gave 95 per cent. or more of fixed acids.

Even the true lactic acid bacteria, however, were shown to yield volatile acids in measurable quantities. Thus Bertrand and Weissweiler[2] obtained 1·5 per cent. of acetic acid and traces of formic acid from cultures of *Bact. bulgaricum*, a type isolated by Grigoroff[3] from yoghurt.

For this reason differentiation of the lactic acid bacteria on the basis of their fermentative activity might seem unsatisfactory, particularly as several investigators, Kayser[1] and Barthel,[4] for instance, have found that the percentage of volatile acid produced increases in the presence of oxygen. It is not to be overlooked, however, that those members of the group which produce appreciable quantities of volatile acids convert fructose into its corresponding alcohol, mannitol, a reaction which is unknown among the true lactic acid bacteria.

A fairly extensive literature is already in existence dealing with the mannitol producing lactic acid bacteria, and some writers have attempted to establish the various intermediary and final fermentation products formed by them. Others, notably Gayon and Dubourg[5] [6] and Müller-Thurgau and Osterwalder,[7] have studied these bacteria from the point of view of their activities as infections in wine.

Kruis and Raymann[8] isolated from malt a type which produced from saccharose formic and acetic acids, traces of ethyl alcohol, mannitol, and lactic acid. Tate[9] studied a type resembling *Streptococcus mesenteroides* (*Leuconostoc*) which gave 2 molecules of ethyl alcohol, 7 to 8 molecules of lactic acid, 1 molecule of succinic acid, and smaller quantities of acetic acid and formic acid, from 9 molecules of glucose. Peterson and Fred[10] investigated other types isolated from manure, silage, and soil. The last-named writers suggest that the mannitol is formed as a coincident product of fermentation —through the reduction of fructose by nascent hydrogen— and that it becomes subsequently broken down to lactic and acetic acids. Previously Gayon and Dubourg[6] and Müller-Thurgau and Osterwalder[7] had failed to secure growth of their mannitol bacteria on media containing mannitol as the sole source of carbohydrate. The organism studied by Tate fermented mannitol with the formation of ethyl alcohol, acetic acid, formic acid, and lactic acid.

A more exhaustive study of the mannitol producing lactic acid bacteria was carried out by Smit[11] in 1916 and by van Steenberge in 1920.[12] The figures recorded in Table III, showing the quantitative yields of fermentation products of a typical mannitol producing lactic acid bacterium, are taken from Smit's paper.

The organism in question, *Bact. lactofermentum* (*Lactobacterium fermentum*), had been described previously by Beijerinck.[13]

It will be seen that qualitatively, and in some respects quantitatively, the fermentation of glucose by this bacterium recalls the mode of action of *Bact. coli commune*, except that hydrogen is absent, that the yield of acetic acid is lower, and that glycerol has appeared as an important product of fermentation. The proportions of carbon dioxide, ethyl alcohol, lactic acid, and of formic acid are of the same order.

How far this can be taken as indicating a similarity in the mode of action of the two types of micro-organisms has not yet been shown.

According to van Steenberge the mannitol producing lactic acid bacteria possess marked reducing powers towards selenium and tellurium salts, and are capable of activating

TABLE III

Fermentation products.	Glucose.	Fructose.
Carbon dioxide - - -	14·1 per cent.	—
Ethyl alcohol - - -	16·9 ,, ,,	1·6 per. cent.
Lactic acid - - -	47·1 ,, ,,	12·3 ,, ,,
Acetic acid - - -	3·7 ,, ,,	12·9 ,, ,,
Formic acid - - -	0·1 ,, ,,	0·2 ,, ,,
Succinic acid - - -	1·2 ,, ,,	1·4 ,, ,,
Mannitol - - -	nil	60·1 ,, ,,
Glycerol - - -	6·3 ,, ,,	nil
Bacterial substance - -	3·5 ,, ,,	—

these salts to function as acceptors for activated hydrogen. This observation supports the view that the formation of mannitol is attributable to the same cause, and that intermediately formed formic acid, therefore, produced at one stage or another in the fermentation of hexoses by these organisms, is decomposed with liberation of atomic hydrogen.

Among the true lactic acid bacteria the activating powers are much less marked. According to van Steenberge they are unable to reduce selenium and tellurium salts, and fructose is converted into lactic acid by them.

They still retain the property of reducing methylene blue to its leuco-compound (Jensen[14]), a reaction which does not involve a preliminary activation of the molecule of the hydrogen acceptor.

Catalase is not produced by the true lactic acid bacteria, an observation which Beijerinck[15] made twenty-five years ago, and which Jensen[14] subsequently confirmed. This must be taken to indicate that hydrogen peroxide is unlikely to be formed as a result of the fermentation of carbohydrates by the true lactic acid bacteria, and indicates no doubt an increased sensitiveness towards oxygen by these organisms. The absence of catalase in the cells of the true lactic acid bacteria was utilized by Beijerinck[15] for detecting their colonies in artificial cultures. He found that a droplet of dilute hydrogen peroxide solution, when placed on these colonies, remained undecomposed for a considerable time.

Though the true lactic acid bacteria are undoubtedly more anaerobic than the mannitol producing types, they still develop—though sparingly—in the presence of oxygen.

A further characteristic of these types is their inability readily to convert methylglyoxal into acetaldehyde and formic acid (Kluyver and Donker[16]). Their action on this important intermediate is restricted almost entirely to a conversion into lactic acid, a reaction which, according to Neuberg and Gorr,[17] gives rise to almost theoretical yields.

Several other observations have been made during recent years which facilitate the interpretation of the course of carbohydrate decomposition among the true lactic acid bacteria. Thus Myrbäck and von Euler[18] have shown that these micro-organisms produce a co-enzyme, and that, as in the case of yeast, a fermentation of glucose by these bacteria is impossible in the absence of the co-enzyme. It can be concluded, therefore, that the first stage in the fermentation of monoses is the formation of hexose phosphoric esters. That these esters are subsequently converted into methylglyoxal is supported by Neuberg and Gorr's researches already referred to.

A certain percentage of the methylglyoxal must be converted into acetaldehyde and formic acid, since Bertrand and Weissweiler[2] observed the formation of the latter substance in cultures of *Bact. bulgaricum*.

Formation of pyruvic acid by the true lactic acid bacteria has recently been reported by Kostytchev and Soldatenkov.[19]

In broad outline the fermentation of glucose by the true lactic acid bacteria may probably be schematized as follows:

glucose→ glucose phosphoric esters→ glyceraldehyde→
                                    methylgloxal
                                  ↙   ↘
              acetaldehyde+formic acid   lactic acid
                         ↓
                    acetic acid
                         ↓
                  ethyl alcohol (?)

The optical properties of the lactic acid produced by bacteria has engaged the attention of many workers. In the early investigations fermentation lactic acid was generally assumed to be inactive (Lewkowitsch[20]).

Reports did not fail to appear, however, containing descriptions of lactic acid bacteria producing either dextro-acid only (Nencki and Sieber;[21] Günther and Thierfelder[22]), or laevo-lactic acid only (Tate[9] and Leichmann[23]). Again, other types were stated to produce a non-compensated mixture of dextro- and laevo-acids (Bertrand and Weissweiller[2] and Harden[24]), the proportions of the two acids depending in many cases (Péré[25]) on the conditions of the growth of the test organisms, notably on the presence in the cultures of a suitable source of nitrogen, or on the temperature prevailing (Kozai[26]). A comprehensive review of the investigations on this subject up to 1907 is given by Heinemann.[27] Some order was brought into the general confusion by McKenzie,[28] who showed that the reason for the divergent views could be ascribed to the methods adopted for the analysis of the acids obtained, it being customary to examine the zinc salts of the lactic acid formed, usually after one or more recrystallizations to ensure purity. By these purifications, however, the true proportions of the lactic acid formed became entirely obscured owing to differences in solubility of the zinc salts, that of the inactive (racemic) lactic acid being less soluble than that of the two active components. McKenzie expressed the view that all fermentation lactic acid consists of an equal mixture of dextro- and laevo-acid.

K

In this view McKenzie is supported by Harden's[24] observation on the optical nature of the lactic acid formed by *Bact. coli commune* and *Bact. typhosum*. Fully aware of the complications due to differences in the solubilities of the zinc salts of the inactive and the active acids, Harden conducted his investigation in such a way as to avoid these difficulties, and found that the lactic acid produced by his two test organisms consisted of a mixture of inactive acid and laevo-lactic acid.

Nevertheless, the question of the optical properties of fermentation lactic acid is still obscure. In investigations by Neuberg and Gorr[29] on the action of *Bact. coli commune* on methylglyoxal it is claimed that inactive acid is produced, and as late as 1926 Pederson, Peterson and Fred[30] asserted that the optical nature of the acid produced by a lactic acid bacterium studied by them was influenced by the presence in the culture of an infection form unable to produce lactic acid.

THE ECONOMIC IMPORTANCE OF THE LACTIC ACID BACTERIA

The very considerable and growing economic importance of the lactic acid bacteria necessitates a short reference to this subject.

The question of the application of these bacteria in the distillery for the checking of undesirable bacterial infections, of their introduction into milk for the preparation of various types of sour milk and all types of cheese, is most conveniently dealt with in an account specially devoted to these subjects and will not be referred to here. The occurrence and activity of the lactic acid bacteria in flour and doughs will be discussed subsequently.

There remains to be reviewed, therefore, the manufacture of lactic acid for medicinal and technical purposes. The first, and at that time universally adopted method, was described by Boutron and Frémy,[31] who worked under the conception that casein was the agency responsible for the conversion of lactose into lactic acid. Subsequently von Blücher[32] observed that saccharose could be similarly converted in the presence of casein, and recommended this method as superior to that of Boutron and Frémy. Gobley,[33] like Boutron and Frémy, added lactose to milk to increase the carbohydrate concentration, but allowed the conversion to proceed spontaneously in the presence of chalk. Bensch,[34] like von Blücher, utilized saccharose as the source of carbohydrate, and added cheese as a source of casein. In order, as he thought, to facilitate the inversion of the saccharose, he added small amounts of tartaric acid to his saccharose solution. The improvement obtained by the introduction of this acid must have been due to other causes, however—probably to the checking of the development of wild yeast and butyric acid bacteria, two sources of infection which invariably affected the yields of acid obtained in the early methods of lactic acid production.

With the realization of the function of bacteria considerable further improvements were introduced. One of the pioneers in the manufacture of lactic acid was Avery,[35] who took out a number of patents during 1881 to 1885 for the protection of his method, in which the danger of undesirable side-reactions, notably of butyric acid and alcoholic fermentations, was guarded against though by no means excluded. A very detailed account of this method was given by Claflin[36] in 1897, an account which appears to have served as a model for the industry until quite recently, when genuine pure culture work was introduced.

Avery's method, as improved by Claflin, conforms on the whole with the requirements of modern technique and may serve as a basis for the description of lactic acid manufacture to be given in these pages.

Though most lactic acid bacteria develop well in milk and whey it is doubtful whether these liquids now serve as the raw materials for the production of lactic acid. The difficulties involved in the recovery of the acid from milk and whey militates against their use in practice. The carbohydrates commonly used are saccharose, in the form of molasses, glucose, and maltose, obtained by the hydrolysis of starch.

The necessary nitrogen, which for preference should be present as organic nitrogen (Kayser[1]), is obtained from bran or from the grain in which the starch is contained. The total nitrogen of the finished mash should amount to 2 per cent. of the available carbohydrates—though obviously it must be lower in the case of the procedure proposed by von Sait-cew,[37] who utilizes molasses without the addition of a nitrogen source.

The concentration of carbohydrates in the mash should not be below 7·5 per cent., preferably about 10 per cent.

If the mash is left slightly acid, at a pH value of about 3·7, its sterilization can be carried out without the application of high pressures, an important point, since pressure treatment is inclined to caramelize the dissolved carbohydrates. In many cases boiling at atmospheric pressure should be sufficient to ensure complete sterility under acid conditions.

The sterilized mash is cooled to 50–55° C. with aseptic precautions, and is then run into a fermentation vat, where it is inoculated with a suitable type of true lactic acid bacteria. In earlier days *Streptococcus* (*Bacterium*) *lactis acidi*, Günther and Thiefelder, was generally used. To-day a type of *Bact. acidificans longissimum*, Lafar,[38] is usually chosen, since it withstands higher temperatures. *Bact. Delbrücki* is recommended by von Saitcew.[37] Calcium carbonate, or lime, in sterile suspension is added to the fermenting mash to maintain its reaction at a pH value of 3·7 to 4·5, which, according to Bachrach and Cardot,[39] represent the optimum hydrogen ion concentrations of most lactic acid bacteria, though Virtanen, Wichmann and Lindström[40] place it at a pH value of 6·2.

When, after 3 to 5 days, the conversion of the carbohydrates is completed, the lactic acid obtained should amount to 98 per cent. of the theoretical yield. The mash is now filtered and immediately concentrated so as to supply, on decomposition of the calcium lactate with sulphuric acid, an acid containing 50 per cent. lactic acid.

The use of zinc oxide or magnesium oxide instead of lime or chalk has been recommended by some workers. According to Mayer,[41] however, these oxides are less favourable than calcium salts.

The crude lactic acid may be purified in various ways, but can be used in most industrial undertakings without further preparation. It finds a growing market in the textile industries, notably in the woollen industries, for mordanting with potassium dichromate. In the leather industry an appreciable quantity is consumed in the deliming of the raw hides before tanning.

The technical production of mannitol was discussed by Strecker[42] in 1854. He obtained it in exceptionally large yields—up to 10 per cent. of the saccharose taken—when fermenting a saccharose solution at room temperature under the conditions recommended by Bensch[34] for the production of lactic acid. Draggendorf[43] obtained 5 per cent. under somewhat similar conditions. Dox and Plaisance[44] recommended isolating mannitol from silage, in which they regularly found it present.

The production of mannitol in appreciable quantities at comparatively low temperatures agrees with the observations that the mannitol producing lactic acid bacteria have a lower optimum temperature for growth than the true lactic acid bacteria.

Before leaving the subject of lactic acid a reference must be made to the many attempts which have been made to introduce systems of classification for the numerous types which have been described at various times. It is questionable whether any of these systems, including those of Beijerinck,[15] Löhnis,[45] Jensen,[46] and van Steenberge,[12] will be found of permanent value. The safest subdivision of the lactic acid bacteria remains at present the division based partly on their morphological characters and partly on their mode of action on fructose, whether they are capable of producing mannitol or not.

Finally, it should be mentioned that the property of fer-

menting carbohydrates with the formation of small quantities
of lactic acid is also met with among certain fungi. This was
observed by Eijkman[47] in the case of *Mucor Rouxii* and confirmed for this fungus by Chrzaszcz[48] and by Saito[49] for
Mucor chinensis.

LITERATURE

1. E. Kayser, *Ann. Inst. Pasteur*, vol. 8, p. 736, 1894.
2. G. Bertrand and G. Weissweiler, *Ann. Inst. Pasteur*, vol. 20, p. 977
   1906.
3. S. Grigoroff, *Rev. méd. de la Suisse Romande*, vol. 25, p. 714, 1905.
4. Chr. Barthel, *Zentrbl. f. Bakt.*, Abt. II, vol. 6, p. 417, 1900.
5. U. Gayon and E. Dubourg, *Ann. Inst. Pasteur*, vol. 8, p. 108, 1894.
6. U. Gayon and E. Dubourg, *Ann. Inst. Pasteur*, vol. 15, p. 527, 1901.
7. H. Müller-Thurgau and A. Osterwalder, *Zentrbl. f. Bakt.*, Abt. II, vol.
   36, p. 129, 1912.
8. K. Kruis and B. Rayman, *Lafar's Tech. Mykologie*, vol. 5, p. 295, 1906.
   Gustav Fischer, Jena.
9. G. Tate, *J. Chem. Soc.*, vol. 63, p. 1263, 1893.
10. W. H. Peterson and E. B. Fred, *J. Biol. Chem.*, vol. 42, p. 273, 1920.
11. J. Smit, *Zeits. f. Garungsphysiol.*, vol. 5, p. 273, 1916.
12. P. van Steenberge, *Ann. Inst. Pasteur*, vol. 34, p. 803, 1920.
13. M. W. Beijerinck, *Arch. néerland* (2), vol. 6, p. 212, 1901.
14. O. Jensen, *Zentrbl. f. Bakt.*, Abt. II, vol. 18, p. 211, 1907.
15. M. J. Beijerinck, *Zeits. f. Spiritusindustrie*, vol. 25, p. 531, 1902.
16. A. J. Kluyver and H. J. L. Donker, *Zeits. f. Chemie d. Zelle und Gewebe*,
    vol. 13, p. 134, 1926.
17. C. Neuberg and G. Gorr, *Biochem. Zeits.*, vol. 173, p. 476, 1926.
18. K. Myrbäck and H. von Euler, *Berichte*, Ser. B, vol. 57, p. 1073, 1924.
19. S. Kostytchev and S. Soldatenkov, *Z. physiol. Chem.*, vol. 168, p. 124,
    1927.
20. J. Lewkowitsch, *Berichte*, vol. 16, p. 2720, 1883.
21. M. Nencki and N. Sieber, *Monatsh. d. Chem.*, vol. 10, p. 532, 1889.
22. C. Günther and H. Thierfelder, *Arch. f. Hygiene*, vol. 25, p. 164, 1895.
23. G. Leichmann, *Zentrbl. f. Bact.*, Abt. II, vol. 2, p. 777, 1896.
24. A. Harden, *Trans. Chem. Soc.*, vol. 76, p. 610, 1901.
25. A. Péré, *Ann. Inst. Pasteur*, vol. 7, p. 737, 1893.
26. Y. Kozai, *Zeits. f. Hygiene*, vol. 31, p. 337, 1899.
27. P. G. Heinemann, *J. Biol. Chem.*, vol. 2, p. 603, 1907.
28. A. McKenzie, *J. Chem. Soc.*, vol. 87, p. 1373, 1905.
29. C. Neuberg and G. Gorr, *Biochem. Zeits.*, vol. 162, p. 490, 1925.
30. C. S. Pederson, W. H. Peterson and E. B. Fred, *J. Biol. Chem.*,
    vol. 68, p. 181, 1926.
31. F. Boutron and E. Frémy, *Ann. Chem. Phys.* (3), vol. 2, p. 257, 1841.

32. H. von Blücher, *Ann. d. Physik und Chem.*, vol. 63, p. 425, 1844.

33. ——. Gobley, *J. d. Pharm. et Chem.* [3], vol. 6, p. 54, 1844.

34. A. Bensch, *Annalen*, vol. 61, p. 174, 1847.

35. C. E. Avery, *Pharmaceut. J.*, vol. 13, Series III, p. 109, 1881–2.

36. A. A. Claflin, *J. Soc. Chem. Ind.*, vol. 16, p. 516, 1897.

37. J. von Saitcew, *Zentrbl. f. Bakt.*, Abt. II, vol. 72, p. 4, 1927.

38. F. Lafar, *Zentrbl. f. Bakt.*, Abt. II, vol. 2, p. 194, 1896.

39. E. Bachrach and H. Cardot, *Comptes rend. Soc. biol.*, vol. 86, p. 1127, 1922.

40. A. I. Virtanen, E. Wichmann and B. Linström, *Z. physiol. Chem.*, vol. 166, p. 21, 1927.

41. A. Mayer, *Jahresber. d. Tierchem.*, vol. 22, p. 598, 1892.

42. A. Strecker, *Annalen*, vol. 92, p. 80, 1854.

43. G. Draggendorf, *Arch. f. Pharm.*, Series III, vol. 15, p. 47, 1879.

44. A. W. Dox, G. P. Plaisance, *J. Amer. Chem. Soc.*, vol. 39, p. 2078, 1917

45. F. Löhnis, *Zentrbl. f. Bakt.*, Abt. II, vol. 18, p. 96, 1907.

46. O. Jensen, *Zentrbl. f. Bakt.*, Abt. II, vol. 44, p. 144, 1915.

47. C. Eijkman, *Zentrbl. f. Bakt.*, vol. 16, p. 97, 1894.

48. F. Chrzaszcz, *Zentrbl. f. Bakt.*, Abt. II, vol. 7, p. 326, 1901.

49. K. Saito, *Zentrbl. f. Bakt.*, Abt. II, vol. 29, p. 289, 1911.

CHAPTER XI

THE FACULTATIVE ANAEROBIC DEHYDROGENA-TION OF HEXOSES, INVOLVING THE FORMA-TION OF LACTIC ACID AS AN ESSENTIAL DECOM-POSITION PRODUCT

III. PROPIONIC ACID BACTERIA

STRECKER'S[1] observations in 1854 on the formation of propionic acid from calcium lactate by fermentation and the still earlier work referred to by him were reinvestigated and confirmed in 1879 to 1880 by Fitz,[2] who found that a solution of calcium lactate inoculated with bacteria contained in cows' dung broke down under the influence of these bacteria to a mixture of calcium propionate and calcium acetate.

His analysis of the fermentation products indicated that the reaction had taken the following course:

$$3 \ CH_3.CHOH.COOCa = 2CH_3.CH_2.COOCa +$$

calc. lactate   calc. propionate.

$$CH_3.COOCa + CO_2 + H_2O$$

calc. acetate.

The first pure cultures of propionic acid bacteria were isolated and described by von Freudenreich and Jensen.[3] They obtained them from Emmenthaler cheese, in which these micro-organisms were shown to be responsible for the formation of 'holes' during the ripening process of the cheeses.

Like the types studied by Strecker and by Fitz, von Freudenreich and Jensen's propionic acid bacteria, *Bact. acidi propionici a* and *b* and *Bac. acidi propionici* (a non-spore-forming rod but longer than the two other species), decomposed the lactic acid, previously formed from lactose in the young cheeses by true lactic acid bacteria.

In addition to the decomposition of lactic acid, two of the types of *Bact. acidi propionici* isolated by von Freudenreich

and Jensen were shown to be capable of fermenting lactose
with the production of carbon dioxide, propionic acid and
acetic acid, the last named in somewhat larger proportions
than those yielded where calcium lactate was fermented.
Two further types resembling *Bact. acidi propionici a* and *b*
were described by Thöni and Allemann[4] under the names of
Bact. acidi propionic var. *fuscum* and *Bact. acidi propionici*
var. *rubrum,* their varietal names referring to the pigmentation of their colonies. A further type inclined to zoogloea
production was isolated by Troili Peterson[5] from a certain
type of Swedish cheese.

More recently, Whittier, Sherman and Albus[6] have studied
the properties of a related type, isolated by Sherman and
Shaw[7] from Emmenthaler cheese. They found this type
capable of fermenting both lactose and its component
monoses as well as saccharose and maltose.

Of these carbohydrates maltose was most readily fermented.
Saccharose and maltose were found by van Niel[8] not to be
fermentable by one of the types isolated by von Freudenreich
and Jensen. Glycerol appears to be fermentable by all known
propionic acid bacteria (van Niel[8]).

The propionic acid bacteria are facultative anaerobes with
a preference for anaerobiosis. Most of them are short, sometimes coccoid, rods, von Freudenreich and Jensen's *Bac.
acidi propionici* being longer. They produce yellowish-brown
to red colonies under suitable conditions of growth. They do
not produce endospores, are Gram positive, and in their
morphology usually resemble *Streptococcus lactis acidi* very
strikingly. Grown under conditions where oxygen can gain
access, the cells become irregular, resembling those of *Bact.
radicicola* found in nodules of *Leguminoseae.* The propionic
acid bacteria, according to Sherman[9] and to van Niel,[8] are
typical catalase producers in spite of their reducing power
towards methylene blue, which Jensen[10] found to be three
times greater than that of the lactic acid bacteria. They all
produce propionic and acetic acids from calcium lactate in
the approximate proportions of $1 \cdot 8 : 1 \cdot 0$ (van Niel[8]).

In addition to the above types, which may be termed the true propionic acid bacteria, reference has been made in the literature to types which are claimed to produce smaller amounts of propionic acid. Botkin[11] mentions one which fermented lactose with the production of butyric acid, butyl and ethyl alcohols, small amounts of acetic and formic acids, and traces of propionic acid. Tissier and Gasching[12] describes another, *Bac. lactopropylobutyricus non liquefaciens*, which resembles *Bac. perfringens*, and which is stated to produce butyric and propionic acids in the proportions 2:1, in addition to appreciable quantities of lactic acid. It is highly probable, as suggested by van Niel, that the detection of propionic acid in the fermentation products of these types is due to misinterpretation of analytical data.

The ability of the propionic acid bacteria to decompose lactic acid has naturally led to this acid being regarded as an important intermediate in the fermentation of carbohydrates by these micro-organisms. Virtanen[13] emphasizes this function of lactic acid, and considers that the hexose which is finally converted into acetic and propionic acids is first dehydrogenated into lactic acid, and the latter subsequently converted into a mixture of the two volatile acids.

He suggests the following scheme for this mode of glucose fermentation.

$$3C_6H_{12}O_6 \rightarrow 6CH_3.CHOH.COOH \rightarrow 4CH_3.CH_2.COOH +$$

glucose   lactic acid   propionic acid

$$2CH_3.COOH + 2CO_2 + 2H_2O$$

acetic acid.

The dehydrogenation of lactic acid to acetic acid and propionic acid has been studied in considerable detail by van Niel,[8] who concludes from his experimental data that the conversion occurs without the intermediate formation of acetaldehyde, since small quantities of this substance added to an active culture of propionic acid bacteria remain essentially undecomposed, and are certainly not converted into acetic acid. In place of acetaldehyde van Niel suggests pyruvic acid $CH_3.CO.COOH$ as the intermediate stage between lactic acid and propionic and acetic acids. Pyruvic acid was found both by Virtanen and by van Niel to be as readily converted into propionic and acetic acids as lactic acid, while acetaldehyde was hardly affected at all. Those traces of the aldehyde which were affected could be recovered as acetylmethylcarbinol, a substance which van Niel detected in small quantities in his culture of propionic acid bacteria. The conversion of pyruvic acid to propionic, acetic, and carbonic acids can be secured only if the pyruvic acid is assumed to function as a powerful hydrogen acceptor, thus:

$$2CH_3.CO.C\overset{\displaystyle O}{\underset{\displaystyle OH}{\diagup}} \quad +2H \rightarrow CH_3.CH_2.COOH+CH_3.COOH+CO_2.$$

That it does so is emphasized by van Niel, who comments also on the importance of this observation that a fermentation of hexoses has here been found in which the production of acetaldehyde is of quite insignificant importance.

The following scheme probably represents the essential phases in the fermentation of glucose by the propionic acid bacteria:

Glucose→glucose phosphoric esters→glyceraldehyde→methylglyoxal→ lactic acid→pyruvic acid→propionic acid+acetic acid+CO_2

Compared with the lactic acid bacteria the propionic acid bacteria have received but slight attention in the past. Though present among the intestinal microflora of herbivorous animals and among that of silage, participation of the propionic acid bacteria in the essential reactions occurring in the intestine and in the silage heap is probably insignificant. Their economic importance is restricted at present to their activity during the ripening of cheese and to the use of propionic acid in the perfume industry.

The use of propionic acid and its esters has been suggested as solvents for pyroxylin and as substitutes for cellulose acetate. To facilitate this application of propionic acid bacteria, Sherman[14] and his collaborators attempted to accelerate the fermentation of carbohydrates by them and to increase the yields of propionic acid. They found that the presence in the cultures of propionic acid bacteria of *Bact. casei*, or of *Bact. alcaligenes* or *Bact. vulgare*, greatly accelerated the formation of propionic acid and favoured the production of the acid at the cost of other fermentation products. Thus, while pure cultures of their test organisms (*Bact. acidi propionici d*) fermented 66 per cent. of the available lactose within 30 days and gave a yield of 1 part of acetic to 1·7 parts of propionic acid, the presence of one of the afore-mentioned micro-organisms not only changed these proportions to 1 part of acetic acid and 11·5 parts of propionic acid, but increased the rate of fermentation of the carbohydrates to an appreciable extent. In a patent taken out by Sherman[14] this mode of propionic acid preparation is suggested as a suitable method for industrial purposes.

In concluding this review of the propionic acid bacteria, it should be mentioned that Virtanen[13] has laid great stress on an observation of his that succinic acid is produced by propionic acid bacteria in considerable quantities, up to about 30 per cent. of the total fermentation products. Most other investigators have obtained succinic acid as a fermentation product of the propionic acid bacteria but in far smaller proportions. Virtanen explains the occurrence of succinic acid as due to the property of the propionic acid bacteria of decomposing hexoses without the intervention of hexose phosphoric esters, a reaction which takes place when a coenzyme is absent or only present in insufficient quantities. By this abnormal fermentation process the glucose molecule is stated to be broken down into succinic acid and acetaldehyde, the latter giving rise to acetic acid formation.

Myrbäck and von Euler[15] hold a similar view. The correctness of this conception, however, is warmly disputed by Maurer.[16] And it must be admitted that it is rendered highly questionable by van Niel's observation on the effect of propionic acid bacteria on added acetaldehyde. Van Niel ascribes the small amounts of succinic acid formed by the propionic

acid bacteria to the action of the organisms on protein substances, on the lines suggested by Ehrlich,[17] Neuberg and
Ringer,[18] and Kostytchev and Frey[19] in the case of yeast, and
by Kozai[20] in the case of bacteria.

LITERATURE

1. A. Strecker, *Annalen*, vol. 92, p. 80, 1854.
2. A. Fitz, *Berichte*, vol. 13, p. 1309, 1880.
3. E. von Freudenreich and O. Jensen, *Zentrbl. f. Bakt.*, Abt. II, vol. 17, p. 529, 1907.
4. I. Thöni and O. Allemann, *Zentrbl. f. Bakt.*, Abt. II, vol. 25, p. 8, 1910.
5. G. Troili Peterson, *Zentrbl. f. Bakt.*, Abt. II, vol. 24, p. 333, 1909.
6. E. O. Whittier, J. M. Sherman and W. R. Albus, *Ind. and Eng. Chem.*, vol. 16, p. 122, 1924.
7. J. M. Sherman and R. H. Shaw, *J. Biol. Chem.*, vol. 56, p. 695, 1923.
8. C. M. van Niel, *The propionic acid bacteria, Dissertation*, publ. by Messrs. Uitzeverszack Boissevain & Co., Haarlem, 1928.
9. J. M. Sherman, *J. Bact.*, vol. 11, p. 417, 1926.
10. O. Jensen, *Zentrbl. f. Bakt.*, Abt. II, vol. 18, p. 211, 1907.
11. S. Botkin, *Z. f. Hygiene*, vol. 11, p. 421, 1891.
12. H. Tissier and P. Gasching, *Ann. Inst. Pasteur*, vol. 17, p. 540, 1903.
13. A. I. Virtanen, *Berichte*, vol. 58, p. 2441, 1925.
14. J. M. Sherman, *U.S. Pat.*, No. 1459959, 1923.
15. K. Myrbäck and H. von Euler, *Berichte*, Ser. B, vol. 57, p. 1073, 1927.
16. K. Maurer, *Biochem. Zeits.*, vol. 191, p. 83, 1927.
17. F. Ehrlich, *Zeits. f. angew. Chem.*, vol. 27, p. 48, 1914.
18. C. Neuberg and M. Ringer, *Biochem. Zeits.*, vol. 91, p. 131, 1918.
19. S. Kostytschev and L. Frey, *Zeits. physiol. Chem.*, vol. 146, p. 276, 1925.
20. Y. Kozai, *Zeits. f. Hygiene*, vol. 38, p. 386, 1901.

CHAPTER XII

THE OBLIGATORY ANAEROBIC DEHYDROGENATION OF HEXOSES

THE PRODUCTION OF N-BUTYRIC ACID AND N-BUTYL ALCOHOL.

THE type of hexose fermentation which results in the production of butyric acid as a chief fermentation product attracted the attention of investigators at an early date in the history of microbiology, not only because of the apparent unusual conversion of the hexose molecule, but also, and perhaps mainly, owing to the remarkable fact, first observed by Pelouze and Gélis,[1] that butyric acid may be produced by the fermentation of calcium lactate, or, according to Fitz,[2] from glycerol, substances which contain three carbon atoms in their molecule as against the four found in the butyric acid molecule itself.

Buchner and Meisenheimer[3] were the first to undertake systematic investigations with a view to throwing light on the reactions involved in the conversion of a three carbon chain substance like glycerol into butyric acid containing four carbon atoms in its molecule. To do so they compared the fermentation products of glucose and of glycerol when fermented by a typical butyric acid producing bacterium.

The result of their quantitative analyses, given in Table IV below, is the first detailed record of the final products of a typical butyric acid fermentation:

TABLE IV

Final fermentation products in percentage

Material.	n-Butyric acid.	Acetic acid.	Formic acid.	Lactic acid.	n-Butyl alcohol.	Ethyl alcohol.	Carbon dioxide.	Hydrogen.
100 gr. glycerine	0·7	1·0	4·0	3·4	19·6	10·4	42·1	1·9
100 gr. glucose	26·0	7·5	3·4	10·0	0·7	2·8	48·1	1·6

Buchner and Meisenheimer utilized for their investigations a culture of *Bac. butylicus* isolated by Fitz[4] from cows' dung and stated to be capable of producing butyric acid under both aerobic and anaerobic conditions. The fermentation products, which amounted to 83 and 85 per cent. respectively of the substances fermented, were found to be identical whether glycerol or glucose were taken, but differed quantitatively. This identity was considered to indicate a common origin. As such Buchner and Meisenheimer suggested lactic acid, which Schade[5] had previously contemplated as a possible mother substance of acetaldehyde and formic acid. Postulating the production of acetaldehyde from lactic acid, Buchner and Meisenheimer explained the formation of butyric acid by assuming that acetaldehyde was first condensed to aldol,

$$CH_3.CHOH.CH_2.C\begin{matrix} O \\ \diagdown H \end{matrix}$$, and this subsequently reduced to

butyric acid. The n-butyl alcohol was thought to have been formed by the reduction of crotonic aldehyde, CH_3.

$$CH.CH.C\begin{matrix} O \\ \diagdown H \end{matrix}$$, which in turn had been derived from aldol.

The ethyl alcohol was considered to have been formed from acetaldehyde on the lines known from the action of yeast on glucose. The origin of the acetic acid was not discussed by Buchner and Meisenheimer.

That acetaldehyde occurs as an intermediate fermentation product in the butyric acid fermentation was first demonstrated by Neuberg and Arinstein,[6] who 'fixed' appreciable quantities of this substance in fermenting cultures of *Bac. butylicus*, Fitz. Though these writers emphasize that the fixing of acetaldehyde by means of sodium sulphite results in the disappearance of butyric acid and of butyl alcohol from the final fermentation products, they decline to accept acetaldehyde as an intermediate of butyric acid. Instead they propose pyruvic acid aldol $CH_3.COH.COOH$, a substance

$$\overset{|}{CH_2.CO.COOH}$$

which they found could be decomposed to butyric acid by *Bac. butylicus*. This conception, as pointed out by Donker,[7] is not likely to be correct, since pyruvic acid $CH_3.CO.COOH$, when added to a culture of *Bac. butylicus*, does not become converted into butyric acid, but is transformed into acetic and formic acids. Neuberg and Arinstein had already observed this to be the case.

Important observations were made on the reactions taking place in the fermentation of glucose by butyric acid bacteria during the investigations carried out between 1917 and 1919 in the laboratory of one of the writers, and subsequently published by Reilly and collaborators[8] and by Thaysen.[9] These investigations showed that the fermentation of glucose by butyric acid bacteria can be divided into two well-defined stages—an early one, during which acids are produced and carbon dioxide and hydrogen evolved, and a later one, during which most of the acids are converted into neutral products.

The acids formed were found to consist essentially of acetic and butyric acids in varying proportions, with smaller amounts of formic and of lactic acids. The neutral products comprised n-butyl alcohol, acetone, and ethyl alcohol.

By the addition of an excess of calcium carbonate to a fermenting culture of the test organism, or by the adjustment of the reaction of the culture medium nearer to the alkaline side of the neutral point, the fermentation could be influenced in such a way that almost the whole of the available carbohydrates was converted into acids, carbon dioxide, and hydrogen, the usual neutral fermentation products being practically eliminated. Similar observations were made by Speakman.[10]

These observations indicated that any attempt made to elucidate the intermediate stages of the butyric acid fermentation had to concentrate in the first instance on the reactions leading to the formation of acids. Unfortunately Reilly and his collaborators did not pursue their investigations in this direction beyond ascertaining that the two volatile acids formed were produced in the proportions of 1 molecule of acetic acid to 1·8 molecule of butyric acid. Speakman's[11] publication on this subject added nothing of interest to the solution of the problem. He suggested that the acids originate direct from the carbohydrate, being formed in equimolecular proportions with simultaneous liberation of oxygen. Other publications have not appeared.

There is, therefore, at present no direct evidence to show how hexoses are broken down into acetic acid and butyric acid by butyric acid bacteria. The experimental data of Neuberg and Arinstein on the intermediate formation of acetaldehyde and those of Donker[7] on the occurrence of formic acid and acetylmethylcarbinol among the fermentation products support the hypothesis, however, that the fermentation proceeds via methylglyoxal—or perhaps dihydroxyacetone—to acetaldehyde and formic acid.

The formic acid would be the mother substance of carbon dioxide and hydrogen evolved, and the acetaldehyde that of butyric acid—through aldol condensation and reduction, of acetic acid, and of acetylmethylcarbinol $CH_3.CO.CHOH.$ CH_3. Support for this hypothesis is found in the results of the quantitative analysis of the fermentation products of a typical butyric acid producing bacterium, *Bac. Pasteurianus* (*Clostridium Pasteurianum*), which was investigated by Donker. Table V shows that the fermentation products of *Bac. Pasteurianus*, when expressed as their equivalent quantities of acetaldehyde, hydrogen, and carbon dioxide, were equal in each case to double the number of gramme molecules of carbohydrates converted. The bearing of similar observations in the case of *Bac. acetoethylicus* on the interpretation of the course taken by a fermentation was discussed in detail in Chapter V, p. 86.

The second stage in the fermentation of carbohydrates by butyric acid bacteria, when the acids formed are converted into neutral compounds, varies very greatly with the species. In some cases the active hydrogen resulting from the break-up of formic acid takes very little part in the subsequent reactions and is given off almost entirely as molecular hydrogen. Here the fermentation invariably comes to a standstill before the whole of the available carbohydrates has been consumed, unless precautions are taken to prevent an accumulation of free acids by the addition of a neutralizing agent such as calcium carbonate. Typical representatives of

TABLE V

Bac. Pasteurianus grown in yeast water containing 2 per cent. of glucose and 1 per cent. of calcium carbonate

Fermentation product.	Percentage of fermentation product calculated on glucose fermented.	Number of gramme molecules produced per 50 gramme molecules of glucose fermented.		
		Carbon dioxide.	Hydrogen.	Acetaldehyde.
Carbon dioxide	47·4	+97·0	—	—
Hydrogen	1·52	—	+68·4	—
Formic acid	—	—	—	—
Acetic acid	11·4	—	−17·1	+17·1
Butyric acid	12·6	—	—	+25·8
n-butyl alcohol	21·2	—	+51·6	+51·6
Acetone	1·1	−1·7	−3·4	+ 3·4
2:3 Butylene-glycol	—	—	—	—
		95·3	99·5	97·9

such strains are *Vibrion butyrique*, Pasteur;[12] *Bac. butyricus*, Prazmowski;[13] *Bac. Pasteurianus*, Winogradski;[14] *Bac. saccharobutyricus (Granulobacter saccharobutyricum)*, Beijerinck;[15] and Grassberger and Schattenfroh's[16] non-motile butyric acid bacillus. The chief hexose fermentation products of these types are butyric and acetic acids, carbon dioxide, and hydrogen.

The strains which activate butyric and acetic acids to function as hydrogen acceptors usually convert the whole of the available hexoses and produce appreciable quantities of neutral fermentation products, notably n-butyl alcohol, acetone and ethyl alcohol. The most characteristic representative of this group is the type introduced by Weizmann[17] for industrial purposes and described variously in the literature as *Bac. granulobacter pectinovorum*, Speakman;[10] as *Clostridium acetonigenum*, Donker;[7] or as *Clostridium acetobutylicum* (Wilson, Peterson, Fred[18]). Colloquially it has become known as the 'acetone bacillus'. In these pages it will be referred to as *Bac. acetonigenus*.

The reactions involved in the production of neutral fermentation products by the strains activating acetic and butyric acids have engaged the attention of several workers since the industrial processes for the manufacture of n-butyl alcohol and acetone by fermentation were introduced. That a connexion existed between the disappearance of n-butyric acid and the formation of n-butyl alcohol was clear from the investigation of Reilly and collaborators, but with the exception of some little known observations by Hall and Randall[19] on the behaviour of *Bac. Welchii*, it appears to have escaped the notice of investigators studying the behaviour of pathogenic types.

It was shown by Reilly that butyric acid added to a fermenting culture of the test organism became converted into n-butyl alcohol through the action of available active hydrogen. It is now generally accepted as correct that n-butyl alcohol is derived from the corresponding acid through hydrogenation. The figures for hydrogen evolution among various types of butyric acid bacteria which have been supplied by Donker confirm that a hydrogenation of butyric acid takes place during the period of the formation of n-butyl alcohol.

The interpretation of the origin of acetone has been debated at great length, but can now be regarded as settled in favour of the view, first advanced by Desborough,[20] that it is formed from acetic acid.

Desborough found that an addition of acetic acid to a fermenting culture of *Bac. acetonigenus* resulted in an increase of acetone, amounting to 80 per cent. of what might be expected from a theoretical conversion of acetic acid to acetone on the following lines, suggested by Kluyver and Donker:[21]

$$CH_3.C{\underset{H}{\overset{O}{\diagdown}}} + CH_3.COOH \rightarrow CH_3.CO.CH_2.C{\underset{OH}{\overset{O}{\diagdown}}} \rightarrow CH_3.CO.$$

acetoacetic acid

$$CH_3 + CO_2$$

Speakman[10, 11] confirmed Desborough's observations, but contended nevertheless that butyric acid was the mother substance of acetone. He suggested the following course for this conversion:

(1) $2CH_3.CH_2.CH_2.COOH + O_2 \rightarrow 2CH_3.CO.CH_2.COOH + 2H_2$
acetoacetic acid

(2) $CH_3.CO.CH_2.COOH \rightarrow CH_3.CO.CH_3 + CO_2$

His suggestion is not based on convincing experimental evidence, and his main argument is apparently the observation of an increase of 10 per cent. in the acetone yields after addition of butyric acid to a fermenting culture of the acetone bacillus—perhaps owing to the presence of acetic acid in the butyric acid used by him. On the other hand he admits that the bulk of the butyric acid is converted into n-butyl alcohol.

That acetoacetic acid should be an intermediate product in the production of acetone was suggested also by Raistrick and Clark.[22]

There is general agreement that the ethyl alcohol formed by butyl alcohol producing bacteria is derived from acetic acid through reduction, and not from acetaldehyde. This is convincingly supported by the fact that ethyl alcohol appears during the second stage of the fermentation only. The acetyl-methylcarbinol and 2:3 butyleneglycol found by Donker in small quantities originate no doubt from acetaldehyde. They may be assumed to have been formed on the lines suggested by Neuberg and Reinfurth[23] and by Kluyver, Donker and Visser't Hooft.[24] According to Wilson, Peterson and Fred,[18] the acetylmethylcarbinol is formed at about the same time as the acetic and butyric acids. These writers confirm that the three substances have a common precursor. They point out also that the yield of acetylmethylcarbinol may be increased by the addition of phosphates, while it decreases on addition of proteins.

Reviewing the processes of hexose fermentation by typical butyric acid bacteria, it may be claimed that, though unproved experimentally, there are good reasons for assuming that co-enzymes are essential for the reaction and that the hexose is first converted into phosphoric esters. These subsequently become converted into methylglyoxal, or possibly dihydroxyacetone, and the three carbon substances to acetaldehyde and formic acid. The latter gives rise to carbon dioxide and hydrogen. The acetaldehyde functions as the mother substance of all the remaining fermentation products, with the exception of lactic acid, which may originate from methylglyoxal direct through intramolecular dehydrogenation.

As regards the formation of lactic acid, Buchner and Meisenheimer[3] maintained that the whole of the methylglyoxal was first converted into lactic acid, the lactic acid giving rise subsequently to acetic and butyric acids, as well as to the remaining normal fermentation products of the group. This is not likely to be the case, seeing that a preliminary intramolecular dehydrogenation of the methylglyoxal to lactic acid, followed by the conversion of this acid to acetaldehyde and formic acid, would require a much greater effort on the part of the activating powers of the cell than a direct dehydrogenation of methylglyoxal to acetaldehyde and formic acid.

Among some of the bacteria producing butyric acid the fermentation ceases at an early stage owing to the accumulation of acidic products. In the case of others which, as already mentioned, are capable of activating butyric acid to serve as hydrogen acceptor, the available hexoses are decomposed and the acidic products converted into neutral compounds. This difference is to-day regarded as the most distinctive within the group and offers a suitable basis for the natural classification of these types. The former may be termed the true butyric acid bacteria, the latter the butyl alcohol bacteria. In both cases the fermentation proceeds best under anaerobic conditions, though some species, for instance *Bac. butylicus*, Fitz, are able to develop also in the presence of oxygen.

Obligatory aerobic bacteria no doubt exist which produce small quantities of butyric acid in the presence of oxygen. Schattenfroh and Grassberger[25] make reference to them in one of their well-known publications. One of the best known of these types is probably *Bac. butylicus*, Hüppe,[26] which is stated by Lehmann and Neumann[27] to be related to *Bac. Megatherium* and *Bac. mesentericus*. Another type, *Bac. mesentericus ruber*, is stated by Dupont[28] to produce not only butyric acid and acetic acid in small quantities, but also traces of valeric acid.

The progress of the hexose fermentation in these cases has not yet been investigated.

A special reference must be made also to those butyric acid bacteria, first isolated by Omelianski,[29] which ferment cellulose. A detailed account of these types, notably of *Bac. methanigenes* and *Bac. fossicularum*, was given in the monograph of Thaysen and Bunker[30] on the microbiology of cellulose and allied substances. Though the activity of these types is restricted to cellulose, glucose probably occurs at one stage or another in the reaction. In other respects the intermediate stages of the fermentation remain entirely unexplored.

Both groups of starch and hexose fermenting anaerobic butyric acid bacteria have acquired considerable industrial importance and are used for the production of butyric acid, n-butyl alcohol and acetone. In the following *résumé* an account will be given of the processes by which butyric acid and n-butyl alcohol may be obtained by fermentation.

THE BUTYRIC ACID FERMENTATION

It was mentioned above that Pelouze and Gélis[1] had found the mixture recommended by Boutron and Frémy[31] for the preparation of lactic acid to undergo a further decomposition when kept under suitable conditions. Pelouze and Gélis found that this secondary fermentation took place with the evolution of considerable quantities of hydrogen and with the formation of butyric acid, derived not from the hexose but from the lactic acid to which the hexoses present had been converted in the first instance.

That this fermentation was due to the activity of microorganisms was first demonstrated by Pasteur.[32] Stricht[33] was able to show that butyric acid can be produced direct from a carbohydrate. Later other investigators, among them Fitz,[34] confirmed this, and showed that butyric acid can be produced also from glycerol. The wide distribution in soil, milk, water, faecal matter and wounds, of bacteria producing butyric acid under anaerobic conditions was abundantly proved by subsequent investigators. Efforts at grouping and describing the numerous types proceeded actively with the isolation of new strains and are still proceeding. Various schemes have been suggested for this classification. The best known are perhaps those of Grassberger and Schattenfroh[16] and of Bredemann.[35] The most recent and the most extensive from the point of the carbohydrate metabolism is that of Donker.[7]

In spite of the interest which has been taken in the butyric acid bacteria little progress has been made with the improvement of the methods for the preparation of butyric acid. It is questionable even whether pure cultures of the most suitable types are in use for the purpose. The comparatively recent method suggested by Lefranc and Co.[36] would appear to indicate this. It is impossible, therefore, to give more than a tentative description of the industrial production of butyric acid as it should be carried out under ideal conditions.

The raw material chosen, usually starch, maltose, saccharose (molasses), or glucose, should be suspended or dissolved in the requisite amount of water and sterilized by heat.

On the whole, starch in the form of maize or rice is preferable as raw material, since its use obviates the necessity for separate processes for the preparation of maltose or glucose.

Where molasses are used it will invariably be found necessary to supply nitrogenous food substances to ensure a normal progress of fermentation. As such may be used extracts of grain, or the gluten remaining after the preparation of starch from rice or wheat (Legg[37]).

The temperatures required for sterilization would depend on the hydrogen ion concentrations maintained in the mash (Chick[38]) and on the concentration of the mash.

The sterile mash would have to be cooled to 37° C. and the cooled mash fed continuously into a previously sterilized vat, containing a vigorously fermenting culture of the selected type of butyric acid bacterium, until the vat was completely filled. While the fermentation proceeded the hydrogen ion concentration of the mash would have to be maintained at its optimum, presumably between pH values of 5·0 to 6·0, so as to prevent the fermentation from coming to a premature standstill. On completion of the fermentation—after two to four days—the mash, containing salts of the volatile acids produced, should be evaporated to dryness and the butyric acid recovered by fractional distillation of the calcium salts in the presence of sulphuric acid or oxalic acid.

THE PRODUCTION OF BUTYL ALCOHOL BY FERMENTATION

Not until 1911 was any serious interest taken in the production of butyl alcohol by fermentation. In that year Fernbach and Strange[39] patented a fermentation process for this purpose, based, it is understood, on the utilization of *Bac. butylicus*, Fitz.

Previously the butyl alcohol producing bacteria had been a subject of research only in connexion with the elucidation of the origin of the 'fusel oils' of crude alcohol. Fitz[2] had raised this question in 1877 and Perdrix[40] had subsequently reverted to it. From his investigations on *Bac. amylozymus*, isolated from Paris tap water, Perdrix had come to the conclusion that the appearance of 'fusel oils' was undoubtedly the result of contamination of worts with this or allied bacteria. A bacterial origin of the 'fusel oils' was favoured also by Emmerling.[41] Pringsheim's[42] investigations of the problem threw doubt on this contention, however, and showed that 'fusel oils' rarely, if ever, contain n-butyl alcohol, but are composed of amyl and propyl alcohols besides iso-butyl alcohol. It was noted also by Pringsheim that bacteria such as *Bac. amylozymus* are unable to develop in worts containing 10 per cent. of ethyl alcohol, a concentration usually established in worts under industrial conditions before the production of 'fusel oils' becomes apparent. The question of the origin of 'fusel oils' was finally settled by Ehrlich,[43] who found that they resulted from the action of yeast on nitrogenous organic substances.

Fernbach and Strange's efforts at producing butyl alcohol on an industrial scale do not appear to have met with marked success, and the industry remained of insignificant proportions until the outbreak of the war of 1914 to 1918, when an abnormal demand for acetone arose.

At this time attention was drawn by Weizmann[17] to the property of butyl alcohol bacteria of producing considerable quantities of acetone. Liberal financial support from public funds made it possible to institute a comprehensive inquiry into the most suitable methods by which the butyl alcohol bacteria could be utilized for the production of acetone. As a result factories were erected in which starch and maltose were fermented under aseptic conditions with a species of butyl alcohol bacterium, supplied by Weizmann, discussed in this treatise under the name of *Bac. acetonigenus*.

The morphology, biology, and fermentative action of this strain have been the subject of fairly detailed investigations by Speakman,[10] Reilly and collaborators,[8] Thaysen,[9] and notably by Donker,[7] who came to the conclusion that it differed sufficiently from other similar organisms studied by him to justify him in regarding it as a new species.

Its most characteristic properties are its marked liquefying action on gelatine and its formation of appreciable quantities of acetylmethylcarbinol. All other similar strains examined

by Donker lacked proteolytic action and reduced any intermediately formed acetylmethylcarbinol to 2:3 butyleneglycol.

A striking feature of the fermentation of hexoses by this
organism is the rise of the titratable acidity of the fermenting
mash to a clearly defined maximum. Under the most favourable conditions this maximum is reached within the first
fifteen hours of fermentation, though it may be delayed
for various reasons until the thirtieth hour. It is followed
immediately by a fall to a minimum which, apart from
slight variations, remains stationary until the completion
of the fermentation. The curve shown in Fig. 1 illustrates
this. A similar rise and fall in the hydrogen ion concentration of the fermenting mash can be observed, but the
maximum concentration is not as clearly defined as in the
case of the titratable acidity. Unpublished observations
by the writers show that a hydrogen ion concentration
equal to a pH value of $4\cdot3$ is established under normal conditions within the first ten hours of the fermentation, and that
this concentration, after an intermediate rise which coincides
with the attainment of the maximum titratable acidity, is again
established towards the end of the fermentation (see Fig. 1).

The evolution of gas, a varying mixture of hydrogen and
carbon dioxide, does not coincide with the rise and fall in
titratable acidity, but commences at a later stage as shown
in Fig. 2.

By checking the relationship between evolution of gas and
the production of titratable acidity at frequent intervals,
valuable information may be gained as to the absence or
presence in the fermenting mash of infecting micro-organisms.
When infections occur the curves both of the titratable
acidity and of gas evolution become affected, that of the
titratable acidity rising either continuously, or after a tem-
porary fall, to concentrations much in excess of those at
which the fermentation can continue its normal course. The
curve of gas evolution shows a correspondingly marked drop
(see Fig. 3).

Thaysen[9] has shown that the most serious infection of the

Hydrogen ion Concentration of fermenting mash.

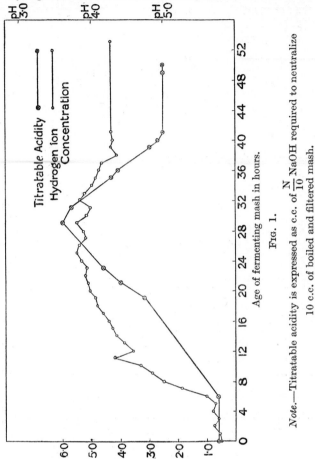

Titratable acidity of fermenting mash.

FIG. 1.

Note.—Titratable acidity is expressed as c.c. of $\frac{N}{10}$ NaOH required to neutralize 10 c.c. of boiled and filtered mash.

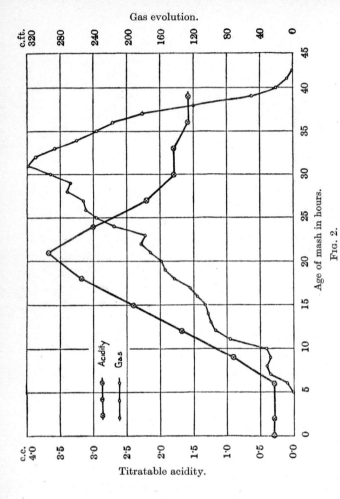

Gas evolution.

Age of mash in hours.

Fig. 2.

Titratable acidity.

Note.—Titratable acidity is expressed as c.c. of $\frac{N}{10}$ NaOH required to neutralize 10 c.c. of boiled and filtered mash.

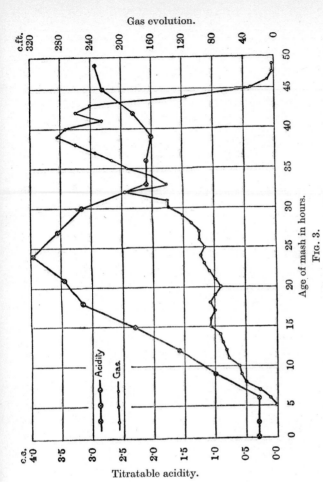

Gas evolution.

Titratable acidity.

Age of mash in hours.

Fig. 3.

Note.—Titratable acidity is expressed as c.c. of $\frac{N}{10}$ NaOH required to neutralize 10 c.c. of boiled and filtered mash.

acetone fermentation is caused by lactic acid bacteria, notably to one described by him under the name of *Bact. volutans*, an organism which cannot be readily distinguished from *Bac. acetonigenus* by microscopical examination except after previous staining of the preparation with methylene blue in the cold. By this technique *Bact. volutans* is seen to contain in its cells two or three granules of purple staining bodies which never occur in the cells of *Bac. acetonigenus*. The seriousness of lactic acid infections has been referred to also by Fred, Peterson and Mulvania,[44] and by Speakman and Phillips.[45] The last-named writers interpret the action of *Bact. volutans* as due to its production of an inhibitory substance which causes *Bac. acetonigenus* to produce lactic acid instead of its usual intermediate fermentation products. The experimental evidence brought forward by Speakman and Phillips in support of this contention is not supported by practical experience.

Various methods have been recommended for counteracting the harmful influence of lactic acid bacteria on the course of the butyl fermentation, such as lowering the fermentation temperature. In the writers' experience none of these recommendations have the desired effect.

Another serious cause of failure of the butyl fermentation has been ascribed by Legg[46] to the occurrence of 'epidemics of sluggishness' in the cultures used for inoculation, presumably indicating the presence of a bacteriophage in such cultures. This interesting observation has not yet been fully explored.

The plant now generally chosen for the production of butyl alcohol is that usually adopted for pure culture fermentation processes and need not be described in detail. The process involves a preliminary sterilization of the raw material, either starch or maltose, followed by the introduction of the cooled mash into a large amount of already fermenting mash. Where starch mashes are used their sterilization requires temperatures far in excess of those usually thought necessary; and an exposure of the mash for 8 hours to 144° C. is found to be essential.

The fermentation is conducted at a temperature between 37° C. and 40° C., and under normal conditions is completed in 28 to 32 hours. The fermentation products, according to Reilly and collaborators, are:

   7   kg. of acetone

103   kg. of n-butyl alcohol

100·3 cubic meters of carbon dioxide

59·1   ,,   ,,   ,, hydrogen

 12   kg. of residual acidity, from

100   kg. of grain, containing 65 kg. of starch.

With the increasing importance of n-butyl alcohol as a basis for the manufacture of dopes and varnishes, attempts have been made to increase the yields of butyl alcohol obtained. According to Boinot[47] this may be achieved by adding calcium lactate to the fermenting mash.

Since the introduction of the industrial production of butyl alcohol by fermentation, the isolation of pure cultures of *Bac. acetonigenus* has become a question of considerable importance, the usual laboratory methods being entirely unsuitable for the purpose. Dorner[48] has maintained that this difficulty is due to the presence in ordinary culture media of inhibitory substances which prevent the ready development of *Bac. acetonigenus*. By the addition of substances such as animal charcoal, soil, or brain to dextrose broth, Dorner claims to have been able to overcome the inhibitory action of the usual laboratory media, and states that he has good development of a single cell by Burri's[49] Indian ink method. The writers have repeated Dorner's experiments, using glucose broth and wort with animal charcoal added. They did not succeed in obtaining growth of *Bac. acetonigenus* in these media when the number of cells inoculated decreased to less than 2,000.

THE PRODUCTION OF HIGHER FATTY ACIDS

The early investigators of the butyric acid fermentation record having isolated other and usually higher fatty acids as fermentation products. Grillone[50] and Fitz[34] obtained caproic acid, Botkin[51] propionic acid, Locquin[52] and Wagner, Meyer and Dozier[53] valeric acid.

Neuberg and Arinstein[6] paid particular attention to these acids and isolated 34·9 grammes of a mixture of caproic, caprylic and capric acids from 3990 grammes of glucose. These higher fatty acids invariably contained an even number of carbon atoms in their chains.

Neither Neuberg and Arinstein nor any other investigators have so far attempted to explain the intermediate stages involved in the production of these acids by micro-organisms. Perhaps it is justifiable to assume that the reactions involved in these cases are similar to those responsible for the syntheses to which references will be made in Chapter XV.

LITERATURE

1. J. Pelouze and Gélis, *Ann. Chim. Phys.*, 3, vol. 10, p. 434, 1844.
2. A. Fitz, *Berichte*, vol. 10, p. 276, 1877.
3. C. Buchner and J. Meisenheimer, *Berichte*, vol. 41, p. 1419, 1908.
4. A. Fitz, *Berichte*, vol. 15, p. 867, 1882.
5. H. Schade, *Zeitschr. f. physikal. Chem.*, vol. 57, p. 1, 1907; vol. 60, p. 510, 1907.
6. C. Neuberg and B. Arinstein, *Biochem. Zeits.*, vol. 117, p. 269, 1921.
7. H. J. L. Donker, *Bijdrage tot de Kennis der Boterzuur-Butyl alcoholen Acetonegistingen*. W. D. Meinema, Delft, 1926.
8. J. Reilly, W. G. Hickinbottom, F. R. Henley and A. C. Thaysen, *Biochem. J.*, vol. 14, p. 229, 1920.
9. A. C. Thaysen, *J. Inst. Brew.*, vol. 27, p. 529, 1921.
10. H. B. Speakman, *J. Biol. Chem.*, vol. 41, p. 319, 1920.
11. H. B. Speakman, *J. Biol. Chem.*, vol. 43, p. 401, 1920.
12. L. Pasteur, *Comptes rend.*, vol. 52, p. 344, 1861.
13. A. Prazmowski, *Botan. Zeits.*, vol. 37, p. 409, 1879.
14. S. Winogradski, *Zentrbl. f. Bakt.*, Abt. II, vol. 9, p. 43, 1902.
15. M. W. Beijerinck, *Verhandl. d. Kon. Akad. van Wetenschap*, Amsterdam, Series II, vol. 3, p. 163, 1893.
16. R. Grassberger and A. S. Schattenfroh, *Archiv f. Hygiene*, vol. 60, p. 40, 1907.
17. Ch. Weizmann, *B. Pat.*, No. 4845, 1915.
18. P. W. Wilson, W. H. Peterson and E. B. Fred, *J. Biol. Chem.*, vol. 74, p. 495, 1927.
19. J. H. Hall and H. B. Randall, *J. Infect. Dis.*, vol. 31, p. 326, 1922.
20. A. P. H. Desborough, J. Reilly, A. C. Thaysen and F. R. Henley, *B. Pat.*, No. 128403, 1919.

21. A. J. Kluyver and H. J. L. Donker, *Zeitsch. d. Zelle und Gewebe*, vol. 13, p. 134, 1926.
22. H. Raistrick and A. B. Clark, *Biochem. J.*, vol. 13, p. 329, 1919.
23. C. Neuberg and E. Reinfurth, *Biochem. Zeits.*, vol. 142, p. 553, 1923.
24. A. J. Kluyver, H. J. L. Donker and Visser't Hooft, *Biochem. Zeits.*, vol. 161, p. 361, 1925.
25. A. S. Schattenfroh and R. Grassberger, *Arch. Hygiene*, vol. 37, p. 54, 1900.
26. F. Hüppe, *Mitt. Kais. Gesund.*, vol. 2, p. 309, 1884.
27. K. B. Lehmann and R. O. Neumann, *Bakteriologische Diagnostik*, 5th edition, Lehmann, München, 1912.
28. C. Dupont, *Comptes rend.*, vol. 134, p. 1449, 1902.
29. V. Omelianski, *Comptes rend.*, vol. 121, p. 653, 1895.
30. A. C. Thaysen and H. J. Bunker, *Microbiology of Cellulose, Hemicelluloses, Pectin and Gums*, Oxford University Press, 1927.
31. F. Boutron and E. Frémy, *Ann. de Chim. et Phys.* (3), vol. 2, p. 257, 1841.
32. L. Pasteur, *Comptes rend.*, vol. 45, p. 930, 1857.
33. C. Stricht, *Jahrsber. f. Chem.*, vol. 21, p. 522, 1868.
34. A. Fitz, *Berichte*, vol. 11, p. 42, 1878.
35. H. Bredemann, *Zentrbl. f. Bakt.*, Abt. II, vol. 23, p. 385, 1909.
36. Lefranc and Co., *B. Pat.*, No. 186572, 1923.
37. I. A. Legg, *U.S. Pat.*, No. 1582408, 1926.
38. H. Chick, *J. Hygiene*, vol. 10, p. 237, 1910.
39. A. Fernbach and E. H. Strange, *B. Pat.*, No. 15204, 1911, and *B. Pat.*, No. 21073, 1912.
40. L. Perdrix, *Ann. Inst. Past.*, vol. 5, p. 287, 1891.
41. O. Emmerling, *Berichte*, vol. 37, p. 3535, 1904; vol. 38, p. 653, 1905.
42. H. Pringsheim, *Zentrbl. f. Bakt.*, Abt. II, vol. 15, p. 300, 1905; *Berichte*, vol. 38, p. 486, 1905.
43. F. Ehrlich, *Berichte*, vol. 39, p. 4072, 1906; vol. 40, p. 1027, 1927. *Jahrb. d. Versuch u. Lehranstalt f. Brauerei in Berlin*, vol. 10, p. 515, 1907.
44. E. B. Fred, W. H. Peterson and M. Mulvania, *J. Bact.*, vol. 11, p. 333, 1926.
45. H. B. Speakman and J. F. Phillips, *J. Bact.*, vol. 9, p. 283, 1924.
46. D. A. Legg, *B. Pat.*, No. 278307, 1927.
47. F. Boinot, *U.S. Pat.*, Ser. B, No. 1565543, 1926.
48. W. Dorner, *Zentrbl. f. Bakt.*, Abt. II, vol. 65, p. 156, 1925.
49. R. Burri, *Das Tuscheverfahren*, Gustav Fischer, Jena, 1910.
50. G. B. Grillone, *Annalen*, vol. 165, p. 127, 1873.
51. S. Botkin, *Zeits. f. Hygiene*, vol. 11, p. 423, 1892.
52. R. Locquin, *Chem. Zeits.*, vol. 26, p. 956, 1902.
53. E. Wagner, K. F. Meyer and C. C. Dozier, *J. Bact.*, vol. 10, p. 321, 1925.

CHAPTER XIII

THE FERMENTATION OF PENTOSES

WHEN discussing the principles underlying the exposition given in these pages of the microbiological dehydrogenation of monoses it was mentioned that the fermentation of pentoses would be dealt with in a separate chapter, as a separate subject. The decision to do so was prompted by lack of information on the reactions taking place, and not by any established dissimilarity between the methods by which micro-organisms utilize pentoses and hexoses. On the contrary, most of the available data point to a striking similarity between the reactions by which pentoses and hexoses are decomposed by micro-organisms. To mention but a few examples, Bertrand[1] found that *Bact. xylinum*, or rather the closely related type the sorbose bacterium, converts xylose to xylinic acid, a reaction which evidently is analogous to the conversion of glucose by the same organism to gluconic acid. In his investigations on *Bact. pneumoniae*, Grimbert[2] observed that xylose was fermented with the production of ethyl alcohol, acetic acid, lactic acid and succinic acid, the substances already ascertained to be fermentation products of glucose. Among the more recent observations might be mentioned those of Peterson and Fred[3] on certain pentose fermenting bacteria, isolated from silage, which showed that acetaldehyde was produced as an intermediate fermentation product from pentoses and from hexoses; and those of Northrop and his collaborators[4] on the action of *Bac. acetoethylicus* on glucose and xylose. Here again the final fermentation products were identical, though formed in slightly varying proportions. In the case of *Bac. acetonigenus*, Peterson, Fred and Schmidt[5] came to the conclusion that the xylose fermentation products were identical with those of glucose, though varying slightly in proportion. And finally in their study of the action of *Fusarium lini*, the wilt of flax, White and Willaman[6] observed the production of ethyl alcohol in quantities over and above those which could have been produced had the pentose molecule been broken down into one three-carbon molecule and one two-carbon molecule.

There are reasons, therefore, for expecting that as experimental evidence accumulates, it will be possible to co-ordinate the intermediate reactions of pentose fermentations with those already discernible for hexoses and for anticipating that the formation of molecules containing three carbon chains must be an important stage in the breakdown of pentoses.

As regards the actual stages in the fermentation, it is to be assumed that the pentose molecule undergoes esterification with phosphoric acid prior to fermentation. On this subject, however, there does not at present appear to exist any information. In support of the view that intermediate products of molecules with three carbon chains are formed, there is important circumstantial evidence to be found in the fact that, as already mentioned, the final fermentation products of pentoses are frequently identical with those of hexoses, and that they are produced in almost equal proportions from both. This quantitative similarity precludes the possibility that the pentose molecule is converted during fermentation into two intermediate molecules, one containing a chain of three carbons and the other a chain of two carbons. As in the case of the hexoses the preliminary formation of but one intermediate with a molecule possessing chains of three carbon atoms appears to be the only conception fitting the facts so far established. This being the case it becomes necessary to assume that the pentose molecule undergoes condensation to a polysaccharide prior to fermentation, a polysaccharide containing a multiple of six carbon groups. Support for this interpretation of the early stages of pentose fermentation may be found in the synthetic activities of micro-organisms, to which reference will be made in Chapter XIV.

The property of fermenting pentoses is probably met with among micro-organisms to a far greater extent than was at one time anticipated, but the question has not yet received the attention it deserves. At a comparatively early date it was established by Stone and Tollens[7] that yeasts are unable to ferment pentoses with the production of ethyl alcohol. That these organisms, nevertheless, can utilize pentoses as a source of energy was shown by Bokorny,[8] who obtained reasonably good growth of yeast in culture media containing xylose or arabinose as the sole source of carbohydrate. According to Abbott[9] traces of carbon dioxide, alcohol, and non-volatile acids are formed by yeast from pentoses. Many other lower and higher fungi are no doubt capable of fermenting pentoses, but experimental evidence is meagre in the extreme. Czapek[10] tested *Aspergillus niger* for its rate of development on various carbohydrates and obtained good growth of the fungus on xylose and on arabinose, observations which Ekman[11] confirmed. White and Willaman[6] reported the production of ethyl alcohol as the result of the action of *Fusarium lini* on xylose.

Peterson, Fred and Schmidt[12] extended these observations to other types of fungi, notably to *Aspergillus, Penicillium,* and *Mucor* species, and found that on the whole *Aspergillus* and *Penicillium* species fermented pentoses—xylose and arabinose—more readily than *Mucor* species. The most rapidly acting types decomposed the available pentoses completely in 4 to 5 days, xylose being the more readily decomposed pentose. The fermentation products were represented almost solely by carbon dioxide and mycelial tissue. No production of alcohol or of volatile acids could be detected and but a very slight trace of non-volatile acids was found.

Nevertheless Amelung,[13] who examined the action of *Aspergillus niger* on xylose and arabinose, reported the formation of citric acid from these carbohydrates by the fungus.

Whether actinomycetes ferment pentoses or not has not yet been definitely ascertained. The frequent occurrence of these micro-organisms in manure and compost heaps, where active fermentation of pentoses and of pentosans takes place, makes it almost certain that many actinomycetes are capable of utilizing pentoses as a source of carbohydrates. This is borne out also by unpublished observations by the writers on the development of actinomycetes in xylose containing food solutions.

The pentose fermenting properties of bacteria have been studied in considerably greater detail than those of the other groups of micro-organisms referred to above. It is known that pentoses can be utilized by bacteria belonging to most of the chief groups of hexose fermenting types, and that this property is of particular economic importance among the lactic acid bacteria (Kayser;[14] Gayon and Dubourg;[15] Fred, Peterson and Anderson;[16] Stiles, Peterson and Fred[17]), and among the many insufficiently described types which are responsible for the destruction of hemicelluloses in the intestine and for the early stages of humus formation in soil and peat bogs (Rege[18]).

In the groups of *Bact. typhosum—Bact. paratyphosum*, a destruction of pentoses has been recommended by Stern[19] as a means for differentiating closely related species. Stern found that xylose, but not arabinose, was fermented by *Bact. typhosum*, while *Bact. paratyphosum A* attacked arabinose and *Bact. paratyphosum B* both xylose and arabinose. The investigations of Peterson and Fred[20] have shown that pentose fermenting lactic acid bacteria actively participate in the silage fermentation, and the microscopic investigations of Henneberg[21] on the destruction of plant tissues by the intestinal flora of man and of herbivorous animals have demonstrated that bacteria are partly responsible for the elimination of the pentosans of plant tissues entering the intestinal tract.

The importance of pentoses and their corresponding polysaccharides in the naturally occurring denitrification processes has been studied by Stoklasa[22] and by Rege,[18] who suggest that pentoses take part in the production of natural humus, a view which has been confirmed recently by Thaysen and Bakes.[23]

The important manure heap inhabitant *Bac. mesentericus*

ruber is reported by Fred, Peterson and Carroll[24] to be capable of fermenting xylose with production of ethyl alcohol and acetone.

A particularly interesting field of economic application of pentose-fermenting bacteria is that opened by Northrop and collaborators[4] with their investigations on a bacterium isolated by them and described under the name of *Bac. acetoethylicus.*

The fermenting of glucose by this organism was studied in detail by Donker.[25] The results of this analysis were quoted in Table II on page 86. According to Northrop and collaborators, the yields of acetone and alcohol obtained from pentoses are somewhat lower than those recorded by Donker from glucose, but too much importance should not be attached to these differences, since the fermentation of carbohydrates by *Bac. acetoethylicus* is dependent to an unusual extent on the cultural conditions prevailing. In Northrop, Ashe and Senior's[4] experiments the following yields of ethyl alcohol and acetone were obtained from the carbohydrates mentioned.

TABLE VI

Carbohydrate fermented.	Yield expressed as percentage of carbohydrate fermented.	
	Ethyl alcohol.	acetone.
Glucose	11–23	9–10
Fructose	24–25	8–10
Maltose	23–24	6–7
Starch	20–24	8–10
Xylose	18–20	4–5
d-Arabinose	12–16	6–7

It is not surprising that these very considerable yields of acetone and ethyl alcohol should have drawn the attention of investigators, including Northrop, to the possibility of utilizing the action of *Bac. acetoethylicus* on pentoses for the industrial production of power alcohol. Numerous analyses have shown that pentoses, notably xylose, occur in the form of polysaccharides in various vegetable waste products—in cacao shells (Churchman[26]), in oat husks (Fred, Peterson and Anderson[27]), in Nile sudd—*Cyperus papyrus*—(Joseph and Martin[28]) and in many other similar materials, of which an extensive list was given by Thaysen and Galloway.[29] With a pentose content of 20 per cent. in such materials, a figure which is often reached and sometimes surpassed, *Bac. aceto-ethylicus* should be capable of producing as much as 90 litres of power alcohol per 1,000 kg. of waste, a yield which would be of the order of that obtained from potatoes, utilized extensively in some countries for the production of power alcohol.

The first attempts at developing a process for power alcohol production in which waste vegetable matter was fermented by *Bac. acetoethylicus* were recorded by Northrop, Ashe and Morgan;[30] Peterson, Fred and Verhulst;[31] Fred, Peterson and Anderson;[27] and Juritz,[32] but none of the methods evolved extended beyond a laboratory scale. Subsequently Thaysen and Galloway[29] undertook a renewed investigation of the problem, and extended their work to include production in a small technical plant.

One of their greatest difficulties was to devise a method by which the pentosans, present in the vegetable debris, could be converted into pentoses, a necessary step in the procedure, since *Bac. acetoethylicus* is unable to hydrolyse pentosans. In the investigations by previous workers this hydrolysis had been carried out by subjecting the vegetable waste to temperatures above 100° C. in the presence of sulphuric acid. But this procedure could not be adopted for work on a technical scale owing to the corrosive action of dilute mineral acids on the steel required for the construction of containers capable of withstanding the high temperatures required. Thaysen and Galloway overcame this difficulty by reducing the temperature required to 100° C. or below, and by increasing at the same time the hydrogen ion concentration of the liquid in which the waste was suspended. As the rate of hydrolysis was found to be directly proportional to the prevailing hydrogen ion concentration at a given temperature, they increased the concentration of acid used to such an extent that complete hydrolysis of the pentosans could be ensured at a temperature of 100° C. At the same time, and in order to avoid an increased consumption of acid, they decreased the bulk of the solution taken for the suspension of the waste during hydrolysis.

The pentoses resulting from the hydrolysis were extracted under aseptic conditions with water sterilized by boiling in the presence of a sufficient concentration of hydroxyl ions to ensure complete destruction of all spores and vegetative cells at 100° C. By choosing an alkaline reaction for the mash during sterilization they introduced the simplification of extracting the pentoses present in the hydrolysed mash and of neutralizing the acid remaining in the waste in one operation. The resulting pentose extract was cooled under aseptic conditions and carried with similar precautions to a suitable container into which a culture of *Bac. acetoethylicus* had previously been introduced. The ensuing fermentation was allowed to proceed at a temperature of 40° to 41° C.

The control of the hydrogen ion concentration of the fermenting mash was found to be a factor of great importance for the smooth conversion of the pentoses into ethyl alcohol and acetone. Previous investigators had recommended conducting this conversion at a reaction corresponding to a pH value of 6·4, a figure which may be established by addition of an excess of calcium carbonate.

Confirming the observations of previous writers that the development of *Bac. acetoethylicus* proceeds faster at a somewhat lower hydrogen ion concentration, Thaysen and Galloway recommended the periodic addition of a sterile calcium hydroxide suspension to the fermenting extract. The pH of the mash was thereby raised at intervals of four hours from the value of 6·4 to one of 7·8. By so doing they obtained a more rapid completion of the fermentation, without a diminution in the yield of acetone which, as Northrop,

Ashe and Senior had shown is greatest—other conditions being equal—in mashes where the reaction has been maintained on the acid side of the neutral point.

The yields of acetone alcohol mixture obtained by Thaysen and Galloway from various waste materials on a semi-technical scale were of the order expected and indicated a complete conversion of the pentoses. A yield of as much as 90 litres per 1,000 kg. of vegetable waste was frequently recorded. Their process is recommended by them for the technical preparation of power alcohol in localities where waste vegetable material is available in abundance and where the price of other liquid fuels for internal combustion engines is sufficiently high to justify the production of power alcohol.

Though undoubtedly useful for this purpose, Thaysen and Galloway's process might be improved in one direction, by eliminating the preliminary acid hydrolysis introduced for the conversion of the pentosans of the waste into soluble pentoses. The elimination of the acid hydrolysis, however, can be secured only by the use of bacteria capable of hydrolysing pentosans prior to the fermentation of pentoses, and such types have not yet been isolated. They are probably found among the microflora of decomposing vegetable substances, but an exhaustive study of this microflora has not yet been undertaken.

Apart from the production of power alcohol, the use of pentose fermenting bacteria has been suggested (Fred, Peterson and Anderson[27]) for the technical production of volatile acids and of lactic acid. These suggestions have not been further developed, and are not likely to become of industrial importance unless the requirements of these acids, notably of lactic acid, should increase to such an extent that the available supplies of hexose residues become inadequate to satisfy the demands.

LITERATURE

1. G. Bertrand, *Comptes rend.*, vol. 127, p. 124, 1898.
2. L. Grimbert, *Comptes rend. Soc. biol.*, vol. 48, p. 191, 1896.
3. W. H. Peterson and E. B. Fred, *J. Biol. Chem.*, vol. 44, p. 29, 1920.

4. J. H. Northrop, L. H. Ashe and J. K. Senior, *J. Biol. Chem.*, vol. 39, p. 1, 1919.

5. W. H. Peterson, E. B. Fred and E. G. Schmidt, *J. Biol. Chem.*, vol. 60, p. 628, 1924.

6. M. G. White and J. J. Willaman, *Biochem. J.*, vol. 22, p. 583, 1928.

7. W. E. Stone and B. Tollens, *Annalen d. Chem. und Pharm.*, vol. 249, p. 257, 1888.

   W. E. Stone, *Berichte*, vol. 23, p. 3791, 1890.

8. Th. Bokorny, *Zentrbl. f. Bakt.*, Abt. II, vol. 47, p. 191, 1917.

9. O. D. Abbott, *Missouri Agric. Exp. Stat. Research Bull.*, No. 85, 1926.

10. F. Czapek, *Hofmeister's Beiträge*, vol. 3, p. 62, 1902.

11. G. Ekman, abst. *F. Czapek's Biochemie der Planzen*, vol. 1, p. 312, 1913. Gustav Fischer, Jena.

12. W. H. Peterson, E. B. Fred and E. G. Schmidt, *J. Biol. Chem.*, vol. 54, p. 19, 1922.

13. H. Amelung, *Zeits. physiol. Chem.*, vol. 166, p. 161, 1927.

14. E. Kayser, *Ann. Inst. Pasteur*, vol. 8, p. 736, 1894.

15. U. Gayon and E. Dubourg, *Ann. Inst. Pasteur*, vol. 15, p. 527, 1901.

16. E. B. Fred, W. H. Peterson and J. A. Anderson, *J. Biol. Chem.*, vol. 48, p. 385, 1921.

17. H. R. Stiles, W. H. Peterson and E. B. Fred, *J. Biol. Chem.*, vol. 64, p. 643, 1925.

18. R. D. Rege, *Ann. App. Biol.*, vol. 14, p. 1, 1927.

19. W. Stern, *Zentrbl. f. Bakt.*, Abt. I, Orig., vol. 82, p. 49, 1918.

20. W. H. Peterson and E. B. Fred, *J. Biol. Chem.*, vol. 41, p. 181, 1920.

21. W. Henneberg, *Zentrbl. f. Bakt.*, Abt. II, vol. 55, p. 242, 1922.

22. J. Stoklasa, *Z. f. das landwirtsch. Versuchswesen in Oesterreich*, vol. 1, p. 251, 1898.

23. A. C. Thaysen and W. E. Bakes, *Biochem J.*, vol. 21, p. 895, 1927.

24. E. B. Fred, W. H. Peterson and W. R. Carroll, *J. Bact.*, vol. 10, p. 97, 1925.

25. H. J. L. Donker, *Bijdrage tot de Kennis der Boterzuur-Butyl alcohol en Acetonegistingen*, publ. W. D. Meinema, Delft, 1926.

26. A. Churchman, *J. Soc. Chem. Ind.*, vol. 44, p. 450 T, 1925.

27. E. B. Fred, W. H. Peterson and J. A. Anderson, *J. Ind. Eng. Chem.*, vol. 15, p. 120, 1923.

28. A. F. Joseph and F. J. Martin, *J. Soc. Chem. Ind.*, vol. 59, p. 91 T, 1920.

29. A. C. Thaysen and L. D. Galloway, *Ann. App. Biol.*, vol. 15, p. 392, 1928.

30. J. H. Northrop, L. H. Ashe and R. R. Morgan, *J. Ind. Chem.*, vol. 11, p. 723, 1919.

31. W. H. Peterson, E. B. Fred and J. H. Verhulst, *J. Ind. Eng. Chem.*, vol. 13, p. 757, 1921.

32. Ch. F. Juritz, *South African Journal of Industry*, vol. 4, p. 905, 1921.

PART THREE

CHAPTER XIV

THE SYNTHETIC ACTIVITIES OF MICRO-ORGANISMS

THE review given in the preceding pages of the decomposition of carbohydrates by micro-organisms would be incomplete without a reference to certain syntheses which have been observed to occur during the early stages of fermentation and which appear to be intimately connected with them. The subject was touched upon in the preceding chapter when discussing the fermentation of pentoses, but must be given closer attention than was there possible.

As the study of the subject has emerged from observations on the microbiological synthesis of glycogen, starch, fat, and hemicelluloses, and is still in an early stage of development, it is most conveniently discussed on the basis of a knowledge of these observations.

In 1899 Cremer[1] found that a yeast press juice when allowed to stand for some time, would lose its glycogen content and that glycogen could be reproduced by the juice when sufficient sugar, notably fructose, was added to it. Henneberg[2] confirmed Cremer's observations in the case of living yeast, and reported that the easiest method to secure storage of glycogen in yeast was to place yeast cells in a 20 per cent. saccharose solution.

During the same period Macfadyen, Morris and Rowland[3] recorded that the amount of carbon dioxide given off by a yeast juice from a sugar is smaller than that to be expected from the amount of carbohydrate which has disappeared. Harden and Young[4] confirmed this and found that the excess of sugar consumed by a yeast juice over and above that represented by carbon dioxide and alcohol amounted on an average to 38 per cent. They showed later[5] that this excess of sugar had been converted into a polysaccharide which they regarded as a condensation product, intermediate between glycogen and hexose, possessing a higher dextrorotation than the latter, or even than that of hexosephosphoric esters, and reconvertible into glucose by hydrolysis.

Buchner and Meisenheimer[6] repeated Harden and Young's work, using a German bottom yeast juice, and confirmed their result, though the excess amount of sugar consumed by the juice in this case was considerably smaller than that observed by Harden and Young.

The investigations referred to had established two important facts: that during yeast fermentations part of the available sugar is condensed to a polysaccharide, related to or identical with glycogen, and that this polysaccharide can be hydrolysed and utilized by yeast when no other carbohydrate is available, giving rise to the same fermentation products as the sugar from which it was formed.

At various times papers have appeared showing that similar condensation products of monoses, giving a reddish brown coloration with iodine, are formed in the cells of many other micro-organisms at certain stages of their evolution. Most investigators, notably Errera,[7] Kayser and Boulanger,[8] Heinze,[9] Wehmer[10] and Zikes[11] regard these condensation products as glycogen. Meyer[12] refers to them as carbohydrates closely related to glycogen and amylodextrin. The conditions favouring their production have not been studied in any appreciable detail. The observation of Kayser and Boulanger that the absence of air favours their accumulation, and that the presence of an acid has the opposite effect, conforms with the generally expressed view. The same may be claimed for Zikes'[11] statement that a rise in the temperature of incubation increases their accumulation.

In the case of the synthesis of polysaccharides by other micro-organisms, the effects of oxygen, hydrogen ion concentration of the medium, and temperature may be different. Observations made on these points will be referred to in the following pages.

The appearance in the cells of micro-organisms of starch or substances related to starch, staining purple to blue with iodine, has been reported by Maupas[13] in the case of infusoria; by Bourquelot[14] in the case of *Boletus pachypus*; by Cramer[15] in the spores of *Penicillium glaucum*; by Alsberg and Black[16] in the case of *Penicillium puberulum*; by Dox and Neidig[17] for *Penicillium expansum*; and notably by Boas[18] for *Aspergillus niger* and by Grey[19] for *Bact. coli commune*.

The association of these substances with the presence in the culture medium of various carbon compounds, notably of monoses, was definitely established by Boas.[20] He found that not only glucose, fructose and mannose, but galactose, arabinose, glycerol, mannitol and certain organic acids, such as citric acid, could be converted into starch-like substances by *Aspergillus niger*.

The significance of this fact appears to have been overlooked by Boas, conceivably because of his having reached the conviction,[21] previously expressed by Lappaleinen,[22] that the accumulation was due to a disintegration of substances of the cell wall of the active fungus, and not to a synthesis activated by an enzyme. Why Boas should have chosen the former interpretation in preference to the latter is not easy to understand, seeing that the assumption of a disintegration of the cell wall to starch-like substances must logically demand the conception of a prior synthesis by the organism of even higher condensation products than starch. The fact remains, however, that Boas has shown that in the presence not only of glucose and of other hexoses, but also of the pentose arabinose, *Aspergillus niger* produces starch-like substances.

The conditions favouring the production of these substances were also investigated by Boas.[23] He recommended the use of a culture medium containing from 5 to 10 per cent. of carbohydrate, 1 to 5 per cent. ammonium sulphate and 0·2 per cent. of magnesium sulphate and potassium dihydrogenphosphate, and possessing a hydrogen ion concentration equivalent to a pH value of between 1·57 and 2·75, varying according to the carbohydrate selected. When cultivated in this medium, between the temperatures of 33° and 37° C., the developing mycelium showed a positive starch reaction after 20 hours incubation.

Grey,[19] on the contrary, definitely associated the production of starch by *Bact. coli commune* with the fermentative activity of the organism. Working with suspensions of *Bact. coli commune* grown in a glucose medium containing an excess of calcium carbonate, Grey reported finding that the solid bacterial debris which settled at the bottom of the container gave a blue coloration, a positive starch reaction, with iodine. The polysaccharide was shown to be present in the cells in greatest abundance after the 16th hour, but before the 40th hour of fermentation. The total amount isolated was equal to only 9 per cent. of the available glucose, but this quantity evidently represented the difference between starch formed and starch consumed. Grey deduces from his experimental evidence that at some stage of the fermentation of glucose by *Bact. coli commune* there is an almost complete transformation of glucose into non-reducing carbohydrates, a great part of which is starch.

Beyond the addition of an excess of calcium carbonate, Grey does not appear to have taken specific precautions to ensure starch accumulation. The presence of this calcium carbonate shows, however, that starch synthesis would proceed at a less acid reaction with *Bact. coli commune* than where *Aspergillus niger* is used. Discussing the synthetic side of bacterial metabolism, Grey suggests that a very large proportion of the various substances which are decomposed by bacterial fermentation are first synthesized into more complex compounds within the bacterial protoplasm and are decomposed only subsequently into those end products which are finally observed. Not only his observations, but the deductions made from them by Grey are rather sweeping and a confirmatory investigation of the synthetic activities of *Bact. coli commune* is undoubtedly required.

Only one paper dealing with the storage of fats has a direct bearing on the question of microbiological synthesis as discussed in this chapter. Before discussing this paper by Smedley McLean and Hoffert[24] it will be desirable to review the existing theories on the production of fats.

It is generally held that fats are built up by condensation of simple compounds such as acetaldehyde (Leathes, see Person and Raper[25]), pyruvic acid and acetaldehyde (Smedley and Lubrzyriska[26]), pyruvic acid (Neuberg and Arinstein[27]), or ethyl alcohol (Lindner[28]). These theories have obtained a measure of experimental support from Haehn and Kinttof's[29] observations on fat production from acetaldehyde, alcohol and pyruvic acid by *Endomyces vernalis*. According to these various theories, sugars, when used as the starting-point for fat production, are broken down in the first instance to acetaldehyde, and this fermentation product is then condensed to fatty acids, which, after esterification with glycerol, yield fat.

Smedley McLean and Hoffert do not deny that acetaldehyde, ethyl alcohol, or pyruvic acid, can be utilized by microorganisms for the storage of fat. On the contrary they find that a considerable accumulation of fat occurs in yeast in the presence of ethyl alcohol and an excess of oxygen. But they are unable to accept these substances, and notably acetaldehyde, as the components from which fats are normally synthesized in yeast. In their experiments they observed that fat synthesis from ethyl alcohol was adversely affected by the addition of sodium sulphite, a salt employed in biological reactions for the fixation of acetaldehyde. They concluded from this that acetaldehyde is an essential stage in the conversion of ethyl alcohol into fat. In those experiments in which Smedley McLean and Hoffert used glucose or fructose as raw material instead of ethyl alcohol, the addition of sodium sulphite did not diminish fat production, indicating that in these cases no acetaldehyde was formed. These apparently contradictory observations are explained by Smedley McLean and Hoffert on the assumption that, where ethyl alcohol forms the raw material for fat production, it is converted into acetaldehyde and the latter synthesized into glucose. The glucose is then further condensed to a longer

N

chain structure such as required for the higher fatty acids of which yeast fat is composed. In the experiments in which glucose or fructose served as raw material, this condensation of the hexose is assumed to proceed direct, without a preliminary disintegration of the molecule.

There is a certain similarity between this assumed direct condensation of monoses to fatty acids and the formation of hemicelluloses by micro-organisms, a process of synthesis which perhaps has been more extensively investigated than any other, and which in practically every case has been shown to be dependent on the presence of a carbohydrate.

It may not have been experimentally proved that the synthesis of hemicelluloses by micro-organisms is the outcome of a direct condensation of monoses, but there is indirect evidence of this. Thus it is almost invariably observed that a hemicellulose which is formed as the result of microbiological activity is the polysaccharide corresponding to that monose present in the culture of the micro-organism from which it can be built up, and to which it can be reconverted by hydrolysis with dilute acids. There appears to be no reason why this should be the case if the monose, prior to its synthesis, were converted into an enolic form or into a substance with a shorter carbon chain.

Another observation supporting the assumption of a direct condensation of monoses to hemicelluloses is that hemicelluloses are formed during the early stages of the development of the active organism before a fermentative activity becomes noticeable. When fermentation has commenced the polysaccharides already produced are broken down into the same fermentation products as the original monose. Had the synthesis proceeded from comparatively simple compounds such as acetaldehyde or pyruvic acid, there would be no reason why it should be so intimately connected with the early stages of development, a period when these compounds have not yet been produced in measurable quantities.

From the account given of the synthesis of glycogen,

starch, starch related substances, fats and hemicelluloses, it will have been seen that micro-organisms which ferment monoses are frequently able to perform syntheses in which the monoses are involved. It is known that in some cases this synthesis affects a very large percentage of the available monoses, but it has not yet been conclusively proved that they are essential stages in the fermentation of a monose as suggested by Grey[19] and by Grüss.[30]

Grüss arrived at the conclusion that glucose, on being fermented by yeast, is first broken down to CHOH groups, these groups synthesized to glycogen by an enzyme of the yeast cell, and the glycogen subsequently hydrolysed to glucose and converted by enzymes into carbon dioxide and alcohol.

Though it may be admitted that this is a somewhat extravagant conception of the reactions taking place in the fermentation of a monose by micro-organisms, it cannot be denied that cases are known which are difficult to explain without the assumption of a preliminary synthesis of a substance into a more complicated compound prior to its resolution into final fermentation products. One of the most striking of these cases, to which reference was made in Chapter XIII, is the conversion of a pentose into practically the same fermentation products—quantitatively as well as qualitatively—as those obtainable from an hexose by the same type of micro-organisms. The view that a preliminary condensation of a pentose occurs prior to its fermentation has undoubtedly been strengthened by the observations of Boas[31] that starch-like substances are produced from arabinose by *Aspergillus niger*.

It has already been emphasized that the subject of the synthetic activity of micro-organisms has remained practically unexplored in the past, that little is known of the conditions governing the reactions, and even less of the reactions themselves. Obviously they are largely of theoretical interest, except in so far as they affect the question of mucus production by micro-organisms, a subject which will be discussed in Chapter XV.

LITERATURE

1. M. Cremer, *Berichte*, vol. 32, p. 2002, 1891.
2. W. Henneberg, *Chem. Zentrbl.*, vol. 73, II, p. 1515, 1902.
3. A. Macfadyen, G. H. Morris and S. Rowlans, *Berichte*, vol. 33, p. 2764, 1900.
4. A. Harden and W. J. Young, *Berichte*, vol. 37, p. 1052, 1904.
5. A. Harden and W. J. Young, *Biochem. J.*, vol. 7, p. 630, 1913.
6. E. Buchner and J. Meisenheimer, *Berichte*, vol. 39, p. 3201, 1906.
7. L. Errera, *L'épiplasme des Ascomycètes et le glycogène des végétaux.* Thèse, Bruxelles, 1892.
8. E. Kayser and E. Boulanger, *Chem. Zentrbl.*, vol. 69, II, p. 440, 1898.
9. B. Heinze, *Zentrbl. f. Bakt.*, Abt. II, vol. 12, p. 43, 1904.
10. C. Wehmer, *Berichte d. deut. botan. Gesellsch.*, vol. 31, p. 257, 1913.
11. H. Zikes, *Zentrbl. f. Bakt.*, Abt. II, vol. 49, p. 353, 1917.
12. A. Meyer, *Flora*, vol. 86, p. 428, 1899.
13. E. Maupas, *Comptes rend.*, vol. 102, p. 120, 1886.
14. E. Bourquelot, *J. Pharm. Chim.*, vol. 24, p. 197, 1891.
15. E. Cramer, *Arch. f. Hygiene*, vol. 20, p. 197, 1894.
16. C. L. Alsberg and O. F. Black, *U.S. Bureau of Plant Indust.*, Bull. No. 270, 1913.
17. A. W. Dox and R. E. Neidig, *J. Biol. Chem.*, vol. 18, p. 167, 1914.
18. F. Boas, *Biochem. Zeits.*, vol. 78, p. 308, 1917.
19. E. C. Grey, *Biochem. J.*, vol. 18, p. 712, 1924.
20. F. Boas, *Biochem. Zeits.*, vol. 81, p. 80, 1917.
21. F. Boas, *Zentrbl. f. Bakt.*, Abt. II, vol. 56, p. 7, 1921.
22. H. Lappaleinen, *Berichte über die gesammte Physiologie*, vol. 7, p. 233, 1921.
23. F. Boas, *Ber. d. deut. botan. Gesellsch.*, vol. 37, p. 50, 1919.
24. J. Smedley McLean and D. Hoffert, *Biochem. J.*, vol. 20, p. 343, 1926.
25. L. K. Person and H. S. Raper, *Biochem. J.*, vol. 21, p. 875, 1927.
26. J. Smedley and E. Lubrzyriska, *Biochem. J.*, vol. 7, p. 364, 1913.
27. C. Neuberg and B. Arinstein, *Biochem. Zeits.*, vol. 117, p. 269, 1921.
28. P. Lindner, *Z. f. techn. Biologie*, vol. 79, p. 100, 1921.
29. H. Haehn and W. Kinttof, *Chem. Zelle und Gewebe*, vol. 12, p. 115, 1925.
30. J. Grüss, *Chem. Zentrbl.*, vol. 8 (5), p. 1577, 1904.
31. F. Boas, *Biochem. Zeits.*, vol. 86, p. 110, 1918.

CHAPTER XV

THE MUCUS FERMENTATIONS

AT an early date in the annals of microbiology attention was drawn to the formation of cartilaginous bodies in stored beet and cane sugar juices, 'la fermentation visqueuse' of Desfosses.[1]

These concretions, described as 'frogs' spawn' by German writers, accumulated at the bottom of containers holding the juices, and in serious cases converted the whole of the juices into a semi-gelatinous substance. Desfosses, and with him several other investigators, notably Boudrimont,[2] were of the opinion that the mucus had been produced by the nitrogen contained in the affected sugar juices. Jubert[3] regarded the concretions as living plants and showed that they could be made to increase in size when placed in saccharose solutions. Durin[4] recorded similar observations, but failed to appreciate their significance, and, like Scheibler,[5] considered the concretions as decomposition products of the cells of the sugar beet.

The connexion of the concretions with the activity of bacteria was first suggested by Pasteur,[6] who attributed their formation to the action of a coccus forming short chains. Mendès,[7] Cienkowski[8] and van Tieghem[9] confirmed Pasteur's observation. They arrived independently at the conclusion that the responsible organism was related to Cohn's species, *Ascococcus Billrothii*, Cienkowski terming the new organism *Ascococcus mesenteroides*, van Tieghem *Ascococcus Mendesii*, in honour of Mendès. In many text-books *Ascococcus mesenteroides* is discussed under the name *Leuconostoc mesenteroides*. By Lehmann and Neumann[10] it is described as *Streptococcus mesenteroides*. Further reference will be made to this organism in Chapters XXI and XXII.

Subsequently mucus production was observed in other carbohydrate containing liquids and was frequently found to cause serious damage to industrial products and articles of food. In infusions of *Digitalis purpurea*, containing saccharose, and in other sweetened medicinal preparations, it was studied by Bienz,[11] Bräutigam[12] and Happ,[13] and was claimed by Bräutigam to be due, in the case examined by him, to the resolution of the cell wall of a coccus, found in large numbers in the infusions.

In 1883 Schmidt[14] recorded a case of mucus production in milk. He was able to reproduce it in normal milk with a coccus isolated from the 'ropy' milk.

At about the same time Laurent[15] discovered mucus formation in bread, where it had been produced by a bacterium termed by him *Bac. panificans*. His investigations were later confirmed and extended, notably by Vogel,[16] who found the micro-organisms of ropy bread to be closely related to *Bac. mesentericus*. The subject of ropy bread will be dealt with in greater detail in Chapter XX.

Pasteur[6] had described mucus production in beer and wine, van Laer[17] confirmed his observations, and described a rod *Bac. viscosus*, which he claimed to be responsible for the ropiness of beer.

These various observations made it evident, not only that mucus can be produced by different types of bacteria belonging to widely separated species, but that the appearance of the mucus is associated with the presence of carbohydrates, not necessarily of saccharose, as maintained by Jubert and by Béchamps,[18] but of lactose, glucose (Schmidt[14]), and galactose (Kramer;[19] and Emmerling[20]). Even the alcohol mannitol was found by Schmidt to be a suitable raw material for mucus production.

More recently the mucus produced by *Azotobacter croococcum* has been shown by Stapp[21] to be a condensation product of a dextro-rotatory monose, and that of *Bact. radicicola* has been shown by Greig Smith[22] to be of a similar nature.

The chemical composition of the mucus from beet juices was investigated in considerable detail by Scheibler, who describes it as a colourless substance when pure, giving a quantitative yield of glucose on hydrolysis. Oxidized with nitric acid it yielded oxalic acid. For this reason Scheibler regarded it as an anhydride of glucose, to which he gave the name dextran. Durin, on the other hand, spoke of the mucus as a cellulose, while Béchamps regarded it as a type of starch. Scheibler found that the gelatinous bodies taken direct from sugar beet juices were usually stained greyish black and contained mannitol, but repeated boiling in a solution of calcium hydroxide—or in other alkaline solutions, in all of which they were found to be soluble—removed the impurities and left a colourless mucus capable of imbibing as much as 85 to 88 per cent. of water, in spite of its being insoluble in this medium.

The origin of the mannitol found in the raw mucus was not discussed by Scheibler, but was subsequently associated by Pasteur with the activity of the mucus producing bacteria. Pasteur's suggestion was verified experimentally by various investigators.

The discovery by Durin of appreciable quantities of fructose in the saccharose solutions in which mucus had been formed showed that its production was associated with a preliminary hydrolysis of the saccharose molecule. Other important features of the mucus formation were discussed by Durin, notably the favourable influence of the presence of calcium carbonate. That reactions close to the neutral point, and especially slightly on its alkaline side, are favourable, has been emphasized by all subsequent investigators dealing with this subject. Where marked acid reactions prevail mucus production rarely occurs. The reason for this has not yet been established, but can hardly be attributed, as suggested by Greig Smith,[23] to the hydrolytic action of the hydrogen ions present under such conditions.

The glucose derivative investigated by Scheibler is not the only condensation product which bacteria synthesize from saccharose. It was found by Lippmann[24] that mucus obtained by him from saccharose yielded fructose on hydrolysis with dilute acids. His observations were confirmed by Greig

Smith and by Fernbach and Schoen,[25] the first-named terming the substance 'levan'.

In these cases glucose accumulated in the saccharose solutions in proportions showing that fructose was the sole source of mucus. Similarly the mucus produced in milk could be shown to be a condensation product of galactose, thus emphasizing the conclusion usually arrived at that microbiologically formed mucus is a condensation product of the one monose from which a particular organism is capable of synthesizing it, and that it is convertible into this monose, and this monose only, through simple hydrolysis with dilute mineral acids. The only observations which cannot be harmonized with this view are those of Schardinger,[26] who records that the galactan investigated by him could be obtained from lactose, saccharose and glucose. A reinvestigation of his observations would be most desirable in view of the consensus of opinion outlined above on the mode of formation of other types of mucus.

It will have been seen that most of the earlier publications on the subject associated mucus production with the activity of bacteria, notably with types which to-day can be recognized as belonging to the mannitol producing lactic acid bacteria. In time a large number of others have been added to the earlier types, *Bact. lactis aerogenes*, for instance, by Emmerling,[20] an ethyl alcohol producing spore-forming organism, *Clostridium gelatinosum*, by Laxa,[27] and more recently *Bac. acetoethylicus* by Northrop and collaborators.[28] Among the obligatory anaerobes the writers have frequently observed mucus formation in young cultures of *Bac. acetonigenus*, particularly when these cultures had been prepared from spores kept for a prolonged period on dried sand.

Another species spoken of as a mucus producer is *Azotobacter croococcum*, one of the most important nitrogen fixing micro-organisms of the soil. Stapp[21] concluded from his investigation that the mucus produced by this organism is of a carbohydrate nature, yielding a dextro-rotatory monose on hydrolysis with dilute acids.

Among the *Phycobacteriaceae* mucus production is responsible for the abnormal forms of *Zoogloea ramigera* produced by this organism, according to Zopf.[29]

In his general survey of mucus production by microorganisms Beijerinck[30] states that the actinomycetes, the yeasts and the fungi are unable to produce this substance. His statement undoubtedly requires revision, at least as regards the yeasts and the fungi. As early as 1879 Binz[11] referred to a fungus capable of producing mucus. Meissner's[31] mucus-producing yeasts or torulae belong here, and the same no doubt is the case with the *Dematium pullulans* studied by Lindner,[32] and the type of the same organism isolated by Massee[33] from a case of gummosis in *Prunus japonica*. In *Aspergillus conicus*, a species closely related to *Aspergillus glaucus*, mucus was observed by Dale.[34]

The isolation in pure culture of the organisms responsible for the production of mucus has frequently met with considerable difficulty. In most cases the raw material contains several species of micro-organisms which take no part in the production of mucus, but which are difficult to separate from the causative organisms by dilution in the usual way owing to the insolubility of the mucus.

To secure pure cultures Liesenberg and Zopf[35] suggested heating the raw material to 75° C. for 15 minutes prior to preparation of plates in order to destroy the entangled secondary microflora. They assumed that the mucus producing micro-organisms would possess higher heat resisting powers than the associated flora. This method was not always successful, and has been replaced by the technique of Zettnow,[36] which is based on the observation that mucus is produced only on media containing carbohydrates.

As a preliminary Zettnow triturates a small amount of raw material with twenty to thirty times its volume of sterile water and repeats this treatment three to five times. Small pieces of the purified raw material are then placed on firm saccharose gelatine plates, though saccharose agar plates might presumably be used for the purpose. The inoculant is now distributed over the surface of the plates by means of a sterile glass rod, suitably bent. The colonies with a slimy appearance developing on the plates are transferred to ordinary broth in which no mucus is formed and the ensuing culture is plated out on ordinary gelatine or agar plates. The colonies forming on these plates are subcultured into ordinary broth and the resulting culture plated out on ordinary gelatine or agar plates. For the purpose of identification, the colonies appearing on the last set of plates, now possessing the normal consistency of bacterial colonies, are placed in a nutrient solution containing carbohydrates from which mucus can be produced by the organism.

For the subsequent storage of the isolated strain Zettnow recommends the addition of calcium carbonate to the culture, and drying. In some cases, for instance in that of a Javanese mucus producing organism, *Micrococcus djokjakartensis*, the organism could be preserved in this way for three years without subculturing.

Like Kramer,[19] and most of the earlier investigators, Beijerinck regarded the property of mucus production as a characteristic of certain types of bacteria, due to the presence in their cells of a specific enzyme 'viscosaccharase'. This conclusion is no longer tenable, and on further investigation will undoubtedly be abandoned in favour of the view referred to in Chapter XIV, that most, if not all carbohydrate decomposing micro-organisms possess synthesizing properties which, under favourable conditions, notably a slightly alkaline reaction and the presence of phosphates (Kramer, Glaser[37]), and during the early stages of their development, give rise to the condensation of hexoses to polysaccharides. In cases where these polysaccharides readily imbibe water, a colloidal solution, i.e. a mucus, is formed.

LITERATURE

1. —. Desfosses, *J. Pharm. et Chim.*, vol. 15, p. 602, 1829.
2. A. Boudrimont, *Comptes rend.*, vol. 80, p. 1253, 1875.
3. —. Jubert, vide van Tieghem, *Annales des Sciences Naturelles* (6), vol. 7, p. 180, 1878.

4. E. Durin, *Comptes rend.*, vol. 83, pp. 128 and 355, 1876.
5. C. Scheibler, abst. Wagner's *Jahresbericht der chem. Technolg.*, vol. 21, p. 790, 1875.
6. L. Pasteur, *Comptes rend.*, vol. 83, p. 176, 1876.
7. T. Mendès, vide van Tieghem, *Bull. Soc. Botan.*, vol. 25, p. 271, 1878.
8. L. Cienkowski, *Botan. Jahresbericht*, vol. 1, p. 501, 1878.
9. Ph. van Tieghem, *Bull. Soc. Botan.*, vol. 25, p. 211, 1878. *Annales des Sciences Naturelles* (6), vol. 7, p. 180, 1878.
10. K. B. Lehmann and R. O. Neumann, *Bakteriologische Diagnostik te* 5, Auflage, publ. J. F. Lehmann, München, 1912.
11. C. Bienz, *Pharmz. Ztg.*, vol. 24, p. 506, 1879; vol. 46, p. 707, 1891.
12. W. Bräutigam, *Pharmz. Zentralhalle*, vol. 32, p. 427, 1891; vol. 33, p. 534, 1892.
13. C. Happ, *Zentrbl. f. Bakt.*, vol. 14, p. 175, 1893.
14. A. Schmidt, *Landwirtsch. Versuchsstat.*, vol. 28, p. 91, 1883.
15. E. Laurent, *Bull. Acad. Royale Sci. Belgique* (3), vol. 10, p. 765, 1885.
16. J. Vogel, *Zeits. f. Hygiene*, vol. 26, p. 398, 1897.
17. H. van Laer, *Bull. Acad. Royale Belgique* (3), vol. 18, p. 37, 1889.
18. A. Béchamps, *Comptes rend.*, vol. 93, p. 78, 1881.
19. E. Kramer, *Monatshefte für Chemie*, vol. 10, p. 467, 1889.
20. O. Emmerling, *Berichte*, vol. 33, p. 2477, 1900.
21. C. Stapp, *Zentrbl. f. Bakt.*, Abt. II, vol. 61, p. 276, 1924.
22. R. Greig Smith, *J. Soc. Chem. Ind.*, vol. 26, p. 304, 1907.
23. R. Greig Smith and Th. Heal, *J. Chem. Ind.*, vol. 21, p. 1381, 1902. *Zentrbl. f. Bakt.*, Abt. II, vol. 21, p. 307, 1908.
24. E. O. v. Lippmann, *Zentrbl. f. Bakt.*, Abt. II, vol. 8, p. 596, 1902.
25. A. Fernbach and M. Schoen, *Comptes rend.*, vol. 155, p. 84, 1912.
26. F. Schardinger, *Zentrbl. f. Bakt.*, Abt. II, vol. 8, p. 144, 1902.
27. O. Laxa, *Zentrbl. f. Bakt.*, Abt. II, vol. 8, p. 154, 1902.
28. J. H. Northrop, L. H. Ashe and J. K. Senior, *J. Biol. Chem.*, vol. 39, p. 1, 1919.
29. W. Zopf, A. Schenck, *Handbuch d. Botanik*, vol. 3, sec. 1, p. 1, 1884.
30. M. W. Beijerinck, *Proceed. K. Akad. van Wetenschap*, Amsterdam, Sect. Science, vol. 12, p. 635, 1910.
31. R. Meissner, *Landwirtsch. Jahrbücher*, vol. 27, p. 715, 1898.
32. P. Lindner, *Wochenschr. f. Brauerei*, vol. 5, p. 290, 1888.
33. G. Massee, *Kew Bulletin*, p. 321, 1898.
34. E. Dale, *Annales Mycol.*, vol. 12, p. 33, 1914.
35. C. Liesenberg and W. Zopf., W. Zopf's *Beiträge zur Physiologie und Morphologie niederer Organismen*, 1892.
36. E. Zettnow, *Zeits. f. Hygiene*, vol. 37, p. 154, 1907. *Zentrbl. f. Bakt.*, Abt. I, vol. 75, p. 374, 1914.
37. F. Glaser, *Zentrbl. f. Bakt.*, Abt. II, vol. 1, p. 879, 1895.

PART FOUR

CHAPTER XVI

THE MICROBIOLOGY OF CEREALS AND CEREAL PRODUCTS

CERTAIN aspects of the action of micro-organisms on starch were dealt with in Chapter II, notably the action of fungi as applied in Eastern countries to the hydrolysis of starch for the preparation of alcohol and articles of diet. In the following pages attention will be concentrated on the general microbiology of grain and flour, on the microbiology of sizing materials and adhesive pastes, and on that of dough and bread.

The relationship which undoubtedly exists between these subjects is largely due to the common origin of many of the organisms involved. An obvious influence is exercised also by the similarity in chemical composition of the substances involved, but on this little need be said.

It may be recalled that all green plants possess an epiphytic microflora which normally subsists on the slight traces of carbohydrates, protein and inorganic salts which dissolve in the water exuding from, or condensing on, the epidermis of the host. This microflora has been studied by Burri[1] and by Düggeli,[2] both of whom agree that it is able to subsist under the most severe climatic conditions to which the host normally becomes exposed, and that at periods of damp and rain it develops luxuriantly, spreading over the whole of the epidermis, including the flower and the seed. Burri points out that the resistance of the epiphytic microflora to low humidities is due to the production by the individual cell of an outer layer of mucus which retards the drying up of the cell, and incidentally fixes it to the surface of the plant tissues on which it lives.

Under damp conditions, when dew or rain covers the epidermis of the host, the mucus dissolves and allows the cells to spread over the epidermis.

The epiphytic microflora consists of comparatively few species, though frequently of very large numbers of cells, sometimes more than are met with in the soil in which the host grows. Düggeli, in his investigation quoted, reported the presence of 1,330,000 bacteria per gramme on oat grains, 1,600,000 on barley, 126,000 on rye, and 500,000 cells per gramme on wheat. These figures are considerably lower in most cases than those previously recorded by Hoffmann[3] for Russian, Rumanian, and German grain, but probably represent more correctly the numbers of the true epiphytic microflora than the figure given by Hoffmann, who sought to determine the number of micro-organisms present in samples of superior and inferior grades of cereals.

Curiously enough the epiphytic microflora is composed almost exclusively of short non-spore forming rods. *Bact. herbicola a aureum*, synonymous with *Bact. mesentericus aureus* Winkler,[4] and described by Beijerinck[5] as *Bact. agglomerans*, is claimed by Düggeli to be the preponderant species of the normal epiphytic flora, followed by *Bact. fluorescens liquefaciens* as a second, but much less frequent type.

In the writers' experience, which harmonizes with the views expressed by Beijerinck,[5] it is not altogether correct to ascribe a dominating influence to *Bact. herbicola a aureum*. It is undoubtedly true that an appreciable percentage of the epiphytic flora consists of short rods, which, when grown on ordinary laboratory media, produce yellow transparent colonies identical with or closely resembling those of *Bact. herbicola a aureum*. But such yellow colonies are produced by a number of species, including the yellow gas producing short rod found by Holliger[6] in flour, *Bact. coli luteoliquefaciens*, the yellow acid producing rod isolated by Levy[7] from flour, and the *Bact. trifolii* (*Pseudomonas trifolii*) of Huss,[8] as well as several other species.

In addition to the above there are found among the epiphytic microflora the short rods isolated by Burri[9] and by Thaysen[10] from grass which, in their morphological and biological characters, resemble the *coli-paratyphosum* groups. These types were regarded by Fränkel[11] and by Papasotiriu[12] as identical with *Bact. coli commune*, but were later shown (Holliger[6]) to differ from this organism in the composition of the gas produced by them and in their lack of indol production.

It is interesting to note from Burri's and from Düggeli's work that the epiphytic microflora remains almost completely unaffected by the microflora of the soil in which the host is growing. It maintains the continuity of its existance by spreading to the seed, and from there to the emerging embryo and the new plant.

The spread to the seed is favoured by the fact that during the period of flowering of the host saccharine liquids are secreted by the flowers, which offer favourable conditions for development. Even among the cereals the exudations of the flower, coupled with the protection against desiccation afforded by the presence of glumes (*paleae*), make these sites particularly suitable growth centres. In this part of the plant the epiphytic microflora is joined, according to Chrzaszcz,[13] by more accidental types brought to the flower with dust and particles of soil. These types comprise true yeasts, torula species, *Dematium pullulans*, *Penicillium* species and *Cladosporium herbarum*, as well as occasional *Cocci* and *Sarcinae*. It is possible that spore bearing rods, notably butyric acid forming bacilli, as well as lactic acid producing bacteria, are also represented, but this was not demonstrated by Chrzaszcz. The various types, which might be regarded as a secondary microflora of the flower, thrive on exuded saccharine substances and develop beside the normal epiphytic flora. The secondary microflora does not possess special means of protection against desiccation and depends for its development on the presence of an abundance of moisture. It is not surprising, therefore, that it should be particularly prevalent during damp seasons. Once established it is shielded from destruction by the glumes which surround the seed of the *Gramineae*. The effectiveness of this protection is most noticeable in cereals, such as barley, where the glumes fuse with the grain during ripening. In such cases the existence of micro-organisms within the normal plant cell may well be thought to occur. This conclusion was actually arrived at by Bernheim,[14] and subsequently by Galippe,[15] who suggested that soil bacteria penetrated the tissues of most plants except garlic. However, Fernbach[16] in France and Buchner[17] in Germany proved that the interior of normal vegetable tissues are free from micro-organisms.

Chrzaszcz describes as an internal infection the whole of the microflora of the cereal seed, consisting of the true epiphytic flora and of the secondary flora, developing in the flower and on the ripening grain in damp seasons, and contrasts this flora with the external infection composed of an entirely accidental microflora which has become mixed with the grain with particles of dirt and soil, and which in most cases has had no opportunity of development.

The external infection can be considerably reduced, and perhaps even completely suppressed, by removal of the soil and dirt adhering to the seed, or by treatment with suitable antiseptics. The internal infection cannot be similarly influenced. Wetting, whether with clean water for washing purposes or with dilute antiseptics, does not destroy it. On the contrary, wetting would in most cases induce a renewed activity which, as already remarked, would be favoured by the presence of carbohydrates. This is important as it explains why an analogy exists between the microbiological changes occurring in grain and flour, in adhesive pastes and sizing materials made from flour, and in dough and bread. In all of these materials there is available a sufficiently large supply of soluble carbohydrates to ensure a rapid growth of carbohydrate decomposing micro-organisms. Under these conditions large populations, such as the normal internal infection of grain, will have every opportunity to outweigh more accidental infections introduced with dirt and soil, and therefore to dominate the microbiological changes taking place.

An account and analysis of the observations made on the microbiology of grain and flour will substantiate the correctness of this statement.

LITERATURE

1. R. Burri, *Zentrbl. f. Bakt.*, Abt. II, vol. 10, p. 756, 1903.
2. M. Düggeli, *Zentrbl. f. Bakt.*, Abt. II, vol. 13, p. 56, 1904.
3. F. Hoffmann, *Wochenschr. f. Brauerei*, vol. 13, p. 1153, 1896.
4. W. Winkler, *Zentrbl. f. Bakt.*, Abt. II, vol. 5, p. 569, 1899.
5. M. W. Beijerinck, *Zentrbl. f. Bakt.*, Abt. II, vol. 15, p. 366, 1905.
6. W. Holliger, *Zentrbl. f. Bakt.*, Abt. II, vol. 9, p. 305, 1902.
7. F. Levy, *Arch. f. Hygiene*, vol. 49, p. 62, 1904.
8. H. Huss, *Zentrbl. f. Bakt.*, Abt. II, vol. 19, p. 50, 1907.
9. R. Burri, *Zentrbl. f. Bakt.*, Abt. II, vol. 28, p. 321, 1910.
10. A. C. Thaysen, *Zentrbl. f. Bakt.*, Abt. I, Orig., vol. 67, p. 1, 1912.
11. F. Fränkel, *Inaug. Dissertation, Würzburg*, 1896.
12. J. Papasotiriu, *Arch. f. Hygiene*, vol. 41, p. 204, 1902.
13. T. Chrzaszcz, *Wochenschrift f. Brauerei*, vol. 19, p. 590, 1902.
14. H. Bernheim, *Münchner med. Wochenschr.*, vol. 35, p. 743, 1888.
15. M. Galippe, *Zentrbl. f. Bakt.*, vol. 3, p. 108, 1888.
16. A. Fernbach, *Ann. Inst. Pasteur*, vol. 2, p. 567, 1888.
17. H. Buchner, *Münchner med. Wochenschr.*, vol. 35, p. 906, 1888.

CHAPTER XVII

THE MICROBIOLOGY OF GRAIN AND ITS MILLING PRODUCTS, BRAN AND FLOUR

IT has been indicated that the seeds of cereals, like those of other plants, possess a specific microflora largely composed of non spore-forming short rods, but containing representatives of true yeasts, lower fungi, such as *Cladosporium herbarum* and *Aspergillus* and *Penicillium* species, and infrequently also of cocci and spore-forming rods. Like all living cells, these types depend for their development on the presence of nutritive substances and of small but definite concentrations of moisture. The required minimum of water will frequently be exceeded while the grain is still developing, but normally should not be reached after ripening. Nevertheless, occasions frequently occur when excess moisture is present in the ripened grain, and when, in consequence, the microflora of the seed develops abnormally. In a study of the behaviour of the seeds of various cereals, stored in glass containers, Atterberg[1] sought to establish the minimum concentration of moisture which allows the development of an indigenous microflora. He found that samples of wheat, containing up to 15·6 per cent. of moisture, remained unaffected by microorganisms during storage, but developed mould growth when this moisture percentage was exceeded. In the case of barley, most samples remained sound when containing less than 14·4 per cent. of moisture, though a few became slightly mouldy at this concentration. Samples of oats remained normal when containing 16·2 per cent. of water. For maize, Black and Alsberg[2] gave 12 per cent. as the maximum permissible concentration. In one case Thom and LeFevre[3] observed development of mould on a sample of maize containing less than 13 per cent. of moisture.

Atterberg concluded that wheat in storage should possess no more than 16 per cent. of moisture and barley no more than 14 per cent., at least not during the warmer seasons, when the prevailing higher temperatures facilitate the devolopment of micro-organisms.

Such percentages are invariably exceeded during wet seasons, when moisture contents of 24 to 28 per cent. have been observed (Atterberg[1]). Microbiological activity, therefore, sets in at such seasons, and the grain becomes more or less seriously damaged. This damage has claimed the attention of many investigators. It is often noticeable in the first instance as an odour of mouldiness (Emmerling[4]), at least when the excess moisture is comparatively slight (König, Spieckermann and Olig[5]). Moisture contents of 30 per cent. and more give rise to bacterial activity. In extreme cases the damage may lead to spontaneous combustion of the stored grain. This was observed by Hoffmann[6] in a case of stored bran, and was described by him as due in the first instance to the respiration of the cells of the damp bran increasing the temperature sufficiently to allow micro-organisms to develop. Their activity was stated to raise the temperature to 70° C., a point at which the absorption of oxygen would proceed at a greatly increased rate, sufficient to bring the temperature to 150° C., when the bran would ignite. Hoffmann's exposition agrees in its essentials with Haldane and Makgill's[7] conception of the spontaneous combustion of hay. An account of Haldane and Makgill's work was summarized by Thaysen and Bunker[8] in their review of the spontaneous combustion of vegetable tissues.

In a recent study of the spontaneous combustion of damp organic materials, James, Rettger and Thom[9] refer to the activity of bacteria contained in damp maize meal in storage. They found that the most pronounced heating was observed when the moisture content of the flour was about 30 per cent. An increase of the microflora of such flour occurred during the time taken for the temperature to rise to 50° C. After that a decrease set in, which became particularly noticeable when the temperature of the flour had been raised by aeration to 62° C. When stored for 4 days at 62° C., practically the whole of the microflora was destroyed.

Between the extremes of a slight mouldy odour and a complete charring of the material, a series of intermediate stages of microbiological damage have been observed in grain and flour. They have been studied chiefly from a hygienic point of view.

As regards the action of micro-organisms on ripening grain, as distinct from that on stored grain and flour, it has been recorded that abnormally wet seasons encourage it. Both Reichard[10] and Becker[11] attribute the loss of germinating power of damp grain to the spread of an excessive microflora over the grain during ripening. Reichard emphasizes that this microflora is composed essentially of lower fungi. This, however, is by no means necessarily the case. Where the excess moisture is comparatively slight, fungi may predominate, but in grain with abnormally high moisture contents, various types of bacteria, belonging to the internal microflora of the grain, will constitute part of the covering microflora. Hiltner[12] mentions that he obtained various bacteria from very damp grain, and refers specifically to a short rod with yellow colonies, *Bact. herbicola a aureum* (?), and also a butyric acid-producing bacillus and *Bact. fluorescens liquefaciens*. Becker, in his paper referred to above, records that he found the bacterial content of barley to vary between five thousand and over twelve hundred millions per gramme, showing that a very dense bacterial flora can exist on grain. The excessive sliminess of infected grain, noted by Becker, also indicates that bacteria participate in the attack on ripening grain, as does the fact that the mucus formed can be removed by steeping and washing.

The washing of infected grain was recommended by Becker for improving the germinating power of damaged barley. He found that the number of seeds capable of developing a normal plant could be greatly increased by this treatment. Reichard, who adopted a disinfection and drying of infected barley with alcohol and ether, or with chloroform, achieved an increase in germinating power of 43 per cent. Such methods for the improvement of the germination power are of the greatest economic importance, not only to the maltster and the brewer, but to any one concerned with the protection of seed in storage.

While it has been fairly conclusively proved that lack of germinating power in grain may be due, not necessarily to a destruction of the seed during its development, but to the action of an excessive microflora on the fully developed germ, it has not yet been shown how this action is to be explained. Becker holds the view that the microflora simply clogs the pores of the germ and thus prevents its respiration, without otherwise damaging the endosperm of the seed. But this explanation would hardly cover cases such as those in which the microflora possesses starch- or pectin-resolving enzymes, the butyric acid producing bacilli, for instance, observed by Hiltner, Schardinger and others, or *Cladosporium herbarum* referred to by Chrzaszcz,[13] types which almost certainly attack not only the endosperm but the tissues of the germinating plant. Future investigations are likely to show that the action of the microflora is a multiple one, depending on the actual micro-organisms comprising the flora ; sometimes causing little structural damage either to the endosperm or to the germ, but sometimes affecting one or both to a marked extent. In this connexion it is of interest to note that Hiltner[14] distinguishes between a microflora which affects the endosperm only, and one which attacks both the endosperm and the seedling.

In the former group Hiltner places the various *Penicillium* and *Aspergillus* species met with on ripening grain. In the more harmful groups, attacking both endosperm and seedling, Hiltner includes two types, one represented by fungi such as *Cephalothecium roseum*, *Botrytis cinerea*, *Mucor stolonifer* and *Pythium deBaryanum*, which attack the endosperm and the seedling indiscriminately, and another to which *Ascochyta Pisi* and *Colletotrichum Lindemuthianum* belong, which first attack the endosperm and subsequently spread to the seedling. To the latter group must be added *Fusarium roseum*, which Jatschewski,[15] and subsequently Gabrilowitsch,[16] isolated from samples of rye which had caused severe disturbances to the health of persons consuming it. The occurrence of rye attacked by *Fusarium roseum* is common during damp seasons, when the fungus invades the seed during ripening and effects the endosperm in a way which renders it toxic. The toxin causes giddiness and affects the sight, with more serious complications on continued consumption, leading in extreme cases to death.

Until recently Italian investigators ascribed a similar origin to pellagra, a disease which affects the poorer classes in countries where maize is consumed as a staple food.

Pellagra usually starts as a more or less extensive rash on the exposed skin, and subsequently affects both the gastrointestinal canal and the nervous system. Severe cases are not infrequently fatal.

The theory of the connexion of pellagra with the development of micro-organisms on ripening maize was first advanced by Lombroso (see Tirelli ; [17] and Pellizzi and Tirelli[18]), and was widely accepted until recently. The explanation given was that fungi, notably species of *Aspergillus*, when developing in maize, produced toxic protein decomposition products which, on continued consumption, gave rise to the symptoms characteristic of pellagra. A very extensive literature exists on this aspect of the action of micro-organisms on ripening grain, and great efforts have been made by various Italian investigators to bring forward evidence in support of the existence of such toxins and of their specific action on animals and man. Summaries of this work were given by Serena,[19] by Bertarelli[20] and by Ceni.[21] Definite conclusions were not reached, however, since it was found (Bezzola[22]) that guinea-pigs fed on an exclusive diet of normal maize showed symptoms resembling pellagra. Bezzola's observations, which he was anxious not to interpret as conclusive evidence, have recently been confirmed by Mouriquand,[23] and notably by Goldberger, Wheeler, Lillie and Rogers,[24] by Goldberger and Lillie[25] and by Marshall Findlay,[26] all of whom attribute pellagra to an exclusive consumption of food deficient in the thermostable part of vitamine B (vitamine 'B_2' of the Committee of Accessory Food Factors). Maize, whether sound or damaged by micro-organisms, is notoriously deficient of this vitamine.

Even after ripening, without being noticeably attacked by micro-organisms, grain and its milling products, bran and flour, may still become microbiologically damaged, not only by types belonging to the internal microflora, but by organisms introduced accidentally with soil and dust. For such damage to occur the presence of moisture is essential. Atterberg[1] stipulated that wheat and oats, when containing more than 16 per cent. of moisture, became liable to attack; rice, according to Haselhoff and Mach,[27] suffered damage in the presence of more than 10 per cent., and barley (Atterberg) became mouldy when containing more than 14 per cent. of water, provided the temperature during storage exceeded a certain minimum. Atterberg did not investigate the influence of the temperature very exhaustively, but he observed that barley, containing as much as 24 to 28 per cent. of moisture, remained sound during the winter months, while it invariably became attacked when warmer weather prevailed. Observations that low temperatures are safer for the storage of damp grain than average room temperatures, were made also by Bell,[28] who nevertheless favoured a warm dry storage room, provided the moisture of the grain or flour had previously been reduced to below the minimum inducing the growth of micro-organisms. Such drying can be achieved in practice by moving the grain from one elevator to another, on endless belts and in a dry atmosphere, when the questionable advantage is incidentally secured of polishing the surface of the individual kernel and of removing superficial growth of mycelium and fungus spores. Black and Alsberg[2] draw attention to the drawback of this removal, and point out that the detection of damaged grain is rendered more difficult by the treatment.

The methods which have been recommended for the detection and determination of microbiological damage in stored grain and flour will be discussed subsequently.

A comparatively slight excess of moisture in stored grain or flour will result in the development of fungi rather than of bacteria, and with equal moisture contents it is generally noticeable (Black and Alsberg) that growth occurs more readily in flour or bran than in whole grain. Haselhoff and Mach observed growth of *Aspergillus oryzae* in rice flour containing no more than 10 per cent. of moisture, while 15 to 20 per cent. were required for *Penicillium glaucum* to develop. Both species, of course, are constant members of the internal microflora of grain. In the case of rye flour, mould growth occurred, according to Arnoldow,[29] in samples with more than 17 per cent. of moisture, and proceeded rapidly, the presence of the fungi being detectable after 24 hours, not only by a mouldy odour, but by the loss of several per cent. of the carbohydrates present, a loss which after three months' storage had increased to more than 60 per cent. In these cases little change was observed in the protein and the fat content of the flour, an interesting observation which was confirmed in the case of the protein of cotton seeds by König, Spieckermann and Olig.[5]

When bacteria, and notably putrefying bacteria, participate in the deterioration of stored grain and its products the protein present undoubtedly becomes affected. This is confirmed by the observations of König, Spieckermann and Olig in the case of cotton seed cake. In such cases toxic protein decomposition products may conceivably be formed as reported by Cortez.[30] On the other hand, Dragendorf investigated an epidemic among swine, said to have been due to the feeding of deteriorated protein residues of a maize starch factory, and was unable to detect the presence of toxic products. The unpalatable appearance of cereal products which have been attacked by bacteria, as distinct from fungi, and their undoubted detrimental action on the intestinal canal of man and beast, are probably due as much, if not more, to the action of butyric acid producing bacteria on the starch as to that of putrefying types on the protein.

The subject of the damage of cereals and their milling

products by bacteria has received little attention in the past in spite of the economic interest which it undoubtedly possesses. It is known from the work of König, Spieckermann and Olig, that bacteria require a higher moisture content to develop, 30 per cent. being the figure given by the writers referred to. And it has been established by Prillieux[31] and by Griffiths[32] that a certain type, *Bact. prodigiosum*, may affect the starch content of damp cereals and discolour them. But the formation of those felted nauseating lumps of grain and flour which may be met with under unsuitable storage conditions, and which sometimes represent a considerable proportion of a total consignment, for instance of sea-shipped grain or flour, have not yet been studied either by bacteriologists, who might elucidate how they arise and the types of bacteria which participate in their formation, nor by chemists and physiologists, who might determine to what extent the damage wrought has rendered the starch present unsuitable not only for consumption but also for industrial purposes.

There are other questions connected with the activity of bacteria in stored cereals and cereal products which are worthy of interest, for instance, the occurrence of the bacteria responsible for the ropiness in bread. The appearance of ropy bread has been definitely traced to the presence of the responsible bacillus, of which more will have to be said later, in the flour used. Laurent[33] and Thomann[34] first made the observation, and subsequent writers, among them Watkins,[35] have shown that a change in the flour used in bakeries where an epidemic of ropy bread has broken out, will invariably result in the elimination of the complaint. But no information is available to indicate how a consignment of flour can become infected with the rope-producing bacillus to such an extent that even fractions of a gramme may suffice to initiate the disease in bread.

There is also the question of the extent to which bacteria participate in the production of acid in stored cereals, an important point since the presence of such acids has been used by various investigators as an indication of micro-biological activity. Bell[36] determined the changes in the acidity of stored flour, and suggested that lower fungi were responsible for an increased acidity, while bacteria caused a liquefaction of the flour. It is highly improbable that a sharply defined subdivision such as this can be justifiable in all cases, but the question requires investigation.

To mention but one more subject amongst many others, there is at present nothing to indicate the fate of the numerous non-spore-forming bacteria of the internal microflora, notably the gas-producing types of the *paratyphosum* group and the lactic acid bacteria, during the normal and abnormal storage of grain and flour. It is not known whether this flora undergoes changes during storage, which might be correlated with the chemical changes suffered by the grain, notably by its protein as observed by Marion,[37] and therefore might be used as a simple means of detecting such changes, and indirectly possibly the age of a stored cereal or cereal product.

The attack of micro-organisms on stored cereals may occur from the surface towards the interior, when fractured surfaces and holes left by grain-boring insects are the ports of entry for the micro-organisms. Or it may start under the cuticle of the grain, and then usually in the cavity surrounding the germ, a site which, it would appear, frequently becomes invaded by a mycelium, notably of *Penicillium* or of *Aspergillus* species. Such hidden growth of micro-organisms is very difficult for the untrained observer to detect. Sometimes it can be detected only with a powerful lens, and appears as isolated conidiophores, with adhering spores, reaching from the surrounding walls towards the centre of the germ cavity. These cases probably indicate a growth which has come to a standstill prior to storage. In other cases faintly bluish-grey to brown spots are perceptible through the tissues covering the embyro cavity, indicating the growth and spread of a fungus. In aggravated cases these spots converge and cover smaller or greater parts of the whole grain. A bluish-grey spotting is usually due to *Penicillium* species, a bronze colour to *Aspergillus fumigatus*, which has been reported present in damaged grain by various observers, most recently by Sartory and Sartory.[38] Where a reddish discoloration occurs, Black and Alsberg attribute it to *Bact. prodigiosum*. In extreme cases the whole surface of an attacked grain may be covered with a fine powder of fungus spores. Such cases, of course, are easily recognized and would require no specific technique for their detection.

In his treatise on maize and maize products, Schindler[39] stipulates that a cereal used for human or animal consumption should contain no more than 5 per cent. of mouldy kernels. Black and Alsberg consider this percentage too high, at least when taken to include the visibly damaged grains only. They suggest 2 to 2·5 per cent. as a maximum figure, a proposal which is not unreasonable. By basing the estimate on visibly damaged grain the necessary analyses are much simplified, at least when such analyses are restricted to an actual counting of the grains, of which 500 should be taken in each case. This method can in the best of cases be approximate only, since it gives little or no information on the types of deterioration in which the damage has failed to reach an advanced state, or where the grain has been treated by rubbing or polishing to remove visible signs of fungus growth. Nor does it suffice in the case of flour. Here other methods have to be adopted.

The first of these, which was suggested by Emmerling,[4] was very crude. It was based on the time taken for a sample of flour, or grain after grinding into flour, to acquire a mouldy odour on mixing with water to form a paste. Emmerling stipulated that a sound flour thus treated should retain its normal odour for at least 24 hours. The method was widely adopted for the testing of various feeding materials, in spite of the fact that it frequently gave inconclusive results, for instance in the cases reported by Gordan,[40] who used it to determine the soundness of various cattle foods, including bran. It is now universally replaced by methods which determine the changes of acidity occurring in stored grain or flour as a result of microbiological activity. The nature of this acidity were studied by Dombrowski.[41] He found it due to the production of acetic and lactic acids.

In their modification of these methods, Black and Alsberg take 500 kernels picked at random, grind them to a fine flour, and place 10 grs. of the flour in a 50 c.cms. glass stoppered flask. The flask is filled to the 50 c.cms. mark with neutral alcohol, of 85 per cent. by volume, and shaken. The mixture is allowed to stand for 24 hours, and 25 c.cms. of the filtered extract is then mixed with 100 to 150 c.cms. of distilled water and its acidity determined by titration against $\frac{n}{20}$ NaOH, using phenolphthalein as indicator. The number of c.cms. of alkali used, multiplied by 10, gives the acidity of 100 grs. of flour expressed in terms of n-alkali. The acidity of various grain and sound flours determined by this method is given below:

TABLE VII

	Acidity, estimated by Black and Alsberg's method, and expressed in c.cms. of n-NaOH.	Remarks.
Sound wheat	............12............	The figures should
„ rye	............4............	be taken as approxi-
„ barley	............8............	mate and in the case
„ oats	............21............	of normal cereals
„ white wheat flour	............5............	may vary slightly on
„ whole meal flour	............15............	either side of the figure given.
„ maize meal	............9............	

Black and Alsberg's method is of considerable value in cases where the deterioration has led to an increase in acidity. It could be improved in its technique by taking 20 gms. of flour and a double quantity of alcohol for extraction. The amounts given by Black and Alsberg are barely sufficient to secure 25 c.cms. of the extract for titration purposes.

In addition to these general methods, other and more specific tests have been recommended for the detection of the microbiological deterioration of cereals, notably of maize, the Gosio[42] phenol test, for instance, and Ori's[43] catalase test. These methods have not been found to be reliable and need not, therefore, be discussed in detail. The germination test advocated by Sclavo,[44] and adopted officially in Italy to ascertain the soundness of maize, demands a minimum of 80 per cent. of germinating power, a figure which is considered too low by Ori,[43] who advocates 90 per cent. Sclavo's test is open to several objections, including the possibility of an otherwise sound grain having been heated too high during artificial drying and its germ destroyed or weakened.

An effort to measure the deterioration of stored grain and flour by microbiological analysis was foreshadowed by Smith (see Black and Alsberg[2]), but work in this direction does not appear to have been followed up.

In spite of the apparent facility with which grain and flour are attacked on storage, one type of cereal at least has been shown to possess properties which actively inhibit the development of certain micro-organisms. In wheat such inhibitory substances were found by Baker and Hulton.[45] Their presence prevents brewer's yeast from being used for the raising of a dough. To what extent a natural resistance against decay occurs in seeds other than wheat has not yet been ascertained.

Considerable attention has been paid to the elimination of micro-organisms from grain and flour. As a sterilization by heat cannot be adopted on account of the resulting damage to the protein, Wollney's cold sterilization process, based on treatment with ether, was tried in the case of flour by Wolffin[47] and by Holliger,[48] who found it of considerable value, while Budinoff[49] and Dombrowski[41] failed to sterilize flour in this way, at least when spore-forming bacteria were present.

As an alternative to ether, Vandevelde[50] recommended the use of chloroform in acetone, and subsequently carbondisulphide, which he says causes less drastic changes in the chemical and physical properties of the flour than any of the other substances recommended.

In the writers' experience none of these methods are entirely satisfactory for the sterilization of grain and flours. Various spore-forming rods will remain alive on grain and flour for periods of more than 10 months when suspended in chloroform, ether, or carbondisulphide.

To prevent microbiological damage to grain and flour on storage, Legendre[51] recommends the addition of small quantities of harmless alkaline materials to the grain. He claims that the change in reaction thereby secured successfully inhibits the formation of sugars by the diastatic enzymes of the grain, and that a multiplication of the bacteria present is prevented in the absence of the resulting sugars. It is highly questionable whether this procedure, even if effective, will be found to be of practical importance.

LITERATURE

1. A. Atterberg, *Landwirtsch. Versuchsstat.*, vol. 39, p. 205, 1891.
2. O. F. Black and C. L. Alsberg, *U.S. Dept. Agric., Bureau of Plant Ind.*, Bull. No. 199, 1910.
3. C. Thom and E. LeFevre, *J. Agric. Res.*, vol. 22, p. 179, 1921.
4. A. Emmerling, *C. f. Agriculturchemie*, vol. 13, p. 472, 1884.
5. J. König, A. Spieckermann and A. Olig, *Z. f. Untersuch. der Nahrungs- und Genussm.*, vol. 6, p. 193, 1903.
6. F. Hoffmann, *Zeits. f. Spiritus Ind.*, vol. 20, p. 287, 1897.
7. J. S. Haldane and R. H. Makgill, *Fuel*, vol. 2, p. 380, 1923.
8. A. C. Thaysen and H. J. Bunker, *The microbiology of cellulose, etc.*, Oxford University Press, 1927.
9. L. H. James, L. F. Rettger and C. Thom, *J. Bact.*, vol. 15, p. 117, 1928.
10. A. Reichard, *Chem. Zeitg.*, vol. 21, p. 21, 1897.
11. H. Becker, *Zeits. f. d. gesam. Brauwesen*, vol. 20, p. 437, 1897.
12. L. Hiltner, *Landwirtsch. Versuchsstat.*, vol. 34, p. 391, 1887.
13. T. Chrzaszcz, *Wochenschrift f. Brauerei*, vol. 19, p. 590, 1902.
14. L. Hiltner, *Arbeit a. d. biol. Abt. am Kais. Gesundheitsamt*, vol. 3, p. 1, 1902.
15. A. A. Jatschewski, *Chem. Zeitg.*, vol. 29, p. 165, Rep. 1905.
16. O. E. Gabrilowitsch, *Biochem. Zentrbl.*, vol. 6, p. 431, 1907.
17. V. Tirelli, *Zentrbl. f. Bakt.*, vol. 16, p. 185, 1894.
18. G. H. Pellizi and V. Tirelli, *Zentrbl. f. Bakt.*, vol. 16, p. 186, 1894.
19. —. Serena, *Zentrbl. f. Bakt.*, Abt. I, Ref., vol. 29, p. 448, 1901.

20. E. Bertarelli, *Zentrbl. f. Bakt.*, Abt. I, Ref., vol. 34, p. 104, 1903.
21. C. Ceni, *Zentrbl. f. Bakt.*, Abt. I, Ref., vol. 39, p. 562, 1907.
22. C. Bezzola, *Z. f. Hygiene*, vol. 56, p. 75, 1907.
23. G. Mouriquand, *Comptes rend.*, vol. 182, p. 347, 1926.
24. J. Goldberger, G. A. Wheeler, R. D. Lillie and L. M. Rogers, *Public Health Report*, Washington, vol. 41, p. 297, 1926.
25. J. Goldberger and R. D. Lillie, *Public Health Reports*, Washington, vol. 41, p. 1025, 1926.
26. G. Marshall Findlay, *J. Pathol. and Bacteriol.*, vol. 31, p. 553, 1928.
27. E. Haselhoff and F. Mach, *Landwirtsch. Jahrbücher*, vol. 35, p. 445, 1906.
28. H. G. Bell, *Operative Miller*, vol. 13, p. 591, 1909.
29. W. A. Arnoldow, *Chem. Abst.*, vol. 2, p. 1017, 1908.
30. —. Cortez, *Draggendorf's Jahresber.*, vol. 13, p. 615, 1878.
31. E. Prillieux, *Bull. Soc. botan. de France*, vol. 21, p. 31, 1874.
32. A. B. Griffiths, *Comptes rend.*, vol. 115, p. 321, 1892.
33. E. Laurent, *Bull. de l' Académ. de Belgique* (3), vol. 10, p. 765, 1885.
34. J. Thomann, *Zentrbl. f. Bakt.*, Abt. II, vol. 6, p. 740, 1900.
35. E. J. Watkins, *J. Soc. Chem. Ind.*, vol. 25, p. 350, 1906.
36. H. G. Bell, *American Miller*, vol. 37, p. 281, 1909.
37. F. Marion, *J. Soc. Chem. Ind.*, vol. 28, p. 808, 1916.
38. A. Sartory and R. Sartory, *Chem. Absts.*, vol. 20, p. 2210, 1926.
39. J. Schindler, *Anleitung zur Beurteilung des Maises und seiner Mahlproducte*, Kgl. und Kaiserl. Statthalterei Innsbruck, 1909.
40. P. Gordan, *Landwirtsch. Versuchsstat.*, vol. 60, p. 73, 1904.
41. —. Dombrowski, *Arch. f. Hygiene*, vol. 50, p. 97, 1904.
42. B. Gosio, *Rivista d' Igiene e Sanità Publica*, vol. 7, p. 825, 1896.
43. A. Ori, *Rivista Critica de Chimia Medica*, vol. 6, p. 165, 1906.
44. V. Sclavo, *Gazzetta Medica di Torino*, vol. 52, p. 853, 1901.
45. J. L. Baker and H. F. E. Hulton, *J. Soc. Chem. Ind.*, vol. 28, p. 778, 1909.
46. R. Wollney, *Zentrbl. f. Bakt.*, vol. 11, p. 752, 1892.
47. A. Wolffin, *Arch. f. Hygiene*, vol. 21, p. 305, 1894.
48. W. Holliger, *Zentrbl. f. Bakt.*, Abt. II, vol. 9, p. 305, 1902.
49. L. Budinoff, *Zentrbl. f. Bakt.*, Abt. II, vol. 10, p. 462, 1903.
50. A. J. J. Vandevelde, *Chem. Absts.*, vol. 14, p. 3112, 1920.
51. H. Legendre, *Comptes rend.*, vol. 185, p. 1156, 1927.

CHAPTER XVIII

THE MICROBIOLOGY OF STARCH-CONTAINING SIZING MATERIALS AND ADHESIVES

SIZING MATERIALS

WHEN a fabric is woven, the warp threads are held parallel in the loom, whilst the weft yarn is passed to and fro by means of a shuttle. In order to smooth and strengthen the warp threads they are usually given a preliminary sizing by being passed through a hot paste or 'size' made of starch or flour. A film of this paste coats the yarn and to some extent penetrates the interstices between the individual fibres. In some cases the size also serves as a means of adding weighting materials such as china clay to the cloth.

In the case of cloths which are to be bleached, the size is removed after weaving, but such cloths are in subsequent processes usually 'finished' with a dressing of some starch preparation.

The starch preparations most commonly used for sizing purposes are wheat flour, potato starch (farina), maize starch, and sago starch. For the preparation of the size the starch-containing material chosen is usually agitated with cold water in an open storage vat until uniformly suspended. Steam is then admitted, and the liquid is heated and stirred for a time, varying from some twenty minutes to four or five hours. The size is next run through a pipe which communicates with the container in which the warp thread is immersed in the size. The supply of size to this container, the 'size box' or 'sow box', is automatically controlled, and the size is maintained at a temperature of about 95° C. The warp threads pass through the hot size and thence to a drying drum. The quantity in the size box is renewed every six to seven hours, through the automatic inflow which replaces the amount removed with the warp. At first sight this procedure appears to ensure the absence of micro-biological activity during the preparation and application of the size, and to guarantee that no living micro-organisms remain on the warp leaving the size box.

A closer analysis of the procedure, however, as well as of the plant used, will show that this is not the case. The vat in which the size is prepared is usually made of wood, and it is so constructed that the last quantity of size, often amounting to 50 or more litres, cannot be drained off. This residue remains behind during the time which elapses between the preparation of two batches of size, a period during which the temperature in the storage vat sinks to approximately room temperature.

As the temperature during the preparation of the size has never exceeded 100° C., and has usually remained somewhat below this figure—at 95° C.—the spores of many micro-organisms must have survived and remained viable in the hot size. It is almost certain that even some non-sporing types must have withstood the heat applied during the preparation of the size. In support of this may be quoted Thaysen's[1] observations—in his account of the fermentation process for making butyl alcohol and acetone—on a lactic acid bacterium, *Bact. volutans*, which withstood an exposure for 2 hours at a temperature of 125° C. when present in a 5 per cent. maize mash. This resistance was due perhaps to the protection afforded by the colloidal nature of the mash, since *Bact. volutans* was found to be destroyed in five minutes at 65° C., when exposed to this temperature in water.

Many types—perhaps even spores of fungi—which thus survive the preparation of the size, would develop in the size remaining in the storage vat when its temperature had fallen below 40° C. Other types might conceivably be introduced from the air. Whilst the former flora would comprise butyric acid bacilli, capable of hydrolysing starch and of rendering it sour, the latter might include spore-forming soil bacilli, also possessed of starch hydrolysing properties and able to render the size an increasingly suitable food for many fermenting types of the internal microflora of grain.

The whole of this microflora would become mixed with subsequently prepared quantities of size and would penetrate the pores of the wood of the tank, where it would form a further nucleus from which future batches of starch could be infected. Attention was drawn by Whewell[2] to this danger of an infection from the wood.

In the size box, the temperature at which its content is maintained would effectively prevent a development of micro-organisms; those present would be transferred to the sized yarn without further numerical increase and would remain inactive until the moisture content of the yarn had reached a figure suitable for growth.

Their numbers would be correspondingly increased if, as sometimes happens, the operator added a quantity of untreated starch or flour direct to the paste in the size box to thicken it.

An attempt has not yet been made to ascertain the numbers and types of micro-organisms present in the size box. This work could very easily be undertaken and would finally decide whether fungus spores and non-spore forming bacteria are introduced with the size to the yarn and cloth, a question which at present remains in dispute.

Where wheat flour is used the size is not prepared as outlined above. Practical experience has shown that a more suitable size can be obtained when the wheat flour is exposed to a preliminary fermentation process either in the absence of or in the presence of an antiseptic. For the latter zinc chloride is usually chosen. Where an antiseptic is added the treatment is described as a 'steeping' process, though the term 'steeped flour' is often loosely used as synonymous with fermented flour.

For fermentation or 'steeping', wheat flour is made into a paste with equal weights of cold or tepid water. The paste is allowed to stand at room temperature for several weeks, two to three months being a not unusual time. During this period the paste is stirred frequently. The stirring would appear to be an essential part of the treatment. Laboratory experiments confirm the suggestion that a certain amount of aeration is necessary to check putrefying micro-organisms.

The microflora of the paste, and the resulting changes, will depend on whether the wheat flour is fermented in the absence or in the presence of an antiseptic; one would expect that in the former case the whole, or at least a substantial part of the normal internal microflora of wheat would secure favourable conditions for growth, while a limitation in activity would occur when an antiseptic was added.

It is not possible to give a very detailed account of the microbiology of the preparation of wheat flour sizes. The observations on the subject given by Stocks[3] are not very exhaustive. Stocks attributes the advantages gained by fermenting or 'steeping' a wheat flour prior to turning it into size, to the protein thereby becoming more readily soluble, and yielding a stronger binding agent. The simultaneous production of organic acids is claimed to prevent putrefying bacteria from developing. Stocks also remarks that the first change noted, when no antiseptics are present, is a considerable frothing of the paste due to the action of yeast on sugars present. A few days later the flour-water mixture develops a pleasant fruity odour, while its acidity commences to rise owing to the formation of lactic and acetic acids. Though the whole of this acidity must necessarily have been formed from the available starch or from its dextrinous decomposition products, the sugars having been previously consumed by yeast, it is frequently asserted that even when the fermentation is prolonged no loss of starch occurs. Bean and Scarisbrick[4] deny this, and state that the introduction of an antiseptic is essential to prevent loss or damage to the starch.

The following hitherto unpublished observations on the microbiological changes during flour fermentation were collected during the examination of a number of mill samples of fermenting flour, and of regular weekly samples from experimental vats.*

* Quoted by courtesy of the Director of Research, British Cotton Industry Research Association.

At ordinary temperatures the fermentation was found to be remarkably regular in character. During the first few days organisms of various types—yeasts and bacteria—multiplied rapidly, and their number often reached 400 million per gram. There was considerable gas evolution due to the action of yeasts on the sugar present. After the first week, however, lactic acid bacteria predominated and the steadily increasing acidity suppressed all other organisms except a small number of yeasts and cocci, which persisted throughout the fermentation. During these later stages the number of organisms per gram remained fairly constant and was about 100 millions. The process bore a general resemblance to the souring of normal milk, where lactic acid bacteria also rapidly predominate and cause the suppression of putrefactive organisms.

Originally no doubt an antiseptic was added with the idea of preventing all microbiological activity (Ermen[5]). It certainly does not do this, though it stops the initial frothing of the flour-water mixture which was attributed by Stocks to yeast activity.

A bacteriological analysis of 'steeped' flour during the early days of fermentation in the presence of 8 to 10 per cent. of zinc chloride reveals that a considerable increase takes place in the yellow short rods belonging to the internal micro-flora of the grain. The acid-producing species, on the other hand, do not appear to show much activity, and there can be no doubt that less severe microbiological changes take place in this case than in the fermentation of flour. For this reason steeping is strongly favoured by Bean, particularly as the resulting product has the same improved 'feel' as fermented wheat flour.

The micro-organisms which have survived the application of the size to a yarn or cloth are reinforced by further infection consisting of fungi and bacteria, derived from the air as well as from other sources. The further development of these organisms frequently leads to discolorations, technically known as 'mildew', and usually due to the growth of mould fungi.

Mildew is of common occurrence in cotton goods, particularly of the unbleached type known as 'grey cloth'. Here the principal source of mildew fungi is the raw cotton itself, which invariably contains considerable fungal mycelium and spores in addition to various types of bacteria.

The mildew fungi of cotton goods were discussed in detail in Thaysen and Bunker's[6] treatise on the microbiology of cellulose. They are principally species of *Aspergillus* and *Penicillium*, together with certain *Fungi Imperfecti*.

In order to prevent the growth of mildew fungi the precaution must be taken either of maintaining the moisture content of the yarn or cloth at a figure below the minimum at which the organisms can grow, or of adding an antiseptic to the size.

It has long been recognized that the various sizes employed in the textile industries do not offer equally suitable food material for micro-organisms. This has been experimentally confirmed in a series of investigations by Morris,[7] who found that, taking the suitability of unfermented 'strong' wheat flour, i.e. wheat flour with high protein content, as a food substance for *Aspergillus* species as 100, other commonly employed starch-containing sizing materials could be placed in the following order:

Rice flour .	108
Cassava flour	106
Maize dextrin (acid) .	100
Maize dextrin (heat) .	98
Farina dextrin (diastase)	97
Farina dextrin (acid)	90
Wheat starch	89
Soluble starch .	85
Maize starch	82
Sago	78
Farina	76
Cassava starch .	74
Soft wheat flour fermented for 10 weeks	72

Exactly the same sequence does not necessarily apply in the case of other fungi. Broadly speaking, however, it may be claimed that starches are less suitable food materials than their corresponding raw materials, and that the fermentation of wheat flour very appreciably reduces its suitability as a food, at least for the growth of some fungi, notably *Cladosporium* and *Fusarium* species. The inhibitory action of fermented wheat flour is less marked in the case of *Aspergillus*, and least in that of *Penicillium* species.

Washing and neutralization of a fermented flour was found by Morris to render it more suitable for mould growth, indicating an antiseptic value of the organic acids produced during fermentation.

Similar investigations with bacteria and with actinomycetes have not yet been made.

A reference was made above to the essential importance of the presence in the size of a certain minimum moisture content for micro-organisms to develop. This minimum was claimed by Armstead and Harland[8] to be approximately 8 per cent. in the case of the *Aspergillus* species studied by them, but may be slightly higher, perhaps even 10 per cent., in the case of other fungi.

To prevent growth of fungi when sufficient moisture is present it is essential to add an antiseptic to the size. The choice of the right antiseptic presents considerable difficulties and cannot be claimed to have been finally made. Hitherto zinc chloride, in the concentration of 8 to 10 per cent., calculated on the starch in the size, has been most extensively used. It is not entirely satisfactory, however, as it does not afford complete protection and under certain conditions may cause damage to the cloth.

A comprehensive review of a large number of other antiseptics was given by Morris,[9] who found 2:4 dibromophenol and tribromophenol the most effective, and thallium carbonate and para-nitrophenol the most generally suitable antiseptics, with an effective antiseptic power of between six and seven times that of phenol. All of these substances, however, have certain drawbacks which may prevent their industrial application.

Morris's investigations were carried out with fungi as test

organisms. The effect of these and other antiseptics on bacteria present in the size has not yet been ascertained.

More recently salicylanilide and certain of its compounds have been recommended for use in sizing, and for other purposes in which a powerful mildew antiseptic is required.[10]

FLOUR AND STARCH ADHESIVES

In addition to their use in the sizing and finishing of textiles, starch pastes are used for a large number of other purposes; in the manufacture of cigarettes, of paper bags, cardboard boxes, in bookbinding, for bill-posting and for paper-hanging. For these purposes the starches, or flours—wheat and rye flour being the most suitable—may be boiled with water or may be given a previous treatment which partly converts the starch into dextrins. Sometimes, as in the process of Vandenberg,[11] it may even undergo a preliminary fermentation process similar to that used in the preparation of fermented size.

It is probably correct to assert, as has been done by de Keghel,[12] that adhesives prepared from starch are less likely to be decomposed by micro-organisms than those made from flour.

The microflora which participates in the destruction of adhesives includes a variety of types. When left to itself at room temperature a paste becomes covered with a layer of bacterial and mould growth, usually composed of species of *Bac. mesentericus* and of fungi of the genera *Aspergillus* and *Penicillium*. The deeper layers show signs of an active fermentation giving rise to the production of gas and of esters and acids. As a result the adhesive properties of the paste are destroyed. A detailed analysis of the participating types has not been made. From the writers' experience it includes yellow short rods as well as many spore-forming types, including butyric acid bacteria.

The antiseptics which have been recommended to check this microbiological activity include zinc chloride, aluminium sulphate, phenol and formaldehyde. The last is added by de Keghel in a concentration of 0·2 per cent. calculated on the finished adhesive, at least when the adhesive is prepared with starch. When flour is taken, a 0·1 per cent. addition is recommended instead of the higher concentration which, according to de Keghel, might coagulate the proteins of the flour and destroy their adhesive properties.

None of these antiseptics is entirely satisfactory, and the question of how to make starch-containing adhesives proof against microbiological attack under all conditions still awaits solution.

LITERATURE

1. A. C. Thaysen, *J. Inst. Brewing*, vol. 27, p. 529, 1921.
2. W. H. Whewell, *J. Soc. Dyers and Col.*, vol. 39, p. 65, 1923.
3. H. B. Stocks, *J. Soc. Dyers and Col.*, vol. 28, p. 148, 1912. *First Report on Colloid Chemistry*, H.M. Stat. Office, London, 1917.
4. P. Bean and F. Scarisbrick, *The Chemistry and Practice of Sizing*, 10th edition, Hutton, Hartley & Co., Manchester, 1921.
5. W. F. A. Ermen, *The Materials used in Sizing*, 2nd edition. Constable & Co., London, 1912.
6. A. C. Thaysen and H. J. Bunker, *The microbiology of cellulose, &c.*, Oxford University Press, 1927.
7. L. E. Morris, *J. Text. Inst.*, vol. 17, p. T1, 1926; vol. 17, p. T23, 1926.
8. D. Armstead and S. C. Harland, *J. Text. Inst.*, vol. 14, p. T475, 1923.
9. L. E. Morris, *J. Text. Inst.*, vol. 18, p. T99, 1927.
10. British Cotton Industry Research Assn., R. G. Fargher, L. D. Galloway, and M. E. Probert, *B. Pat.*, 323579.
11. —. Vandenberg, *U.S. Pat.*, No. 521517, 1894.
12. M. de Keghel, *Fabrication des Colles*, Gauthier-Villars et C^{le}, Paris, 1926.

CHAPTER XIX

THE MICROBIOLOGY OF BAKING

OF the various microbiological changes which cereals undergo from the time of milling to their consumption as bread by far the most important take place during the preparation and the ripening of the dough.

The stages by which man discovered the importance of dough fermentation obviously cannot be traced. It is not unreasonable to assume, however, as suggested by Chicandard,[1] that they were intimately connected with the custom of primitive races of consuming the bulk of their cereal food in the form of porridge. Like porridge, dough is in principle but a mixture of finely divided grain and water, cooked in its original form on hot stones instead of in a pot.

Even the crudest power of observation and deduction must have sufficed to establish that a mixture of flour and water, when left for some time prior to baking, yields a lighter and more palatable product than one placed on hot stones immediately after mixing.

From this stage to that of retaining part of a successful dough as a leaven to be included in subsequent batches there would appear to be but a short and very natural step. The addition of such leavens to a dough must have been practised for untold generations, and is undoubtedly much older than that known to have prevailed in the Roman Empire of adding fermenting grape juice to the dough. Some writers, Lafar,[2] for instance, consider that originally all natural leavens were derived from additions to the dough of fermenting grape juice or similar liquors, and base their assumption on some of Holliger's[3] experiments which showed that a mixture of flour and water, though capable of leavening a dough, does so through the activity of bacteria and not through the evolution of gas by yeast, which, as has been demonstrated repeatedly, is an essential constituent of all biological dough leavens used technically.

Though Holliger may have failed in his attempts to produce a leaven, functioning through the activity of its yeast, when starting from a dough containing flour and water only, it does not necessarily follow, as Lafar would imply, that a typical leaven can be produced only where saccharine liquors in active fermentation are added. It is known from the work of Chrzaszcz[4] that species of true saccharomycetes occur in the internal microflora of grain, types which might quite well have been the progenitors of the yeast met with in dough leavens.

The addition to a dough of natural leavens, whatever their origin, is still the recognized technical procedure in the making of some types of bread, notably of rye bread. In the form used for this purpose the leaven is known as sour dough, a preparation which will be discussed subsequently in greater detail.

The apparent ease with which a dough can be ripened by the addition of a biological leaven by no means implies that the reactions taking place during dough fermentation are simple and easily controlled. More than forty years of study have been devoted to this subject, and yet all that can be claimed is that certain groups of reactions have been recognized as essential for the successful fermentation of a dough. Bailey and Sherwood[5] enumerated these reactions as (1) diastatic changes, (2) hydrolytic changes of the available disaccharides, (3) fermentative changes, (4) proteolytic changes, and (5) changes in the hydrogen ion concentration of the dough.

One of the objects of the following pages will be to inquire into the participation of micro-organisms in these changes. For this purpose the subject-matter has been divided into four sections, one dealing with the diastatic and other hydrolytic changes affecting the carbohydrates of the dough, the remaining three referring to Bailey and Sherwood's other groups of reactions. As a preliminary an account will be given of the principles of the technique of dough making, of the various micro-organisms which occur in the dough, and of their relationship to the normal microflora of the flour.

When flour and water are mixed to form a stiff paste, and are left at a suitable temperature, say 20° C. to 30° C., a spontaneous fermentation sets in, as was shown by Dünnenberger[6] and by Boutroux.[7] The dough is ripened and can be baked, yielding a fairly satisfactory loaf. Holliger[3] carried out a study of the microflora present in the dough during this fermentation. He found it to be dominated by two non-sporing bacteria, one already known under the name of *Bact. levans*, and the other a gas-producing rod forming yellow colonies on ordinary laboratory media. Both types may be claimed to belong to the normal internal microflora of grain.

Bact. levans was first isolated and described by Wolffin,[8] who obtained it from sour dough and from flour; from the latter most readily after a preliminary incubation of a flour and broth mixture at 37° C. for 24 hours.

The organism achieved considerable notice at the time, and was studied in detail by a number of workers, including Lehmann,[9] Fränckel,[10] and Papasotiriu,[11] who expressed the view that it was closely related to, if not actually identical with, *Bact. coli commune*. This similarity, incidentally, induced Lehmann to test the leavening power of *Bact. coli commune*, which he found to be considerable.

The relationship of *Bact. levans* to the most common intestinal inhabitant was discussed afresh by Holliger, who was able to show that apparent similarity to *Bact. coli commune* was restricted to its morphology. In its biochemical reactions *Bact. levans* differed markedly from *Bact. coli commune*, yielding no indol and producing a gas mixture composed of hydrogen and carbon dioxide in the proportions of one-third of the former to two-thirds of the latter, as against two-thirds of hydrogen and one-third of carbon dioxide produced by *Bact. coli commune*.

The yellow gas-producing rod found by Holliger in spontaneously ripened dough has never been described in detail. In morphology it is identical with the short yellow rods which characterize the epiphytic microflora of vegetable tissues.

Observations can readily be made on the microbiological

changes which occur in a spontaneously fermenting dough by intermittent bacteriological analyses. Such analyses reveal that the original microflora, of a sound wheat flour for instance, which consists of short rods of the size of *Bact. coli commune*, interspersed with spore bearing types of the groups of aerobic soil bacilli, changes during the first 20 hours into one composed almost exclusively of non-sporing rods forming yellow colonies on ordinary media. The number of micro-organisms present in the dough at the end of this period may represent a 25,000 fold increase or more in the original flora. Macroscopically also certain changes are noticeable. The protein has softened and gas bubbles have began to appear in the dough. An accumulation of acid has not yet become noticeable and can be detected only after the fermentation has proceeded for 30 to 40 hours. At this stage the number of short rods, which dominated the microflora previously, has given way to some extent to types of lactic acid bacteria, sometimes of the *Streptococcus lactis acidi* type and sometimes of the *Bact. acidificans longissimum* type, and to spore-bearing rods of the butyl alcohol-producing group. It is during this period that a vigorous gas evolution occurs in the dough.

From this it is clear that, where a spontaneously fermenting dough is used as a leaven to initiate fermentation in a fresh batch of dough, the value of the addition will depend on the age of the leaven. Vigorous gas evolution will be achieved only when the leaven has reached a stage when spore-bearing anaerobes of the butyl alcohol-producing bacilli have developed. A leaven of this type is employed in the Southern States of the United States of America to prepare the so-called 'salt-risen' bread. Kohman[12] has given a detailed description of the preparation of salt-risen bread. He remarks that yeasts are seldom met with as an important group of the microflora. In this type of leaven, therefore, the active microflora is essentially of bacterial origin.

On examination of a sample of sour dough, the type of leaven which in earlier days was extensively used for the raising of all types of dough, and which is still employed technically in the preparation of rye bread, the impression is gained that similar conditions prevail and that bacteria take an important part in the gas evolution. Microscopic preparations and bacteriological analyses have frequently been made of sour doughs and the preponderance of bacteria in the microflora has usually been commented upon. Schiötz-Christensen,[13] for instance, found 8 bacteria to every 3·5 fungi and 2·5 yeast in a sour 'dough' of Danish origin. The bacteria were principally lactic acid bacteria, acetic acid bacteria, and butyric acid producing types, while the fungi included *Penicillium glaucum*, *Cladosporium herbarum*, and *Oidium lactis*. Among the yeasts were both typical saccharomycetes and species of *Torula*.

Nevertheless, the activity of bacteria is not essential for the proper functioning of a 'sour dough', at least not for the production of gas, a reaction for which species of saccharomycetes are responsible. This has now been experimentally confirmed, but had already been indicated by Girard's[14] observations in 1885, that the proportions of alcohol and carbon dioxide given off by a 'sour dough' are identical with those produced in the fermentation of sugar by yeast.

It is scarcely relevant to discuss in detail all the earlier work on the microbiology of sour dough. The observations made were frequently of a highly speculative character—for instance those of Chicandard,[1] who regarded the active organism as a bacillus producing gas by decomposition of the protein of the flour—or they bear unmistakable evidence of the technical difficulties which prevailed at the time and which made an exhaustive study difficult, if not impossible. This applies to the investigation of Engel,[15] who reported the presence in 'sour dough' of a specific type of yeast, *Saccharomyces minor*, to the studies of Marcano,[16] Laurent[17] and Popoff,[18] who held that bacteria were responsible for the leavening action of sough dough, and to those of Dünnenberger,[6] Boutroux[7] and Jago,[19] who regarded yeast as the sole active type.

A more exhaustive investigation, which involved closer attention to technical difficulties, revealed that the action of sour dough leaven is due to a combined activity of yeast and bacteria. Peters[20] arrived at this conclusion after isolating three types of yeasts, including one resembling *Saccharomyces minor*, and five bacteria from samples of 'sour dough'. And Wolffin[8] expressed a similar opinion, finding the function of 'sour dough' to be due to a combined action of *Saccharomyces minor* and *Bact. levans*.

This conception, however, requires that the gas given off by a 'sour dough' should contain a certain percentage of hydrogen, since *Bact. levans* produces a mixture of carbon dioxide and hydrogen. But hydrogen is not a component of the 'sour dough' gas. This has been shown both by Gerard and by Jago.

In Holliger's,[3] in Burri and Holliger's,[21] and in Budinoff's[22] investigations the function of the bacteria of 'sour dough' is considered to be of secondary importance, being limited to the production of acids, notably lactic acid and acetic acid, which, according to Lehmann,[23] are normally present in bread prepared from sour dough. The concentration produced during the leavening of rye bread is equal, Schiötz-Christensen remarks, to that of a 0·75 per cent. solution of sulphuric acid. Assuming the acids to have been lactic and acetic acids, their concentration must have been equivalent to a pH value of 2 to 4, depending on the buffering action of the rye flour. The gas evolution is attributed solely to species of saccharomycetes, either *Saccharomyces minor* or other species of the genus, including *Saccharomyces cerevisiae*. That this view is correct is confirmed by Schiötz-Christensen's statement that bakeries in Copenhagen produce a normal bread, when the dough has been leavened with pure cultures of *Saccharomyces* species.

Such bread obviously must be less acid than samples in which considerable numbers of lactic acid and acetic acid bacteria have been allowed to develop, and Schiötz-Christensen does not comment on the extent to which its flavour compares with that of ordinary rye bread which Knudsen[24] and Beccard[25] state requires the presence of acid-producing bacteria to develop its desired flavour. Nevertheless, the fact remains that the leavening action of 'sour dough', and notably its gas-producing properties, are due to the action of various species of yeast. In principle, therefore, there is little difference between the leavening secured by the addition of 'sour dough' and that obtained by the introduction of active yeast in some other form.

The origin of the yeast found in 'sour dough' has not yet been traced. That it is not necessarily identical with brewer's yeast or wine yeast has been established, and indicates that, originally, it may have been introduced with the natural microflora of the flour, used for the preparation of the leaven. Another source of yeast for leavening purposes was available in the Roman Empire, and probably in other wine-growing countries, in the form of fermenting grape juice, which, as already mentioned, was utilized at an early date for this purpose. In northern countries a similar leaven was prepared by the addition to a dough of fermenting beer wort, the 'foam' or 'barm', of such beer wort. In the course of time numerous methods have been devised for the preparation of suitable barms, a subject which was discussed in some detail by Jago,[26] and more recently by Ellis.[27] Of these various methods, the only one still in practical use, at least in the British Isles, is that termed Parisian barm. As its micro-biology is more or less representative of all other types, the subject of barm preparation will be dealt with by describing the procedure in the preparation of Parisian barm.

A mash is prepared from 2 to 3 kgs. of malt and 9 litres of water, previously heated to 70° C. This mash is maintained for 2 to 3 hours at a temperature of 60° C. and is then filtered through fine muslin.

The resulting wort is warmed to about 65° C., and at this temperature is mixed with a handful of flour in such a way that the flour becomes evenly distributed and uniformly gelatinized. The wort is now allowed to cool and to stand for 2 days or more at 45·5° C. During this period it becomes slightly sour, presumably owing to the development of lactic acid bacteria. When the acidity has reached the desired degree, the wort is inoculated with a quantity of old barm, usually about 3 per cent. Like sour dough this barm consists essentially of species of yeast which set up a vigorous fermentation in the wort. The fermentation is usually completed in 16 to 24 hours, when, after cooling, the fermented wort is ready to be mixed with flour for the preparation of dough. In many cases this dough is, or was, prepared in two stages— perhaps, as suggested by Jago,[26] to facilitate the incorporation of the flour.

The final stage consisted in the mixing of the barm (perhaps originally the whole, but subsequently usually half or a quarter) with flour sufficient to form a thick paste or 'sponge'. This was left for 12 hours at a temperature of 28° C. to 37° C. By that time the remaining flour could be mixed to form the final dough with less effort than if the mixing had been done in one operation. This final dough was then allowed to stay in a warm place for $1\frac{1}{2}$ to 2 hours, sufficient to ensure its satisfactory aeration. During this time the dough would usually be kneaded once to assist the fermentative changes taking place by introducing additional oxygen, thus favouring the activity of the yeast.

During the 'resting' of the sponge a fermentation of the available sugars would set in and carbon dioxide be developed. At the same time the colloidal suspension of the flour proteins would become more pliable, the starch slightly hydrolysed, and a flavour developed in the sponge; all of which, when imparted to the bread, would render its crumb lighter, more aromatic and less likely to dry up.

As implied by the name barm, the active type of microorganism in dough prepared by this method was yeast, beer-yeast, or 'brewer's yeast' as it is generally called, of the top yeast type. When barm dough was widely used this type of yeast was apparently found satisfactory. It has since been found to be much inferior to the bottom yeasts used by distillers and supplied commercially to bakers as 'pressed yeast'. The reason for the superiority of the latter type has been shown by Baker and Hulton[28] to be the presence in flour of some thermolabile toxic substance to which distiller's yeast has become acclimatized, while brewers yeast has not.

It is a question of some economic importance to devise means whereby the fermenting power of brewer's yeast, when growth in flour and water mixtures can be increased to become more nearly equal to that of distiller's yeast. Baker[29] suggests that one way of doing this is to cultivate brewer's yeast for three generations in typical distiller's mash, that is, in solutions which have not been heated to temperatures high enough to destroy the thermolabile flour toxin.

In course of time barm preparations were replaced by distillery yeast, a change which to some extent could be regarded as an improvement, since it eliminated the dangers due to faulty barms.

In the preparation of dough with pressed yeast the microbiological aspects became restricted to the making of 'sponge' and the subsequent fermentation of the dough. A further simplification was introduced when powerful kneading machines became available, and in most bakeries to-day direct preparation of the dough in one operation is the usual procedure. The risk of faulty fermentation is reduced to a minimum in this 'straight dough' procedure. A considerable saving in time is also secured, since the whole of the dough can be completed in 3 to 5 hours if sufficient yeast is added in the first instance. But in spite of these advantages the adoption of the straight dough procedure has not been entirely satisfactory. The suggestion has been made that the bread made by the straight dough procedure is lacking in something desirable in flavour and keeping properties. And, of course, an added expenditure is incurred by the addition of a larger quantity of yeast.

It is very natural, therefore, that efforts should have been made to secure the advantages of the earlier methods of dough fermentation for the technically less complicated straight dough procedure. The efforts made in this direction will be discussed later, when an account has been given of the microbiological changes which take place in the straight dough preparation itself.

From a microbiological standpoint these changes are naturally considerably simpler than those taking place in barms. A comparatively pure culture of yeast is utilized, and in quantities sufficiently large to ensure the desired changes being completed within a few hours. There is little if any opportunity therefore for other micro-organisms to develop. The straight dough fermentation may be regarded as essentially a pure yeast fermentation.

(1) THE HYDROLYTIC CHANGES TAKING PLACE IN THE CARBO-HYDRATES OF THE FLOUR DURING DOUGH RAISING

As yeast does not hydrolyse starch, it may be asked how this organism can produce a volume of carbon dioxide sufficient to aerate a dough which consists essentially of starch, water, and protein.

It is true that most flours contain a certain percentage of sugars, notably saccharose and glucose, but these quantities are not sufficient to ensure an ample evolution of gas. Von Liebig[30] gives for wheat flour a sugar content of 1·0 to 1·5 per cent. of saccharose, and 0·1 to 0·4 per cent. of glucose; a total of approximately 2 per cent. of carbohydrates fermentable by yeast.

Experimentally von Liebig showed that a two-hour fermentation with yeast resulted in a loss of 1·42 to 2·05 per cent. of sugar, indicating that the original sugar would be utilized by the yeast before the dough fermentation had been completed. Additional sources, therefore, are required if the dough fermentation is to proceed normally. Von Liebig showed that additional sugar became available through the activity of the flour itself, and found that the percentage of reducing sugars in a dough in which micro-organisms were absent increased during 14 hours' incubation at 30° C. to as much as 4·6 per cent., calculated as glucose. The sugar formed was chiefly maltose, and its rate of production corresponded to a diastatic power equal to one-seventh of that of a kiln-dried malt in the case of patent wheat flour, and to one-third in the case of whole meal wheat flour.

It need hardly be emphasized that certain conditions must prevail for the amylase of wheat flour to function at its optimum, conditions which it is desirable, if not essential, to maintain during the fermentation of a dough.

The various conditions governing the activity of the amylase of micro-organisms were discussed in Chapter II. The three most important requirements were there shown to be the presence of sufficient moisture, an optimum temperature, and an optimum concentration of hydrogen ions. Though these requirements may be asserted to be of paramount importance also for the proper functioning of the flour amylases, they have not yet received much attention by investigators of the dough fermentation.

It has been shown by Vandevelde[31] that an increase by 30 per cent. in the water content of the dough increases the fermentative power of a yeast by 6·5 per cent. But it is not indicated whether this increase is due to the effect of the added water on the diastatic activity of the flour or to an action on the yeast itself.

And though the establishment of an optimum temperature is generally accepted as of the greatest importance for the successful completion of a straight dough fermentation, there does not appear to be any publication dealing specifically with the influence of temperature on the diastatic functions of the dough.

The influence of a suitable hydrogen ion concentration on the diastatic activity of a flour has been specifically referred to by Bailey and Sherwood,[5] by Sörensen,[32] and by Greeve and Bailey,[33] the last named ascribing the chief value of this factor to its influence on the amylases of the flour.

An improvement in diastatic action might of course be achieved also by deliberate addition of extraneous amylases, for instance in the form of malt, malt extract or other diastase containing substances. The effect thereby secured has been studied by Gore[34] in the case of sweet potatoes, which are rich in amylase, and by Collatz and Racke[35] in the case of malt extracts. The latter investigators found that too large an addition of malt extract tended to render the dough soft or 'wet' and lowered the quality of the resulting bread.

The hydrolytic changes of disaccharides, to which Bailey and Sherwood refer as the second important group of reactions taking place in straight dough fermentations, have not yet been studied in detail. Bailey and Sherwood suggest that these reactions are carried out by maltase and saccharase secreted by the yeast.

Like the diastatic enzymes, maltase and saccharase are greatly influenced in their activity by temperature and by hydrogen ion concentration.

(2) FERMENTATIVE CHANGES IN THE DOUGH

The actual fermentation of a straight dough, the breakdown of monoses to carbon dioxide, alcohol and traces of other substances, is due exclusively to the action of the yeast, and these reactions are influenced not only by temperature, but also by the prevailing hydrogen ion concentration.

Before discussing the importance of these factors, it is desirable briefly to refer to the conditions under which the fermentation is carried out in general practice. After the flour and water have been mixed in the appropriate quantities with the desired amount of pressed yeast and salt, the whole is kneaded by machine until a uniform dough results. This dough is incubated, or 'set', at a temperature of 26° to 27° C., by placing it in a room kept at about 28° C., and is allowed to stand at this temperature until it has risen to its maximum volume and collapses when a finger is inserted into it. The time taken for this stage to be reached varies with the type of flour used, high protein flours—'strong' flours—taking longer than flour of low protein content— 'weak flours'. The time is markedly influenced also by various factors, to which reference will be made later. Under normal conditions the time will be from six to eight hours. The dough is now re-kneaded in order to incorporate fresh supplies of oxygen, is weighed off to the requisite amounts, and placed at a temperature of 32–37° C. for about two hours. During this period of 'proofing' a rapid fermentation ensues, which recharges the matured dough with fresh carbon dioxide and gives it its final volume.

The baking is usually done between 230° C. and 248° C., but these temperatures are never reached in the interior of the loaf nor even on its surface. The actual figures will depend to some extent on the size of the loaf and on the duration of the baking. Roussel[36] registered a maximum temperature in the interior of the dough of 101° C. to 103·5° C., and on the surface of 125° C. to 140·5° C. Brewster-Morison[37] recorded a temperature of 63° C. in the interior of a 500 gramme loaf after 15 minutes in the oven.

Speaking generally, the factors which influence the course of a dough fermentation may be divided into two groups, one of which affects the growth of the yeast, and the other influences the enzymatic changes initiated by the yeast.

This subdivision is indicated by Neumann and Knischewsky's[38] observations that actual growth of yeast takes place during dough fermentation. By adopting a special technique Neumann and Knischewsky were able to count the actual number of yeast cells present in a dough at various stages of the fermentation. They ascertained in this way that a noticeable cell production took place when the quantity of yeast incorporated was equal to, or smaller than the amount normally added, even after a short period of three, or sometimes even of two hours' fermentation. On the other hand, where the amount of yeast was appreciably in excess of the normal quantity of 0·25 per cent., no reproduction occurred; on the contrary, a reduction of the number of cells was often noticeable.

To the growth-promoting factors belong the various food substances such as organic or inorganic nitrogen compounds, which were recommended by Kohman and collaborators[39] and by Elion[40] as dough stimulants. Malt and malt extracts were favoured by Collatz and Racke;[35] for the same purpose, bran extracts by Quine,[41] and by White;[42] and carbamide —potassium chlorate—magnesium sulphate mixture by Epstein.[43]

The effect produced by these various substances can only be of advantage where a reproduction of the yeast is desired and where the number of yeast cells finally present in the dough does not exceed the maximum which can be incorporated without imparting a 'yeasty' flavour. This maximum is usually very much in excess of the quantity of yeast normally taken; in the case of rye bread it was estimated by Holdefleiss and Wassling[44] as 4 per cent. calculated on the flour taken. Nevertheless it is within the bounds of possibility that it may be exceeded during fermentation unless the initial yeast addition is kept low. Where the initial addition of yeast is low the use of growth-promoting substances is of practical importance from the point of view of reducing the percentage of yeast required for the normal raising of a dough.

The second group of factors, the enzyme accelerating substances which increase the rate of gas evolution, and sometimes the total amount of gas produced, are controlled by the presence or absence of acids. Wahl[45] came to the conclusion that a dough, fermented by yeast in the presence of lactic acid bacteria of the type of *Bact. Delbrücki*, gave a more uniformly aerated and a better flavoured loaf than dough fermented in the absence of such bacteria. A similar, though not quite so pronounced effect, was observed where lactic acid was added instead of lactic acid-producing bacteria. Chabot,[46] who dealt with the subject, found that the addition of acid caused an increased fermentation so long as a maximum hydrogen ion concentration was not exceeded. With little, if any justification, this observation has been interpreted as proving that an addition of acid guarantees an early maturing of a dough. Thus Wagner and Glaban[47] maintained that the changes suffered by the flour protein during dough fermentation could be brought about by the addition of acids. This is not correct, however, and is contradicted by Bailey and Johnson's[48] observations, which showed that doughs, made from flour which for some reason or other had acquired an abnormally high acidity, and which, according to Wagner and Glaban, should have matured in a shorter period than normal doughs, gave unsatisfactory loaf characteristics, unless fermented for the normal period.

A number of other substances have been recommended as useful for accelerating the dough fermentation. Kohman[49] recommended iodates and bromates, or their corresponding free acids, which he added in concentrations of 0·0005 per cent. calculated on the flour. Potassium salts were also found by Kohman and his collaborators[39] to have a slightly beneficial action. The effect of ethyl alcohol, caraway seed, onions and various essential oils, such as clove oil, was determined by Neumann and Knischewsky.[50] They found that all of these substances except onions, which were doubtful in their action, favoured the dough fermentation when added in very small quantities. This observation lends experimental evidence in support of the old custom prevailing in some countries of mixing caraway seed with the dough.

The interpretation given by Neumann and Knischewsky of the action of ethyl alcohol, that its presence checks the development of harmful bacteria, is probably not correct. In the concentration of 1 per cent. in which it was found to act most favourably, it could not prevent the development of the bacteria of the normal microflora of the flour.

Oxidizing agents were tested by James and Huber,[51] who could find no improvement in the dough after their addition. Oxygen itself, however, is an important accelerator. Though no actual investigation appears to have demonstrated this, it is clear from experience that this is the case. It has long been recognized that thorough and repeated kneading, which introduces a fresh supply of oxygen into a dough, is of the greatest value for successful maturing. The action of the oxygen is probably that of a hydrogen acceptor, and it therefore functions primarily in the conversion of the sugars into carbon dioxide and alcohol. It should be replaceable therefore by other hydrogen acceptors, methylene blue for instance. It would not be without theoretical interest to ascertain whether this is the case.

In this connexion the observations of Masters and Maughan[52] on the accelerating influence on the dough fermentation of small quantities of fresh ox-serum are noteworthy. Additions of 1 per cent. of this substance were claimed to improve the fermentation sufficiently to cause an increase in volume of the finished loaf of between 15 and 16 per cent. The action was not due, as might have been thought, to the introduction of additional nitrogen, since serum more than three days old showed little if any action. The nature of the stimulant contained in fresh ox-serum has not yet been established. The agent is apparently thermolabile since it was found to be rapidly destroyed on boiling. Lower temperatures, 60° C. for instance, were withstood for some time. On standing the serum was inactivated after a few days; it could be preserved, however, for a considerable time when precipitated as part of the protein precipitate obtained on saturating the serum with ammonium sulphate. Addition of small concentrations of formaldehyde to fresh ox-serum also preserved it.

Against these observations on substances which favour the dough fermentation must be set the observations which have been made on innocuous and inhibitory substances.

To the first group belong the chlorides, nitrites, nitrates and sulphates, tested by Kohman and his collaborators. Phosphates, at least when a sufficiency of phosphates is already present in the dough, were also ineffective.

These observations of Kohman's, which were confirmed by Neumann and Knischewsky, are of particular interest as regards the chlorides, since common salt has for years past been regarded as a retarder of the fermentation, checking also the development of undesirable bacteria and fungi.

Vandevelde's statement that a high gluten (protein) content in a flour affects the fermentation disadvantageously may appear surprising. If confirmed this may be found to be due to the fact, elucidated by Bailey and Johnson,[48] that an optimum hydrogen ion concentration takes longer to establish in a dough with high gluten content than in one with a normal or small percentage, owing to the increased buffering action of the flour with high gluten percentages. It cannot be due to a direct inhibitory influence exercised by the large protein content.

An inhibitory influence is undoubtedly caused by the addition of larger doses of certain spices or their corresponding essential oils and of many chemicals. It has not been determined whether the action in these cases affects the development of the yeast cells or the functioning of their enzymes.

For the study of the dough fermentation, that is for the elucidation of the conditions affecting it, and of the substances interfering with its normal course, it has been important to devise tests which indicate a normal progress of the fermentation, the attainment of a maximum gas evolution, and the completion of the fermentation.

In the bakehouse such tests have been empirically evolved and have been restricted to ascertaining when a dough was ready for proofing (weighing). This may be done by inserting a finger into the dough, which, if matured, will recede or collapse.

The explanation given by Bailey and Johnson of this test is that the gluten of a mature dough has been softened to such an extent that it can no longer prevent the escape of gas, which, in consequence, is being lost at a rate faster than that at which it can be replaced, probably because of the rupturing of vesicles of gas at the surface of the dough and perhaps indirectly owing to an exhaustion of the available sugar supplies setting in. At this stage, therefore, the dough must have reached its maximum volume.

Basing their efforts on this assumption, Bailey and Johnson have attempted to evolve a reliable method of ascertaining when a dough has matured sufficiently to be proofed and made ready for baking. They argue that, since at a given stage there is a rapid loss of carbon dioxide, it should be possible to determine this stage by measuring the carbon dioxide evolution of the dough at intervals. They do this by absorbing the gas given off with a dilute solution of alkali possessing a hydrogen ion concentration corresponding to a pH value of 7·8. The time taken for this pH value to decrease to 7·0, as indicated by the changes in phenol red from pink to yellow, is taken as a measure of the rate of carbon dioxide evolution.

In their experiments Bailey and Johnson found that a sharp increase in gas evolution from a dough was indicated by this method and coincided with the time of ripening of the dough. A somewhat similar method has been advocated by James and Huber[51] for flour and water suspensions. Here the fermentation is allowed to proceed in a flask and the carbon dioxide given off is collected in an inverted tube in which it moves a registering arm recording the changes. Either of these methods appears to be superior to that by which the ripening of a dough is correlated with changes in hydrogen ion concentration.

Since Jessen-Hansen[53] first drew attention to the connexion between changes in the hydrogen ion concentration and the ripening of a dough, the view has gained ground that once the optimum pH value of 5·0 has been established, the gas evolution of a dough has reached its maximum and the fermentation should therefore be arrested (Brewster Morison[37]). It was suggested that a simple measurement of the hydrogen ion concentration of a dough would suffice to show when proofing could be commenced. It is not surprising to hear that more recent investigations have had to revise this view.

The various flours used in bread-making, even various types of wheat flour, differ too markedly in chemical composition, notably as regards their protein content, to justify the conclusion that the establishment of a given hydrogen ion concentration in a given time is unaffected by the nature of the flour. This is clear from the observations of Bailey and

Sherwood,[5] who found that the hydrogen ion concentration of a dough made with wholemeal flour increases more slowly than that of a dough prepared from patent flour. Bailey and Johnson[48] recorded that, in the case of a wholemeal dough which is allowed to ferment until its optimum pH value of 5·0 has been reached, the resulting bread was inferior, the protracted fermentation having rendered the crumb wet, and having greatly increased the loss of dry matter. As a contrast these writers record that, where the fermentation of a patent flour which for some reason or other had acquired an abnormally high acidity, was arrested through the hydrogen ion concentration of the dough had reaching its optimum, the resulting loaf was harsh and 'unfinished'. It is hardly safe to assert, therefore, as has occasionally been done (Wagner and Glaban[47]), that the time of fermentation of a dough may be shortened, and perhaps even almost completely eliminated by artificially establishing an optimum hydrogen ion concentration in the dough.

Apart from the attention paid to the changes in the hydrogen ion concentration of a dough and to the production of carbon dioxide and alcohol, surprisingly little time has been spent on the study of the biochemical changes which take place as a result of the activity of yeast and perhaps of other micro-organisms. Undoubtedly there is here a wide field for future investigations.

It is realized that the increase in hydrogen ion concentration during fermentation is due to the production of one or more acids, but their exact nature has not been determined. It seems likely that the carbon dioxide, which has been known since Chicandard's time to constitute the bulk of the gas included in a dough, may take a part in the lowering of the pH value, though the chief agencies in this respect are probably the various acids formed during fermentation. The increase in pH value of a loaf which can be noticed during baking, and to which Bailey and Sherwood drew attention, indicates that part of the dough acidity must be of a volatile nature. The bacteria responsible for its production are

identical with or related to *Bact. acidificans longissimum,*
Lafar, a type which is added in many distilleries to the wort
to encourage the growth of the yeast and to suppress other
bacteria.

The appearance and disappearance of ethyl alcohol, the
second important fermentation product of yeast, during
dough raising and on baking respectively, has been discussed
by some writers. Graham demonstrated very forcibly the
possible economic importance of this question when pointing
out, according to Pohl,[54] that more than a million and a
quarter litres of alcohol were allowed to escape yearly from
the ovens of the bakeries of London.

The percentage of ethyl alcohol present in straight doughs
may be placed at somewhat more than 1 per cent., the figure
obtained by Snyder and Voorheer,[55] and subsequently confirmed by Czapek.[56] During baking the bulk of this alcohol
escapes, but the finished bread, nevertheless, contains
measurable quantities. The figure obtained by Bolas[57] for
fresh London bread was 0·314 per cent., and for a week old
bread 0·120 to 0·139 per cent. These figures are possibly
somewhat high and are probably based on analyses of bread
made with barm or sponge. The more recent data of Pohl,
which refer to straight dough bread, are lower and record
0·0508 per cent. of alcohol in fresh bread. All the investigations carried out on the presence of alcohol in bread have
confirmed Sandberg's[58] conclusion that the original alcohol
content of fresh bread is reduced on the week's storage by as
much as 55 per cent.

Recently attempts have been made to recover the very
appreciable quantities of alcohol which are produced in the
bakehouse. Andrusiani[59] describes one such attempt which
would appear, however, to have met with little economic
success. It is based on an alteration to the bakeoven which
makes it possible to withdraw and to condense the vapours
emanating from it. These vapours were claimed by Mousette[60]
to contain 1·6 per cent. of ethyl alcohol and 0·06 per cent. of
acetic acid.

Since the quantity of ethyl alcohol produced during the dough fermentation may amount to over 1 per cent. of the total weight of the dough, and knowing that the quantity of carbon dioxide evolved must be even greater, it will be appreciated that the inroad made during fermentation on the carbohydrates of the dough cannot be regarded as negligible. It was with a view to restricting this loss of carbohydrates that the various attempts already referred to of shortening the fermentation period were made. Their practical value has been questionable.

A more promising method would appear to be that advocated by Dorée and Kirkland[61] of combining the old fashioned barm method of preparation of dough with the simplicity of the straight dough process. They attain this by preparing a 9 per cent. malt extract solution, and by fermenting it with 1 lb. of yeast per sack of flour. The fermentation completed, the extract is mixed with the whole of the flour and the dough is allowed to ferment for 3 hours after kneading in the usual manner. In this way they utilize a yeast culture in a liquid medium as a starter instead of pressed yeast. This procedure was found by Scliber and Bovshik[62] to be more economical than the use of pressed yeast, as regards consumption of raw material for the production of the yeast cells required to raise a given unit of dough.

An entirely different method of reducing the consumption of carbohydrates during dough raising is achieved in the making of 'salt-risen' bread, a type of bread which is extensively prepared in the Southern States of the United States of America. The leaven for this type of bread is made from maize meal, salt, soda, and milk, which are mixed into a batter and kept warm, usually for 15 to 20 hours, until gas begins to be formed. The batter is then made up with wheat flour into a slack dough and is allowed to ferment for 1 to 3 hours. According to Kohman[12] the gas evolved is a mixture of carbon dioxide and hydrogen in the proportions of 1 part of the former to 2 parts of the latter, indicating that bacteria are primarily responsible for the gas production. This is confirmed by microscopic examination and bacteriological analysis of the dough. One of the bacteria isolated by Kohman was *Bact. levans*. Except for small quantities of acids no fermentation products other than hydrogen and carbon dioxide are produced during salt dough raising, and less flour is therefore required for leavening than in the case of a yeast raised dough.

Koser[63] refers to a similar method of leavening adopted by certain bakeries in Washington. Here an anaerobic butyric acid producing bacillus can be identified as the responsible micro-organism. Koser refers to the close relationship of this type to the pathogenic *Bac. Welchii*, a species which he utilized to leaven experimental dough samples.

(3) PROTEOLYTIC CHANGES IN THE DOUGH DURING RIPENING

No less important than the fermentation of the available carbohydrates is the fourth group of reactions which occur during the leavening of a dough, those affecting the proteins present. Bailey and Sherwood refer to this group of reactions as the proteolysis or hydrolysis of the gluten. This proteolysis proceeds simultaneously with the conversion of the carbohydrates (Sharp and Schreiner[64]) and is markedly influenced by the hydrogen ion concentration of the dough, a pH value of 5·0 representing an optimum.

Sharp and Schreiner[64] have shown that the plasticity of the protein increases to a maximum as the yeast fermentation proceeds, but there is no definite experimental evidence to show that proteolytic enzymes, secreted by the yeast, are responsible for this change. In fact it is still an open question whether the softening, or increased plasticity of the gluten during dough making, is due to enzymes produced by the yeast, by the flour, or by other agencies. Perhaps it may be taken as an indication that, since barms give rise to a more plastic protein than the straight dough fermentation, the proteolytic activity is governed by other factors than the enzymes of yeast and flour.

(4) CHANGES IN HYDROGEN ION CONCENTRATION OF THE DOUGH DURING RIPENING

Turning to the last of Bailey and Sherwood's five important groups of reactions which governs the fermentation of a dough, it may be recalled that an optimum hydrogen ion concentration must be established in a dough for the various reactions to take place under favourable conditions.

It is a remarkable and fortunate coincidence that these various hydrogen ion concentration requirements should be practically identical, and that not only the diastatic changes of the flour, but also the hydrolysis of the disaccharides thereby produced, the gas evolution, and the proteolysis of the gluten should proceed most favourably on the acid side of the neutral point. Jessen-Hansen[53] and most other investigators give the optimum hydrogen ion concentration as equivalent to a pH value of 5·0 to 5·2. This reaction is considerably more acid than that of the flour itself, at least under normal conditions and in the case of patent wheat flours, for which Chabot[46] records a pH value of 6·0 to 6·4, and Fisher and Halton[65] pH 5·8. During the fermentation of a dough production of acid is therefore essential to establish an optimum reaction.

There are in existence a number of data, determined by Bailey and Sherwood, which show the rate of increase in hydrogen ions of straight doughs prepared with wheat flour.

TABLE VIII

Treatment of the dough.	Age of dough in minutes.	Hydrogen ion concentration of dough.
		pH value
Dough mixed	0	6·2
After — minutes fermentation	108	5·88
After — minutes fermentation	156	5·78
After — minutes fermentation	180	5·76
After proofing	270	5·67
Bread after baking	300	5·75

They are average figures of determinations from seven individual experiments. They indicate that the most suitable hydrogen ion concentration is not normally reached by this method of dough raising.

A nearer approach to optimum conditions was obtained by Bailey and Sherwood when the dough was prepared by sponging. In this case the following hydrogen ion concentrations were recorded.

TABLE IX

Treatment of dough.	Age of dough in minutes.	Hydrogen ion concentration of dough.
		pH value
Sponge prepared	0	5·71
Sponge after — minutes fermentation	120	4·49
Sponge after — minutes fermentation	240	5·20
Sponge on completion	340	4·94
Dough after mixing	360	5·53
Dough after proofing	425	5·34
Bread after baking	460	5·42

It is not to be overlooked that the increase in acidity of a dough during fermentation is influenced by other factors than that of the mode of ripening. It is influenced also by the buffering properties of the flour used. Morison and Collatz[66] give several instances of how the addition of identical quantities of the same acid to two different flours bring about a greater hydrogen ion concentration in the dough made from one flour than in that made from the other. Similar results were obtained by Fisher and Halton.[65] As a rule it may be claimed that the hydrogen ion concentration of doughs made from a 'clear' flour—which possesses very pronounced buffering properties—is less readily changed than those of doughs made from patent flour.

There may be cases, therefore, where in practice it will be difficult, if not impossible, to bring the hydrogen ion concentration of a dough to the figure which until recently has been considered the most suitable for ripening purposes. According to Fisher and Halton[67] this would appear to be unimportant, provided that the reaction of the dough is not allowed to change from the acid side of the neutral point to the alkaline side. Also according to them it is infinitely more important to ascertain that the reaction of a dough does not fall below a pH value of 5·0, than to secure that it is maintained near this figure, since their experiments have convinced them that a rapid deterioration of the dough and the loaf results from carrying out the dough fermentation at pH values of 4·8 or less.

While this is probably correct, it is difficult to harmonize Fisher and Halton's statement that the hydrogen ion concentration of a dough is unimportant provided it is maintained on the acid side of the neutral point and does not fall below the pH value of 4·8, with the observations of other workers on the value of the addition of acids to improve the baking qualities of a dough.

There are the findings of White, for instance, showing that an acidulated extract of bran, when added to a dough, improves the fermentation more than a neutral extract of the same bran, and there are the observations of Wahl[45] on the value of the addition of lactic acid to a dough, a value which is ascribed by him to the increased hydrogen ion concentration thereby secured.

The nature of the acids responsible for the increase in hydrogen ion concentration of a fermenting dough has not been clearly established. The fact that the acidity decreases during baking must be interpreted, as already mentioned, as proof that part at least of this increase is due to volatile fermentation products such as carbon dioxide and acetic acid, the latter of which was observed in sour doughs by Lehmann.[23]

LITERATURE

1. G. Chicandard, *Moniteur Scientif.*, vol. 13 (3), p. 927, 1883.
2. F. Lafar, *Handb. d. tech. Mykologie*, vol. 2, p. 504. Gustav Fischer, Jena, 1907.
3. W. Holliger, *Zentrbl. f. Bakt.*, Abt. II, vol. 9, p. 305, 1902.
4. F. Chrzaszcz, *Wochenschr. f. Brauerei*, vol. 19, p. 590, 1902.
5. C. H. Bailey and R. C. Sherwood, *J. Ind. Eng. Chem.*, vol. 15, p. 624, 1923.
6. C. Dünnenberger, *Arch. der Pharm.*, vol. 22, p. 226, 1888.
7. L. Boutroux, *Comptes rend.*, vol. 113, p. 203, 1891.
8. A. Wolffin, *Arch. f. Hygiene*, vol. 21, p. 268, 1894.
9. K. B. Lehmann, *Zentrbl. f. Bakt.*, vol. 15, p. 350, 1894.
10. F. Franckel, quoted by W. Holliger, *Zentrbl. f. Bakt.*, Abt. II, vol. 9, p. 305, 1902.
11. J. Papasotiriu, *Arch. f. Hygiene*, vol. 41, p. 204, 1902.
12. H. A. Kohman, *J. Ind. Eng. Chem.*, vol. 4, pp. 20 and 100, 1912.
13. —. Schiötz-Christensen, *Z. f. ang. Chem.*, vol. 25, p. 221, 1892.
14. A. Girard, *Comptes rend.*, vol. 101, p. 601, 1885.
15. —. Engel, quoted by E. Laurent, *Bull. de l'Acad. de Belgique* (3), vol. 10, p. 765, 1885.
16. V. Marcano, *Comptes rend.*, vol. 96, p. 1733, 1883.
17. E. Laurent, *Bull. de l'Acad. de Belgique* (3), vol. 10, p. 765, 1885.
18. M. Popoff, *Ann. Inst. Pasteur*, vol. 4, p. 674, 1890.
19. W. Jago, *J. Soc. Chem. Ind.*, vol. 6, p. 164, 1887.
20. W. L. Peters, *Botan. Ztg.*, vol. 47, p. 405, 1889.
21. R. Burri and W. Holliger, *Zentrbl. f. Bakt.*, Abt. II, vol. 23, p. 99, 1909.
22. L. Budinoff, *Zentrbl. f. Bakt.*, Abt. II, vol. 10, p. 462, 1903.
23. K. B. Lehmann, *Arch. f. Hygiene*, vol. 44, p. 214, 1902.
24. S. Knudsen, *Kgl. Veterinaer og Landbohøjskoles Aarsskrift*, 1924.
25. E. Beccard, *Ger. Pat.*, No. 350874, 1922.
26. W. Jago, *The Science and Art of Breadmaking*. Simpkin, Marshall, Hamilton, Kent & Co., Ltd., London, 1895.
27. D. Ellis, *The Industrial Chemist*, vol. 2, p. 249, 1926.
28. J. L. Baker and H. F. G. Hulton, see J. L. Baker, *J. Soc. Chem. Ind.*, vol. 36, p. 836, 1917.
29. J. L. Baker, *J. Soc. Chem. Ind.*, vol. 36, p. 836, 1917.
30. H. J. von Liebig, *Landw. Jahrbüch.*, vol. 38, p. 251, 1909.
31. A. J. J. Vandevelde, *Chem. Abst.*, vol. 3, p. 341, 1909.
32. S. P. L. Sörensen, *Amer. Food Jour.*, vol. 19, p. 556, 1924.
33. E. Greeve and C. H. Bailey, *Cereal Chem.*, vol. 4, p. 261, 1926.
34. H. C. Gore, *J. Ind. and Eng. Chem.*, vol. 15, p. 1238, 1923.
35. F. A. Collatz and O. C. Racke, *Cereal Chem.*, vol. 2, p. 213, 1925.
36. J. Roussel, *Rev. intend. militaire*, vol. 20, p. 127, 1908.
37. C. Brewster-Morison, *J. Ind. and Eng. Chem.*, vol. 15, p. 1219, 1923.

38. M. P. Neumann and O. Knischewsky, *Zentrbl. f. Bakt.*, Abt. II, vol. 25, p. 314, 1909.

39. H. A. Kohman, C. Hoffman, T. M. Godfrey, L. H. Ashe and A. E. Blake, *J. Ind. Eng. Chem.*, vol. 8, p. 781, 1916.

40. L. Elion, *Z. f. ang. Chem.*, vol. 41, p. 230, 1928.

41. J. H. Quine, *U.S. Pat.*, No. 1018441, 1912.

42. H. L. White, *J. Ind. Chem.*, vol. 5, p. 990, 1913.

43. A. K. Epstein, *U.S. Pat.*, No. 1657379, 1928.

44. P. Holdefleiss and R. Wessling, *J. Soc. Chem. Ind.*, vol. 28, p. 808, 1910.

45. A. Wahl, *J. Ind. Eng. Chem.*, vol. 7, p. 773, 1915.

46. G. Chabot, *Bull. Soc. Chim. de Belgique*, vol. 32, p. 346, 1923.

47. T. B. Wagner and C. A. Glaban, *B. Pat.*, No. 235874, 1926.

48. C. H. Bailey and A. H. Johnson, *Cereal Chem.*, vol. 1, p. 293, 1924.

49. H. A. Kohman and others, *U.S. Pat.*, Nos. 1148328 and 1148329, 1915.

50. M. P. Neumann and O. Knischewsky, *Zentrbl. f. Bakt.*, Abt. II, vol. 28, p. 256, 1910.

51. T. R. James and L. X. Huber, *Cereal Chem.*, vol. 5, p. 181, 1928.

52. H. Masters and M. Maughan, *Biochem. J.*, vol. 14, p. 586, 1920.

53. H. Jessen-Hansen, *Comptes rend. trav. lab. Carlsberg*, vol. 10, p. 170, 1911.

54. O. Pohl, *Z. f. ang. Chem.*, vol. 19, p. 668, 1906.

55. H. Snyder and L. A. Voorheer, *U.S. Dept. Agric. Bull.*, No. 67, 1899.

56. O. Čzapek, *Österreich. Chem. Ztg.*, vol. 29, p. 83, 1926.

57. T. Bolas, *Chem. News*, vol. 27, p. 271, 1873.

58. T. Sandberg, *Annales Falsif.*, vol. 16, p. 531, 1923.

59. M. Andrusiani, *F. Pat.*, No. 603218, 1926.

60. —. Mousette, *Comptes rend.*, vol. 96, p. 1865, 1883.

61. C. Dorée and J. Kirkland, *Report on Research at the National Bakery School*, p. 21, 1925.

62. G. Scliber and G. Bovshik, *Chem. Abst.*, vol. 20, p. 1118, 1926.

63. S. A. Koser, *J. Infect. Dis.*, vol. 32, p. 208, 1923.

64. P. F. Sharp and O. M. Schreiner, *Cereal Chem.*, vol. 3, p. 90, 1926.

65. E. A. Fisher and P. Halton, *Cereal Chem.*, vol. 5, p. 192, 1928.

66. C. B. Morison and F. A. Collatz, *Amer. Inst. of Baking*, Bull. No. 5, 1921.

67. E. A. Fisher and P. Halton, *Cereal Chem.*, vol. 5, pp. 18 and 97, 1923.

CHAPTER XX

DISEASES OF BREAD

THE introduction of the ripened dough into the baking oven, which usually is maintained at temperatures between 230° C. and 248° C. (Brewster Morison[1]), is the starting-point for far-reaching microbiological changes in the dough. After a brief interval of greatly increased activity as the temperature of the dough rises, all enzymatic activity comes to a standstill, probably at a temperature between 65° C. and 75° C. The moment for this cessation of the enzymatic functions will depend on the volume of the dough. In loaves of the usual commercial size it probably occurs twenty minutes after placing the loaf in the oven. As the baking proceeds the temperature of the dough increases and finally reaches a maximum, determined by Roussel[2] as 140·5° C. for the surface and 103° C. for the interior of the loaf. Other observers, Russell[3] for instance, doubt whether the internal temperature of the loaf ever exceeds 100° C.

The effect of the maximum temperature on the microflora of the dough has not been investigated in very great detail. Nevertheless there are sufficient observations to show that though this effect is destructive it does not completely eliminate micro-organisms, at least not in the case of the spore-forming bacteria occurring in the crumb. On the surface of the dough, in the crust, no micro-organisms or their spores can withstand the temperature of the baking, and this part of the loaf leaves the oven sterile.

The fate of fungus spores during baking, when contained in the interior of the crumb, was investigated by Welte,[4] who placed large numbers of the spores of *Penicillium glaucum*, *Aspergillus nidulans* and *Mucor stolonifer*, enclosed in filter paper, in the centre of a dough ready for baking. He found that, on removal of the test loaves from the oven, all of these spores had been destroyed.

The resistance to the baking temperature of non-spore-forming bacteria enclosed in the dough was studied by Roussel and by von Fenyvessy and Dienes,[5] who agree that these forms are destroyed during baking. Roussel points out, however, that tubercle bacteria present in the dough retain their viability after baking. Nevertheless there is little doubt that Roussel's conclusions are essentially correct, and that normally non-spore-forming bacteria, as well as yeasts and fungi and their spores, are destroyed during baking. Types which may be found in the crumb comprise cocci and sometimes lactic acid producing bacteria of the type of *Streptococcus lactis acidi*. These organisms can be shown occasionally to have survived by emulsifying a piece of the crumb of a newly baked loaf, collected under the strictest aseptic conditions, with sterile physiological salt solution and incubating the emulsion for 24 hours or more at 30° C.

In contrast to the spores of fungi, those of spore-forming bacteria, notably of the group of aerobic soil bacilli, are frequently found in fresh bread. They have undoubtedly survived the temperature of baking.

Where they occur, and also in the more exceptional cases of the survival of cocci and lactic acid bacteria, there is a possibility of microbiological activity starting in the interior of loaves which remain stored for some time, provided their water content does not fall appreciably below the normal of 45 to 48 per cent. In practice little, if any harm, is done by this surviving microflora, except where the crumb is infected with certain types of *Bac. mesentericus*, or where butyric acid producing bacteria have survived. In the first case a loaf may become ropy on storage—a complaint which has been, and to some extent still is, of considerable economic importance. In the second case sour bread results, a complaint which in earlier days was regarded as a fairly common disease of bread (Atwater[6]). The subject of ropy bread will be dealt with in some detail in this chapter.

When a loaf has left the oven, its sterile crust becomes exposed to infection with micro-organisms which may be air borne or may be carried by insects (Roeser[7]) or man. This infection comprises both bacteria and fungi, the latter being the more important, since they develop at comparatively low moisture contents. Welte[4] mentions that he observed growth of fungi on bread containing no more than 25 per cent. of moisture.

A more detailed discussion of observations made on the action of fungi on bread will form a section of this chapter. Their range of activity comprises the whole loaf, sliced bread and other baking products which are unprotected by a crust.

The various products of the bakery are affected also by infections other than the common bread fungi, infections which may be either bacterial or fungal in origin. The appearance of imaginary blood on bread and the formation of 'chalky' bread are cases in point which may well lay claim to separate discussion.

There remains to be recorded the fact that the growth of actinomycetes has not yet been associated with the deterioration of bread and other baking products. This may well appear surprising in view of the ubiquitous occurrence of the actinomycetes and of their marked starch hydrolysing properties. Research in this field remains to be initiated.

ROPY BREAD

The disease of bread, technically described as 'rope', manifests itself in its early stages as a brownish to reddish-brown spotty discoloration of the crumb and imparts to the affected bread a faint sickly smell. The brownish spots subsequently coalesce and spread, finally turning the whole of the crumb into a brown, semi-liquid, mucilaginous mass which may sometimes be drawn out into long threads. By this time the odour of the crumb has become most objectionable, not unlike that of a mixture of rotten fruit and over-ripe cheese.

The disease does not usually become evident until about 12 hours after a loaf has left the oven, but once started it spreads quickly through the crumb and may destroy it in the course of a day when conditions are favourable. In this connexion it is noteworthy that rope has not been observed in stale dry bread and that the most dangerous period for the outbreak of rope is the time during which the loaves are cooled subsequent to their removal from the oven.

The first investigator to associate micro-organisms with the appearance of rope was Laurent,[8] who isolated a bacillus from affected bread and described it under the name of *Bac. panificans*. According to him this bacillus was responsible also for the normal fermentation of a dough, and caused rope only where the bread contained insufficient acid. As a means of preventing rope Laurent recommended the addition of acetic acid during periods when and in places where the disease occurred.

Though subsequent investigations have shown that *Bac. panificans* is neither the specific organism of the normal dough fermentation nor the causative agent of rope, Laurent's observations have been of permanent value by connecting the occurrence of rope with the reaction of the affected bread. Without exception subsequent investigators have found that bread and dough possessing a definite acidity are less susceptible to the disease of rope than neutral or slightly alkaline bread. The reaction which is regarded as sufficient to protect bread was stated by Lloyd and McCrea[9] to be equivalent to a hydrogen ion concentration of the pH value 5·0 to 5·5. Cohen, Wolbach, Henderson and Cathcart's[10] investigations indicated that an even higher acidity might be necessary, and in Morison and Collatz's[11] experiments it was shown that an acidity corresponding to a pH value of 4·8 to 4·9 is required to prevent rope. At this hydrogen ion concentration, however, a satisfactory loaf can no longer be produced from patent flour. In the best of cases, and taking Lloyd and McCree's highest figure, there is therefore, as Fisher and Halton[12] point out, only a very slight margin of safety between the reaction required for the prevention of rope and that at which bread can be produced, at least when acids such as acetic and lactic are used to establish the desired hydrogen ion concentration. Fisher and Halton would appear to have overcome this difficulty by selecting acid calcium phosphate instead of free acids for the adjustment of the reaction. They use this salt in quantities of 2 lb. per 280 lb. of flour, or at the rate of 0·71 per cent., and claim that this concentration successfully prevents rope in bread without reducing the pH value below the figure of 5·0; a pH value of 5·19 being the usual reaction observed.

A convincing explanation of this interesting observation is not given by Fisher and Halton. It is made clear by them, however, that the action cannot be due to a specific property of the phosphoric acid radical.

While the reaction of a loaf is thus of paramount importance for its protection against rope, two additional causes have been elucidated which are undoubtedly of significance. Both the percentage of moisture in the bread and the temperature at which the loaf is stored influence the development of rope to a marked degree as already mentioned. Thus, it has repeatedly been found that a wet crumb, containing more than the normal 45–8 per cent. of moisture, is more susceptible to rope than a drier loaf.

The influence of the temperature is perhaps less clearly defined than that of moisture, but is, nevertheless, very real. The spread of the disease within a loaf is greatly favoured by comparatively high temperatures, 39° C., according to Fisher and Halton, representing the optimum. Rapid development is observed also at temperatures down to 25° C., and only below 18° C. can a loaf be stored with what Watkins[13] considers safety. Even here, however, protection is no more than relative, and given time there is nothing to prevent the disease from appearing in bread stored at temperatures as low as 6° to 8° C. (Vogel[14]).

On the whole, however, it may be claimed that rope, which occurs most frequently during the damp autumn months, can be controlled when care is taken to ensure that the hydrogen ion concentration of the bread is kept at pH values between 5·0 and 5·2, when the loaves are cooled rapidly on removal from the oven, and when they are stored in a dry cool store-room.

It was mentioned above that the first micro-organism to be associated with the appearance of rope was described by Laurent under the name of *Bac. panificans*. A few years later Kratschmer and Niemilowicz[15] investigated the case of ropiness in a loaf of Graham bread (wholemeal bread). They ascribed this to the activity of *Bac. mesentericus vulgatus*, Flügge, better known under Migula's name of *Bac. vulgatus*, a type which is closely related to, but usually larger than, *Bac. mesentericus fuscus* of Flügge, renamed *Bac. mesentericus* by Lehmann and Neumann.[16] Another type, described by Flügge under the name of *Bac. liodermos*, which is closely related to *Bac. vulgatus*, was made responsible by Uffelmann[17] for a case of rope in rye bread. Vogel,[14] who described two types of rope-producing bacteria, *Bac. mesentericus panis viscosi* I and II, and all subsequent investigators have arrived at the conclusion that *mesentericus* forms are the causative agents of rope. It has not been possible, however, to allocate the disease to one well-defined species.

In the light of the conception of the mucus fermentation of carbohydrates as given in an earlier chapter this is not surprising, seeing that the property of producing rope must be possessed by all micro-organisms which can utilize bread as a food material under semi-anaerobic conditions and which under such conditions and at alkaline reactions synthesize hexoses to hexosans.

In accepting this explanation of the appearance of mucus in 'rope', it must be admitted that some writers, König, Spieckermann and Tillmanns,[18] for instance, attribute the appearance of mucus to the dissolution of the cell walls of the responsible micro-organisms. The evidence in favour of this view is far from convincing, and usually rests on the observation that the responsible organism fails to produce mucus in a medium composed of starch and peptone. Whether a medium such as this had the required reaction on the alkalin, side of the neutral point or not is not stated. Nor is it very convincingly proved that this medium is favourable for the growth of the organism in question.

Since the spores of the rope-producing types of *Bac. mesentericus* are able to withstand the temperature of baking, and since the disease invariably manifests itself as a deterioration of the crumb, it is clear that the origin of the responsible bacteria must be sought in the dough itself, or perhaps in the raw materials used for the preparation of the dough, rather than in an infection of the loaf subsequent to baking. Of the various likely raw materials, the yeast was suspected by Russell[3] in one case. In the great majority of cases, however, it has been possible to trace the infection to the flour itself, and Watkins[13] goes so far as to suggest that the rope-producing *mesentericus* forms may be regarded as members of the normal microflora of cereals. As a rule rye flour has been found to be infected more frequently than wheat flour, a fact which has been emphasized both by Vogel[14] and by Fuhrmann.[19]

For the discovery of the rope bacillus in flour Watkins elaborated a technique which he claimed to be sensitive enough to give a positive result with as little as 0·02 gr. of rope infected flour. Essentially the method consists in the inoculation of aseptically prepared pieces of crumb of normal bread with increasing quantities of a 2 per cent. pasteurized water suspension of the suspected flour, followed by incubation of the inoculated crumb at 28° C. for 24 hours or longer. If no rope develops in the test samples of crumb within 48 hours, the suspected flour is regarded as normal.

The value of Watkins's method is rendered doubtful by the fact that it does not guard sufficiently against the serious source of error which is introduced by omitting to adjust the hydrogen ion concentration of the crumb used as medium. This is probably the reason why Fisher and Halton,[12] in their experiments with Watkins's method, were sometimes unable to detect the rope bacillus in samples of flour known to contain it. Fisher and Halton favour the baking of a test loaf instead of the use of Watkins's method, a procedure which may meet the case where sufficient flour is available. Where that is not so, Watkins's method should be adjusted to obviate the source of error referred to. It would then constitute a valuable asset to the bacteriologist endeavouring to trace a rope infection to its source.

As no method is known of eliminating an infection with rope bacteria in flour without destroying its baking properties, protection against rope can be secured only by establishing a reaction in the dough which is unfavourable for the development of the causative organism, by reducing the moisture content of the bread to the lowest possible figure through selection of suitable flours and yeast mixtures, and by rapid cooling and subsequent cold storage of the loaf.

SOUR BREAD

It was mentioned above that the aseptically removed crumb of loaves may occasionally contain lactic acid bacteria which have survived the baking process.

Under storage conditions of excessive warmth and damp these bacteria may develop and give rise to sour bread. Where this complaint occurs and gives rise to dietetic disorders, however, it is not the lactic acid bacteria which are the cause, but butyric acid bacteria, the spores of which have been introduced into the dough with inferior flour or yeast, and remaining unaffected by the temperature of the baking process, have developed in the finished loaf.

MOULDY BREAD

Normally fungi do not survive the baking. This was demonstrated experimentally by Welte.[4] A case is known, however, where the spores of a fungus undoubtedly did do so and in which the pores of the crumb of the infected loaf became covered with a whitish dust of spores and mycelium. Buchwald,[20] who studied this case, isolated the responsible fungus and identified it as *Monilia variabilis*, described by Lindner[21] as the causative agent of the 'chalk disease' of bread, a complaint which occurs in the pores of the crumb of sliced bread when kept for two or three days after infection. A similar complaint in a loaf kept for some weeks was described

by Lindner[22] as due to *Endomyces fibuliger*, a type intermediate between *Willia* and the true *Hyphomycetes*.

In the great majority of cases the mildewing of bread is
due to an infection of the loaf with fungus spores subsequent
to baking. The infection spreads from the surface of the
crust to the crumb, cracks in the former serving as places of
entry for the hyphae. The mode of infection of the crust was
referred to in the introduction to this chapter as being due
either to the settling of air-borne spores adhering to flour
dust, or to the deposition of spores by insects or man.

According to Herter[23] the deposited fungus spores appear
to develop more readily on the crust than in the crumb,
possibly owing to the presence in the crust of dextrins and
water soluble carbohydrates which represent a more readily
absorbable food than the starch of the crumb. The germi-
nated spore will continue to develop when the moisture content
of the bread exceeds 25 per cent., at least where the fungus is
Penicillium glaucum or *Aspergillus nidulans* (Welte[4]). Since
it is almost impossible to prevent infection with fungus
spores, normal bread, with its water content of 45 to 48 per
cent., is seriously exposed to fungus attack on storage unless,
as suggested by Herter and Fornet,[24] it is wrapped in paper
immediately after removal from the cooling trays.

The time taken for a fungus infection to become visible to
the naked eye varies with the conditions prevailing, notably
with the temperature. Under favourable conditions it may
be between 3 and 4 days. The problem of mildewing, therefore, is no longer of such practical importance as it was when
a supply of bread was baked, which sufficed for a week's
consumption.

One of the best-known epidemics of mouldy bread which
was carefully investigated by a number of workers, was that
discussed by Payen[25] as having affected the bread supplies
of the military bakeries of Paris in 1842. The responsible
fungus in this case was shown to be *Oidium aurantiacum*,
which gives rise to orange red spots in the crumb, and imparts
to it an unpleasant musty odour. The same fungus is reputed

by Scheurlen[26] to have been the cause of the infection of the bread supplies of the armies of Alexander the Great in his campaign against Tyre, when its growth was associated with the miraculous appearance of human blood, an interpretation which from the earliest days of civilization and until the beginning of the nineteenth century was given also to the appearance of *Bact. prodigiosum* on various articles of food.

In addition to *Oidium aurantiacum* and to *Penicillium glaucum* and *Aspergillus nidulans* referred to above, a number of fungi isolated from the mouldy bread have been studied by Herter and Fornet.[24] They include *Aspergillus candidus*, *Aspergillus fumigatus*, *Aspergillus glaucus*, *Aspergillus niger*, *Mucor pusillus*, *Mycoderma cerevisiae*, *Oospora lactis*, *Oospora variabilis*, *Penicillium crustaceum*, and *Penicillium olivaceum*.

Mucor stolonifer has also been met with on bread (Welt[4]), and *Mucor mucedo* was identified by Jalade[27] as a common bread fungus. In the epidemic investigated by him it was not this fungus which was the causative agent, but *Monilia sitophila*, which imparted to the crumb a rose-coloured fluorescence interspersed with spots of a reddish-orange or yellow. The growth of the *Monilia*, which occurred chiefly on sliced bread 2 to 3 days after baking, could be completely checked by the addition of acetic acid sufficient to raise the hydrogen ion concentration of the loaf to a pH value of about 3·1 (0·2 per cent. acetic acid), an interesting point since the addition of acids is not usually a suitable means for arresting the development of fungi. For this purpose the addition of antiseptics such as salicylic acid has been found more effective by Herter and Fornet, a procedure which to-day can no longer be adopted, at least in the United Kingdom. Nor should it be necessary, if due attention is paid to the handling and storage of the loaf after removal from the oven. In this connexion it may be recalled that Herter[23] observed that *Mucor stolonifer* and *Penicillium crustaceum* were the only two of the test organisms which developed at a temperature below 10° C. The maximum temperature at which Herter observed development of fungi on bread was

50° C., at which *Mucor pusillus* and *Aspergillus fumigatus* were still able to grow.

It has been stated (Chalmers Robertson[28]) that the consumption of mouldy bread gives rise to intestinal disturbances. It is very doubtful, however, whether this is the case; Decaisne's[29] negative feeding experiments carried out on rats and on himself certainly do not support it.

DISCOLOURED BREAD

Apart from the discoloration due to the development of *Oidium aurantiacum* and *Monilia sitophila*, pigmentation of bread and other baking produce may be due to the development of *Bact. prodigiosum*. The discoloration is then limited to the surface of the exposed bread, which acquires the appearance of having been covered with a layer of coagulated blood. Apart from the presence of the causative organism, the complaint requires relatively high temperatures to develop, preferably more than 30° C., and high humidities.

A highly interesting historical study of the occurrence of bleeding bread and Eucharists was published in 1896 by Scheurlen.[26] From this it would appear that epidemics of *Bact. prodigiosum* infections can be traced back to the early Egyptian civilization.

Both Ehrenberg[30] and Scheurlen attribute the religious ban on the consumption of white beans, which was in force in Egypt and among the Pythagoreans, to the belief that not infrequently this article of food showed signs of bleeding, that is, became infected by *Bact. prodigiosum*.

The first historic record of the occurrence of an epidemic of *Bact. prodigiosum* is stated by Ehrenberg to have been in 332 B.C., when 170 women were done to death in Rome owing to the spontaneous appearance of blood on articles of food, an incident which was interpreted by the priesthood as an indictment against them.

Throughout the Middle Ages persecutions or civil disturbances followed regularly on the appearance of 'bleeding' Hosts and amylaceous articles of food. On the last occasion, during the summer of 1819, a peasant, living in the village of Legnaro, near Padua, observed the phenomenon on a dish of polenta—maize porridge—which he had kept overnight in a drawer. He threw the polenta away, but on the following day observed that a dish of rice soup, a rusk, and a cooked chicken had become similarly affected. Subsequently the phenomenon spread to the whole of the village and the anxiety of the populace induced the authorities to appoint a commission to investigate the matter. Pietro Melo, director of the botanical gardens of Savonara, who, with Vicenzo Sette, a local physician, was a member of the commission, ascribed the phenomenon to a spontaneous fermentation of the polenta, which caused the maize meal used to be transformed into a coloured mucilage.

Sette expressed the view that the bleeding was due to the development of a microscopic plant, and a similar conclusion was arrived at by Bizio[31] in his letter to the priest Angelo Bellani. Bizio described the imaginary agent as *Serratia marcescens*, in honour of the Italian inventor Serafino Serrati, who constructed a steam-driven boat.

Subsequently, in 1850, Cohn[32] demonstrated the true nature of the agent of bleeding Hosts and gave it the name *Bact. prodigiosum*. Wasserzug,[33] in his study of the organism, observed that the red pigment is most readily formed in the presence of acids, a fact which may well have added to the mystery surrounding the occurrence of these epidemics of 'bleeding' on articles of food.

LITERATURE

1. C. Brewster Morison, *J. Ind. Eng. Chem.*, vol. 15, p. 1219, 1923.
2. J. Roussel, *Rev. intend. militaire*, vol. 20, p. 127, 1908.
3. H. L. Russell, *Zentrbl. f. Bakt.*, Abt. II, vol. 5, p. 234, 1899.
4. E. Welte, *Arch. f. Hygiene*, vol. 24, p. 84, 1895.
5. B. von Fenyvessy and L. Dienes, *Zeits. f. Hygiene*, vol. 69, p. 223, 1911.
6. H. W. Atwater, *Bread and the Principles of Bread-making*, U.S. Dept. Agriculture, Farmers Bull. No. 112, 1900.
7. P. Roeser, *Arch. de médecine et de pharm. militaire*, vol. 16, p. 462, 1890.
8. E. Laurent, *Bull. de l'Acad. de Belgique* (3), vol. 10, p. 765, 1885.

9. D. J. Lloyd and E. D. McCrea, *Roy. Soc. Report Food (War) Committee,* No. 48, 1918.

10. E. J. Cohn, S. B. Wolback, L. J. Henderson and P. H. Cathcart, *J. Gen. Physiol.,* vol. 1, p. 221, 1918.

11. C. B. Morison and F. A. Collatz, *Amer. Inst. Baking,* Bull. No. 5, 1921.

12. E. A. Fisher and P. Halton, *Cereal Chem.,* vol. 5, p. 192, 1928.

13. E. J. Watkins, *J. Soc. Chem. Ind.,* vol. 25, p. 350, 1906.

14. J. Vogel, *Zeits. f. Hygiene,* vol. 26, p. 398, 1897.

15. —. Kratschmer and —. Niemilowicz, *Zentrbl. f. Bakt.,* vol. 6, p. 501, 1889.

16. K. B. Lehmann and R. O. Neumann, *Bakteriologische Diagnostik,* part II, 5th edition. J. F. Lehmann's Verlag, München, 1912.

17. J. Uffelmann, *Zentrbl. f. Bakt.,* vol. 8, p. 481, 1890.

18. J. König, A. Spieckermann and J. Tillmanns, *Zeitsch. f. Untersuch. d. Nahrungs- und Genussmittel,* vol. 5, p. 36, 1902.

19. E. Fuhrmann, *Zentrbl. f. Bakt.,* Abt. II, vol. 15, p. 385, 1905.

20. J. Buchwald, see *F. Lafar's Handbuch d. technischen Mykologie,* vol. 2, p. 528. Gustav Fischer, Jena, 1905–8.

21. P. Lindner, *Wochenschr. f. Brauerei,* vol. 15, p. 209, 1898.

22. P. Lindner, *Zeitschr. f. Spiritusindustrie,* vol. 31, p. 162, 1908.

23. W. Herter, *Angewandte Botanik,* vol. 1, p. 51, 1919.

24. W. Herter, and A. Fornet, *Zentrbl. f. Bakt.,* Abt. II, vol. 49, p. 148, 1919.

25. A. Payen, *Ann. de Chim. et de Phys.* (3), vol. 9, p. 5, 1843.

26. —. Scherulen, *Arch. f. Hygiene,* vol. 26, p. 1, 1896.

27. E. Jalade, *Rev. intend. militaire,* vol. 20, p. 269, 1908.

28. J. Chalmers Robertson, *The Lancet,* vol. 2, p. 518, 1887.

29. E. Decaisne, *Comptes rend.,* vol. 73, p. 507, 1871.

30. Chr. G. Ehrenberg, *Ber. u. d. z. Bekanntmach geeign. Verhand. der Kgl. Preuss. Akad. der Wissensch.,* vol. 1, p. 5, 1850.

31. B. Bizio, see C. P. Merlino, *J. Bact.,* vol. 9, p. 527, 1924.

32. F. Cohn, *Beiträge z. Biologie d. Pflanzen,* vol. 1, p. 127, 1850.

33. E. Wasserzug, *Ann. Inst. Pasteur,* vol. 1, p. 581, 1887.

PART FIVE

CHAPTER XXI

THE MICROBIOLOGY OF SUGAR-CANE, SUGAR-BEET, AND THEIR RAW JUICES

In giving an account of the microbiology of bread-making, it was found necessary to consider the normal microflora of grain and flour. A similar course must be adopted here in discussing the microbiology of sugar manufacture. As in bread-making, no process of sterilization is used to purify the raw materials, sugar-cane and sugar-beet, which are living tissues with a normal microflora of their own, and which are exposed for prolonged periods to infection from the air and the soil.

In attempting to give an account of the microflora of the raw materials of sugar manufacture, one is faced by the difficulty that no exhaustive investigation has been carried out to establish the identity of the various micro-organisms which are met with on sugar-cane and sugar-beet.

That an indigenous, epiphytic microflora occurs on these plants, or at least on sugar-cane, is clear from Wolzogen Kühr's[1] experiments. He found that out of 597 samples of aseptically removed healthy sugar-cane, only six, taken from isolated mountain districts, yielded a sterile juice when pressed under aseptic conditions. The remaining 591 samples showed a microflora consisting of various saprophytic bacteria. In some cases at least this microflora comprised types of bacteria producing yellow colonies on ordinary laboratory media, thus resembling *Bact. herbicola a aureum*. Geerligs[2] confirms that the cane arriving at the sugar-mill contains an extensive microflora on its surface, but he gives no details as to the nature of this flora. It is not unreasonable to expect that, in addition to types resembling the typical epiphyte *Bact. herbicola a aureum*, it comprises others met with among the normal epiphytic microflora of grain, such as *Bact. fluorescens liquefaciens* and members of the gas-producing *paratyphosum*-resembling group already referred to in Chapter XVI. On the other hand, it does not necessarily follow from Hutchinson and Ramayyar's[3] isolation from fresh cane juice of a yeast of *Saccharomyces cerevisiae* type and an *Aspergillus* species that these micro-organisms are members of the normal microflora. These species, together with others, such as *Bac. subtilis* and acid-producing types, may have been introduced into the juice with particles of soil adhering to the cane.

The epiphytic microflora of sugar-beet is even less well defined, probably because of an extensive contamination with the microflora of the soil adhering to the beet and its rootlets.

In order to acquire further information on this subject it is necessary to analyse the reports on the micro-organisms found in freshly extracted beet-sugar juices. But even so it is impossible to obtain more than a vague impression of the types composing the epiphytic microflora of beet, since little has been done to identify the micro-organisms met with. Most satisfactory in this respect is the information compiled by Schöne,[4] who determined the number of micro-organisms not only in freshly extracted juice but on freshly washed and cut beet slices, technically known as 'cossettes'. The latter were found to contain from several hundreds to over four thousand micro-organisms per gramme sometimes of gelatine-liquefying types, and probably related to or identical with *Bact. fluorescens liquefaciens*. Schöne does not state whether his *coli paratyphosum*-resembling types were obtained from the cossettes or from the juice extracted from the beet slices. Their presence in several varieties appears to indicate their frequent occurrence, and since they are not members of the normal flora, it may well be assumed that they belong to the epiphytic microflora of sugar-beet. In addition Schöne records the occasional presence in fresh sugar-beet juice of *Bact. prodigiosum*, *Cocci*, a *Torula*, and two species of *Monilia*-like fungi. It is not disclosed whether some or all of these secondary types were derived from the beet itself or from soil, nor can this be settled as regards the two species of *Streptococcus* to which Schöne makes special reference owing to their mucus-producing properties. It is probable that part of the microflora mentioned must have been introduced with the water used for the extraction of the cossettes.

The members of the *mesentericus-subtilis* group to which Schöne refers as having been isolated from cossettes and other products of manufacture were probably introduced with the soil adhering to the beet rather than with the beet itself.

Apart from these various micro-organisms, there is a possibility of the introduction into the various manufacturing processes of plant pathogenic organisms responsible for the development of disease in sugar-beet. Herzfeld[5] draws attention to such cases, which are discussed also by Schöne.[6]

In spite of the very scanty information available on the microbiology of sugar-cane and sugar-beet, there is overwhelming evidence to show that numerous micro-organisms of considerable variety enter the sugar-cane mill and the beet-sugar factory with the raw materials employed, and that these various organisms play an important part, at different stages of manufacture, in the deterioration of sugar juices and of finished sugar.

It will be the purpose of the following pages to justify the claim that micro-organisms are dangerous agencies in sugar manufacture and to support this by an analysis of the published information on the subject. To facilitate this analysis a brief description will be given of the main processes of the manufacture of cane- and beet-sugar.

In cane-sugar manufacture the raw material, after removal of leaves and roots, is placed on specially designed crushers and is passed through these to squeezing rollers arranged in sets of three. In passing through the squeezers the crushed cane is exposed to a pressure of 450 to 600 tons per square inch and is thereby reduced to a pulp resembling saw-dust, while the juice contained in the cane flows off and is collected in vats, where stones and sand can be separated by settling.

This raw juice contains debris of the cane and other impurities, which necessitate its being passed through sieves before it is subjected to the next process of 'tempering', a process during which it is mixed with lime and heated to boiling-point, usually after a prior treatment with sulphur dioxide. After tempering the juice is allowed to settle for the separation of the impurities coagulated during boiling. The sediment is drawn off as a mud from the bottom of the settling-vat, while the clear juice is removed from the top and stored until mixed with the filtered residual juice recovered in a filter-press from the sediment. The clarified juice is evaporated under suitable conditions, and when it is sufficiently concentrated, left to crystallize.

In beet-sugar manufacture the chief processes are similar in principle. The beet, usually stored in large quantities, are conveyed by a stream of water and by elevators to washing-tanks in which they are freed from adhering stones and soil. After washing they are lifted to a higher floor of the building, weighed, and then passed on to the slicing-machines which cut them into narrow strips already referred to as cossettes. The cossettes are filled into vats known as diffusers. Of these there are usually 10–14 in one set, or battery. From the bottom of these vats hot water, or preferably hot juice of a previous batch is run in so as to heat the cossettes sufficiently to kill the beet-cells and thus facilitate extraction of the juice. It is important that the liquid used for extraction should not be heated higher than 75° C. to 80° C., since higher temperatures tend to render the cossettes soft and pulpy. In such case they sink into a solid mass through which the extraction water cannot penetrate. The extract flowing from the first diffuser enters the second of the battery after having been first heated to between 75° C. and 80° C., and thence passes on to the third and so on, warmed up each time prior to entering a fresh diffuser. In this way the temperature of the juice is maintained between 75° C. and 80° C. during the greater part of the extraction. Since the filling of the first diffuser takes no more than 10 minutes, only a comparatively short period occurs during which microbiological development could normally be possible during diffusion. On leaving the diffusion battery the juice is sent to vats in which it is 'defecated', i. e. mixed with an appropriate quantity of lime to increase its pH value from between approximately 4·8 and 5·2, to between 7·2 and 8·5. This change in reaction, coupled with boiling, clarifies the juice, which after filtering and treatment with carbon dioxide, followed by additional filtering, is evaporated sufficiently for the crystallization of the saccharose contained in the thick juice or massecuite to take place.

The approximate number of micro-organisms found in the crude cane juice and crude diffusion juice of sugar-beet has been ascertained on various occasions with more or less accuracy. From 25 samples of raw cane juice Owen[7] found an average total of 280,000 cells per cubic centimetre, comprising yeasts, moulds, and bacteria. Kopeloff and Kopeloff[8] record 2,618 fungus spores and over 710,000 bacteria per cubic centimetre of cane juice, the figures ranging from no fungi and 123,000 bacteria to 7,700 fungi and 1·5 million bacteria.

While Owen paid particular attention to some of the bacteria found, which he states comprised *Bac. vulgatus*, *Bac. mesentericus* and other aerobic soil bacilli, Kopeloff and Kopeloff analysed the fungi in considerable detail. Those most frequently met with by them were *Aspergillus Sydowi*, Bainier, and *Aspergillus flavus*, while *Aspergillus niger*, *Aspergillus repens*, *Penicillium divaricatum*, a *Citromyces*, a *Cladosporium*, a *Syncephalastrum*, and a *Trichoderma* also occurred on several occasions.

The microflora of cossettes and of fresh sugar-beet diffusion juice has been enumerated by Schöne,[4] who counted 860 and 4,200 bacteria respectively per gramme of cossettes supplied by two different factories, and 1,481,000 as an average count per c.cm. of raw diffusion juice supplied by four different factories. The bulk of this microflora consisted of bacteria, including, as already mentioned, *Streptococcus* (*Leuconostoc*) *mesenteroides*, two other mucus producing *Streptococci*, several *Micrococci*, five types of short *paratyphosum*-like rods,

Bac. mesentericus, Bac. subtilis, Bact. prodigiosum and *Bact. fluorescens liquefaciens.* Of fungi Schöne refers only to two *Monilia*-resembling species, a *Torula* and a true *Saccharomyces.* Laxa,[9] who had studied the microflora of diffusion juices prior to Schöne, had also found it to be numerous and varied, but gave no details of the numbers found.

There is a very striking difference between Schöne's figures for cossette infection and for diffusion juice infection, a difference which undoubtedly indicates contamination of the juice with impure water used for the extraction of the cossettes, since the time required for the filling of the diffusers and for the extraction of the cossettes would be far too short for an increase in numbers by growth such as that observed.

In the case of the sugar-cane juices examined by Kopeloff and Kopeloff, no water was used for extraction, and the whole of the microflora found must either have been indigenous to the cane and the soil introduced with the cane, or must have had an opportunity to develop prior to the analysis of the juice, during the time when the cane passed through the mill, unless it can reasonably be assumed that the machinary used for the pressing of the cane contained infections sufficiently extensive to contaminate the raw juice to the extent shown. There is not sufficient experimental evidence for the occasional very large infection observed by Kopeloff and Kopeloff to be definitely ascribed to one or more of the causes mentioned. On the other hand there are certain observations which indicate that in ordinary practice all of the three factors mentioned, the cane itself, the machinery, and the time factor, are contributory causes to the increase in the juice infection.

It has already been mentioned that Wolzogen Kühr[1] had found that the bulk of the sugar-cane samples examined by him possessed an indigenous microflora. As regards the machinery, Orth[10] came to the conclusion that under favourable conditions the deterioration, i. e. the hydrolysis of the saccharose in the juice through microbiological action, was very slight during the transit of the juice from the mills to the heaters, in which the temperature of the juice is increased beyond that at which micro-organisms can develop. However, where extreme cleanliness is not maintained, accumulation of particles of crushed cane and other dirt occurs in corners and gutters of the mills and indirectly gives rise to inversion of saccharose. It has been observed by McCleery[11] that the infection is more marked in a juice pressed towards the end of the week than in one prepared immediately after the cleaning of the machinery. In such cases the mill itself, and particularly such types of mill as facilitate the accumulation of dirt, must be partly responsible for the increase in the microflora of the juice.

In trying to ascertain the connexion between time and increase in the microflora it must not be overlooked that, normally, the interval elapsing between the removal of a sample of juice from the aseptic surroundings of the cane cells and its arrival in the heaters, where microbiological activity would become arrested, is too short to allow of appreciable growth, at least when the micro-organisms present consist only of the comparatively few epiphytic organisms and of the types introduced with soil. Orth[10] found that crusher juice, that is, juice which has exuded from the cane during its preliminary crushing prior to milling, deteriorated little when kept for five hours, indicating but a very slight microbiological activity.

In the juice emanating from the last mill of a 'train', however, Orth detected a rapid hydrolysis of the saccharose of the juice, a hydrolysis which could be readily measured after 30 minutes standing of the juice at room temperature. Similarly, Sprankling[12] records a case in which a crude cane juice standing for six hours lost 14·3 per cent. of its saccharose, that is, 0·04 per cent. a minute, and in the case of sugar-beet juice, Neide[13] recorded a considerable loss of sugar during the one and three-quarter hours required by the juice to pass through a diffusion battery. In such cases of apparently heavily infected juices time has become an important factor, and a slight delay in the delivery of the juice to the heaters may occasion considerable damage.

The time factor is of particular importance in cases where samples of juice—either cane juice or sugar-beet diffusion juice—have to be kept for chemical analysis. The methods adopted for the prevention of deterioration in such cases will be referred to later.

The question of the relative importance of the micro-organisms found in cane and beet juices, though touched upon by various writers, has never received the same degree of attention as the subject of the respective importance of bacteria and fungi for the deterioration of stored crude and refined sugar.

It has already been mentioned that, in raw juices, bacteria have been found to be far more numerous than fungi, indicating that the former are more important than the latter. In accepting this conclusion, however, it should not be over-looked that cases may occur where certain fungi predominate in the juice. Laxa,[14] for instance, refers to a juice in which yeast predominated, and it is highly probable that similar conditions prevail when cane-sugar juices are allowed to undergo spontaneous fermentation as in the West Indies, where this juice is used for the manufacture of vinegar (Sprankling[12]).

Another case where a fungus, *Oidium terricula*, prevailed is referred to by de Haan.[15] This organism, however, did not hydrolyse saccharose, but produced acids from the reducing sugars present.

Of the various bacteria constituting the microflora of raw juices, those capable of producing mucus are particularly important.

When discussing mucus fermentations in Chapter XV it was mentioned that the first of the bacteria known to syn-thesize dextran had been isolated from a sugar solution taken from a beet-sugar factory. Most writers emphasize the fre-quent occurrence of *Streptococcus* (*Leuconostoc*) *mesenteroides* and other mucus-producing types in sugar juices. Boekhout[16] and Velich[17] suggest that these bacteria enter the raw juice with soil in which, according to Stoklasa and Vitek,[18] they have their natural habitat. This is probably correct. With the soil, these organisms are deposited in gutters and settling tanks, places where they find favourable conditions for growth and from which they are difficult to remove, not only because of the adhesive properties of their mucus, but also owing to the protection which the mucus offers them against penetration of heat and antiseptics.

Though the juice contained in gutters and settling-tanks favours the growth of mucus-producing bacteria, it does not necessarily follow that the actual mucus formation is encouraged. It was pointed out in Chapter XV that an alkaline reaction is favourable, if not actually essential, for the synthesis of dextran and levan, the carbohydrates composing the mucus. The reaction both of raw cane and of beet juice, however, is on the acid side of the neutral point, and mucus may not always be found, therefore, when the juice is infected by these bacteria. In such cases *Streptococcus* (*Leuconostoc*) *mesenteroides* is present as an ordinary *Streptococcus* (Schöne[4]), but still capable of exercising its two most important harmful functions, the hydrolysis of the saccharose of the juice and the conversion of part of the resultant reducing sugars into acids, principally lactic acid.

The same is true of the various other mucus-producing bacteria, with the exception that lactic acid may be replaced by other fermentation products, notably by a mixture of acetic and formic acids. It is a mistake therefore to assume, as did Knauer,[19] that the addition of acids to a juice prevents the development of *Streptococcus mesenteroides*. All that can be claimed for this treatment is that it inhibits the synthesizing functions of the organism.

Where an accumulation of mucus-producing bacteria is extensive, their influence on the juice is very marked indeed, and the mere passing of the juice over a heavily infected surface, a mill gutter or a press cloth for instance, may suffice to invert appreciable quantities of saccharose. Hutchinson and Ramayyar[3] compare such conditions to those existing on the filter beds of a sewage purification plant.

The impression has prevailed in many quarters that the occurrence in raw sugar juices of lactic acid bacteria was entirely independent of and unconnected with the presence of mucus-forming bacteria. This is not correct. The two phenomena are very closely connected, inasmuch as a considerable number of mucus producers and certainly the most dreaded type *Streptococcus mesenteroides* form lactic acid as their chief fermentation product. In the early days of the study of mucus formation by bacteria, Béchamp[20] analysed the fermentation products of a type other than *Streptococcus mesenteroides*, and found them to comprise lactic acid and a small percentage of acetic acid. The frequently observed formation of mannitol in cultures of mucus-producing bacteria is a further proof that these organisms, or at least those of them that produce mannitol and lactic acid, are nothing but lactic acid bacteria in disguise—not only *Streptococci*, but non-spore-forming rods such as *Bact. pediculatum* Koch, and Hosaeus,[21] *Bact. viscosum sacchari*, Kramer,[22] or *Bact. gelatinosum betae*, Glaser.[23]

The mucus producers which do not form lactic acid have in practically every case been found to be spore-forming rods, described in the first instance as definite species such as *Clostridium gelatinosum*, Laxa,[14] and *Bac. levaniformans*, Greig-Smith and Steel,[24] but subsequently (Schöne[4]; Owen[7]) revealed as members of the group of aerobic bacilli related to or identical with *Bac. mesentericus, Bac. liodermos*, &c. These types, therefore, are related to the bacilli responsible for the production of ropiness in bread, discussed in Chapter XX.

In normal raw juices the detection of spore-forming mucus-producing bacteria and of spore-forming rods as a whole is rendered difficult by the large number of non-spore-forming bacteria present. Few details are available at present on the properties of the latter types. It has already been mentioned that they comprise rods resembling or identical with *Bact. herbicola a aureum*. They include also *paratyphosum*-like rods which were found by Schöne to produce ethyl alcohol, carbon dioxide and certain non-specified acids. Since saccharose is hydrolysed by them they must participate in the deterioration of sugar juices when present in considerable numbers.

In addition various species of *Micrococcus* have occasionally been reported present, but there is no information to show that they affect saccharose. *Bact. xylinum*, an acetic acid-producing rod, has been found by Browne[25] in cane-sugar juice. It may be the organism which is responsible for the spontaneous conversion of fermented cane-sugar juice into vinegar to which Sprankling[12] refers. Browne found that this acetic acid bacterium was capable of producing a substance resembling cellulose—obviously by synthesis of saccharose, since, according to Hoyer,[26] *Bact. xylinum* is capable of hydrolysing saccharose. To what extent it is normally active in sugar juices has not been revealed.

In discussing the bacterial flora of crude sugar juices it must be mentioned that various earlier investigations assumed the presence of butyric acid bacilli. Dehérain[27] endeavoured to substantiate this assumption experimentally by mixing sugar-beet diffusion juice with soil and allowing it to ferment in the presence of an excess of calcium carbonate. As was to be expected, he found that butyric acid was actually formed and hydrogen evolved. Nevertheless it is remarkable that, as pointed out by Schöne, no case is known in which butyric acid has actually been isolated from fermented raw juice. The participation of this group of micro-organisms in the deterioration of raw juices is not likely therefore to be considerable. This is not surprising, seeing that in passing through the mills or diffusers to the heaters the juice is not exposed to the anaerobic conditions essential for the development of butyric acid bacteria.

The explosive gases, presumably hydrogen, which, in the early days of the diffusion process, occasionally collected at the top of the diffusers and gave rise to serious explosions, must have been produced by other agencies than butyric acid bacteria. That they resulted from an action of acetic and other organic acids on the iron walls of diffusers was suggested by Chevron.[28] This is not a satisfactory explanation, however, and was only proposed because of the difficulty of reconciling their production in the diffuser at high temperatures with microbiological activity. However, if it can be assumed that, at the time of the occurrence of these explosions,* high temperatures—between 70° C. and 80° C.—were not reached in the diffusers, then it becomes probable that the production of the explosive gases was in whole or in part due to the activity of the *paratyphosum*-like bacteria of the epiphytic cossette microflora.

Attempts have been made by some writers to ascertain the extent of damage, as expressed in loss of saccharose, which can be attributed to the microflora of the raw sugar juices under normal working conditions. For this purpose McCleery[11] determined the increase in acidity of a juice from the time of pressing until delivery to the heaters, assuming the increase observed to be proportional to the saccharose destroyed.

It is clear that a method such as this cannot give more than an approximate conception of what actually takes place, since it is based on the assumption that all saccharose hydrolysing organisms found in the juice produce the same organic acids, at the same time and to the same extent.

A glance at the account given in the preceding pages of the microflora met with will show that the types active in the juices are too varied to admit of this possibility.

Efforts to estimate the extent of the deterioration by polarization of the juices must lead to equally unsatisfactory conclusions, or must at least involve highly complicated analyses, since the figures obtained must be influenced not only by the extent to which one or other of the liberated monoses is consumed by the microflora, but also by the degree to which they are utilized for the synthesis of dextran or levan.

More recently Paine and Balch[29] have advocated the use of inverting enzymes for the exact determination of saccharose

* In the early days of the working of the diffusion process the temperatures utilized for the extraction of cossettes often did not exceed 60° C., and probably failed to rise beyond 40° C. in some of the beet slices.

and raffinose in juices, a method which, when used for the estimation of saccharose after boiling of the test samples, should offer reasonable prospects of reliable results. Until such analyses have been carried out, the question, which has been raised on various occasions, for instance by Mügge[30] and by Neide[13], whether microbiological activity in raw sugar juices can be responsible for the so-called 'undetermined losses' of saccharose during manufacture, must remain unanswered. These losses have been placed as low as 0·1 per cent. of the saccharose present in the juice and as high as 1·5 per cent. Gredinger[31] in 1925 recorded from 0·38 to 0·5 per cent. for beet-sugar juices, a figure which may well be taken as a conservative average.

Whether large or small, it is obviously desirable to avoid losses in sugar juices which may be due to microbiological activity. The evolution of the methods devised for this purpose are not without interest and throw some light on a procedure which is still commonly adhered to in sugar manufacturing practice, that of maintaining an alkaline reaction throughout the various manufacturing processes as well as in the finished sugar. There is no doubt that up to 1877, when Gayon[32] published his observations on the phenomenon, the general conception of the cause of deterioration of crude sugar on storage was, that the acids present gave rise to an hydrolysis of the saccharose with liberation of reducing sugars. It was important, therefore, to neutralize these acids and to render the sugar slightly alkaline. But since the acids of the finished sugar had been derived, at least in part, from the acidic compounds responsible for the acidity of the respective raw juices, a protection of the juices against inversion would likewise have to be secured through neutralization. This was done as early as possible in manufacture by the addition of sufficient limestone or slaked lime, not only to neutralize the juices, but also to render them slightly alkaline.

In spite of the evidence collected by Gayon and subsequent workers that the deterioration of stored sugar is due to the activity of micro-organisms, the custom of maintaining a

T

slight alkalinity in the finished sugar by the addition of lime to the raw juices has remained an important stage in manufacture, no longer for the purpose of preventing deterioration, but to facilitate the precipitation of many colloidal impurities present (Bomonti[33]). The stage of lime addition, as already mentioned, is technically known as 'tempering'. It is carried out as soon as the raw juice has been pressed and freed from major impurities, such as stones, sand, pieces of cossettes and sugar-cane. In tempering, the pH value of the fresh crude juice is raised from between 4·8 (Schmidt[34]) and 5·8 (Rao and Ayyar[35]) to 8·0 (Walton, McCalip and Hornberger[36]), or even 8·5 (Williams and Gebelin[37]), though one as low as 7·2 may be sufficient in some cases (Gebelin[38]). Boiling of the juices at these reactions has been found to have a much greater destructive action on the micro-organisms present than boiling at the original reaction of the juice, so much so in fact that, as will be shown in Chapter XXII, the tempered juices may, in many cases, be found sterile after boiling. It is important, therefore, that the tempering should be carried out with the least possible delay.

With the practical elimination of micro-organisms from the juice during tempering, efforts in the direction of preventing microbiological deterioration can be concentrated on the period prior to tempering.

Here addition of antiseptics and increased cleanliness are the only possible means of counteracting the hydrolytic action of the normal microflora. Both methods have been advocated and adopted, the former perhaps more frequently than the latter.

For factory purposes the use of hydrofluoric acid and aluminium fluoride was recommended by Herzfeld and Paetow,[39] who found them suitable in arresting slight infections, but incapable of preventing inversion of saccharose in heavily infected juices, presumably owing to their failing to destroy invertase which had accumulated in such cases.

Ammonium fluoride, which Heerma van Voss[40] recommended, was considerably more efficient than the above substances. Applied to the juice in the proportion of 10 to 15 grammes per hectolitre, ammonium fluoride completely arrested the growth of micro-organisms and prevented inversion of the saccharose. In general practice, however, this antiseptic is too expensive and is inferior therefore to formaldehyde, recommended by a number of workers, Schott,[41] Friedrich,[42] Owen,[43] and Orth.[10] More recently, a proprietary article, a calcium hypochlorite, has been found as effective as formaldehyde by Haldane[44] and markedly cheaper. Haldane recommends its periodical addition to mill beds and gutters, while the crushing of cane is being carried out, using a sufficiently strong concentration to ensure the presence of 2 per cent. chlorine. Further, he advises that a continuous trickle of a solution of the antiseptic of 1 in 500 should be allowed to flow into all juice gutters where dirt and mucus-producing bacteria may accumulate.

Within the last few years Jonáš[45] has drawn attention to the valuable antiseptic properties of sulphur dioxide as used in the cane-sugar mill for the treatment of the raw juice immediately before tempering. Jonáš finds that, in concentrations of from 0·05 to 0·01 per cent., it destroys *Streptococcus mesenteroides* instantaneously, while the spores of mucus-producing soil bacilli are killed by a 0·5 per cent. solution.

Of interest are the efforts which have been made to prevent microbiological activity in sugar juices which have to be kept for the purpose of chemical analysis. A variety of antiseptics, including those already referred to as well as lead acetate (Scheibler[46]), have been recommended for the purpose. Most of them, however, suffer from the disadvantage that in one way or another they affect properties of the juice which it is important or essential to preserve. One of the very few which do not do this is the essential oil of cinnamon recommended by Courtonne[47] for this purpose, and which was stated by him to prevent microbiological deterioration when added in proportions ensuring a concentration of one in a thousand. Even half of this concentration has been found sufficient by the writers in some cases. The methods of securing protection by increased cleanliness are too obvious to need any emphasis. They should result in ensuring the use of healthy cane and beet, free from adhering soil and washed in water containing a minimum of micro-organisms. More frequent cleaning and sterilization of the plant, either by antiseptics or by steam, is a further means by which accumulation of harmful micro-organisms could be prevented in the actual machinery and the various tanks required for the extraction of the juice.

LITERATURE

1. C. A. H. v. Wolzogen Kühr, *Arch. Suikerind.*, 31, *Meddel.* Proefstat. Java Suikerind, No. 9, p. 321, 1923.

2. H. C. Prinsen Geerligs, *Cane sugar and its Manufacture*, 2nd edition. Normal Roger, London, 1924.

3. C. M. Hutchinson and C. S. Ramayyar, *Agric. Res. Inst. Pusa*, Bull. No. 163, 1925.

4. A. Schöne, *Zeitsch. des Vereins d. D. Zuckerind. Tech. Teil*, vol. 51, p. 453, 1901.

5. A. Herzfeld, *Zeitsch. des Vereins d. D. Zuckerind. Tech. Teil*, vol. 41, p. 44, 1891.

6. A. Schöne, *Zeitsch. des Vereins d. D. Zuckerind. Tech. Teil*, vol. 56, p. 737, 1906.

7. W. L. Owen, *J. Ind. Eng. Chem.*, vol. 3, p. 481, 1911.

8. N. Kopeloff and L. Kopeloff, *Louisiana Bull.*, No. 166, 1919.

9. O. Laxa, *Zeitsch. f. Zuckerind. in Böhmen*, vol. 24, p. 423, 1899–1900.

10. W. K. Orth, *Intern. Sugar J.*, vol. 25, p. 474, 1923.

11. W. L. McCleery, *Intern. Sugar J.*, vol. 27, p. 543, 1925.

12. C. H. G. Sprankling, *J. Soc. Chem. Ind.*, vol. 22, p. 78, 1903.

13. E. Neide, *Zeitsch. des Vereins d. D. Zuckerind. Tech. Teil*, vol. 56, p. 726, 1906.

14. O. Laxa, *Zeitsch. f. Zuckerind. in Böhmen*, vol. 26, p. 122, 1901–2.

15. J. S. de Haan, *Arch. v. d. Suikerind. in Ned. Ind.*, vol. 22, p. 1352, 1914.

16. F. W. J. Boekhout, *Zentrbl. f. Bakt.*, Abt. II, vol. 6, p. 161, 1900.

17. A. Velich, *Zeitschr. f. Zuckerind. in Böhmen*, vol. 27, p. 475, 1903.

18. J. Stoklasa and E. Vitek, *Zentrbl. f. Bakt.*, Abt. II, vol. 14, p. 102, 1904.

19. —. Knauer, *Zeitsch. des Vereins d. D. Zuckerind. Tech. Teil*, vol. 38, p. 240, 1901.

20. A. Béchamp, *Comptes rend.*, vol. 93, p. 78, 1881.

21. A. Koch and H. Hosaeus, *Zentrbl. f. Bakt.*, vol. 16, p. 225, 1894.

22. E. Kramer, *Monatsch. f. Chem.*, vol. 10, p. 467, 1889.

23. F. Glaser, *Zentrbl. f. Bakt.*, Abt. II, vol. 1, p. 879, 1895.

24. R. Greig-Smith and T. Steel, *J. Soc. Chem. Ind.*, vol. 21, p. 1381, 1902.

25. C. A. Browne, *J. Amer. Chem. Soc.*, vol. 28, p. 473, 1906.

26. D. P. Hoyer, *Die Deutsche Essigindustrie*, vol. 3, p. 1, 1899.

27. P. P. Dehérain, *Zeitsch. des Vereins d. D. Zuckerind. Tech. Teil*, vol. 34, p. 269, 1884.

28. L. Chevron, *Jour. des Fabric. de Sucre*, vol. 24, p. 320, 1883.

29. H. S. Paine and R. T. Balch, *J. Ind. Eng. Chem.*, vol. 17, p. 240, 1925.

30. —. Mügge, *Zeitsch. des Vereins d. D. Zuckerind. Tech. Teil*, vol. 54, p. 888, 1904.

31. W. Gredinger, *Zeitsch. des Vereins d. D. Zuckerind. Tech. Teil*, vol. 50, p. 1597, 1925.

32. U. Gayon, *Comptes rend.*, vol. 84, p. 606, 1877.

33. H. F. Bomonti, *Chem. Absts.*, vol. 21, p. 665, 1927.

34. E. Schmidt, *Zeitsch. des Vereins d. D. Zuckerind. Tech. Teil*, vol. 51, pp. 628 and 665, 1926.

35. T. L. Rao and G. G. Ayyar, *Madras Agric. Dept. Year-book* (1925), p. 73, 1927.

36. C. F. Walton, M. A. McCalip and W. F. Hornberger, *J. Ind. Eng. Chem.*, vol. 17, p. 51, 1925.

37. W. J. Williams and J. A. Gebelin, *Facts about Sugar*, vol. 17, p. 202, 1923.

38. J. A. Gebelin, *Louisiana Planter*, vol. 71, p. 172, 1923.

39. A. Herzfeld and U. Paetow, *Zeitsch. des Vereins d. D. Zuckerind. Tech. Teil*, vol. 41, p. 678, 1891.

40. A. J. Heerma van Voss, *Zeitsch. des Vereins d. D. Zuckerind. Tech. Teil*, vol. 50, p. 438, 1900.

41. A. Schott, *Zeitsch. des Vereins d. D. Zuckerind. Tech. Teil*, vol. 50, p. 434, 1900.

42. O. Freidrich, *G. Pat.*, No. 146871, 1902.

43. W. L. Owen, *Louisiana Bull.*, No. 153, 1915.

44. J. H. Haldane, *Intern. Sugar J.*, vol. 29, p. 367, 1927.

45. W. Jonáš, *Z. f. d. Zuckerind. d. Cechoslov. Republ.*, vol. 51, p. 161, 1927.

46. C. Scheibler, *Scheibler's Neue Zeitsch. f. Rübenzuckerind.*, vol. 18, p. 255, 1887.

47. H. Courtonne, *Chem. Absts.*, vol. 17, p. 3427, 1923.

CHAPTER XXII

THE MICROBIOLOGY OF CANE JUICE AND BEET JUICE IN MANUFACTURE

WITH the tempering of the raw juice far-reaching changes occur in the microflora present. Attempts have been made from time to time to follow these changes experimentally both in the case of raw cane-sugar and in sugar-beet diffusion juices. Most detailed in this respect are the observations supplied by Owen,[1] who studied the microflora of cane juices in the course of conversion into sugar.

Owen gives the following figures as the average for the microflora of nine different sets of samples taken during the various stages of manufacture.

TABLE X

Type of raw material.	Number of micro-organisms per gramme.	Type of micro-organisms.
Raw juice	280,000	Yeast and other fungi; bacteria
Sulphited juice	35,000	Yeast and other fungi; bacteria
Limed juice	37,500	Bacteria predominating
Defecated juice (limed juice after boiling)	750	Spore-forming bacilli
Syrup (evaporated juice)	400	
Massecuites	450	Spore-forming bacilli
Sugar	600	
Molasses	35,000	A mixed microflora

The data supplied by Kopeloff and Kopeloff[2] are much less detailed, but confirm the impression that a striking reduction of the original microflora takes place during the stages through which the raw juice passes before being set aside for the crystallization of the sugar contained in it, a reduction which particularly affects the non-spore-forming bacteria and the various fungi. This conclusion was arrived at also by Schöne,[3] who studied the microflora of sugar-beet diffusion juices. After liming and saturation with carbon dioxide, the juice was practically sterile in Schöne's experiments.

It is clear, therefore, that the infection which is noticeable in all molasses must have been introduced subsequent to defecation, the process in which the colloidal impurities of the juice are precipitated by boiling in the presence of an excess of calcium hydroxide.

The stage at which this infection occurs is to some extent revealed in Owen's experiments. During evaporation prior to crystallization the microflora of the juice and of the finished massecuites remains practically stationary (see Table X), in spite of the diminution in volume of the various liquors, showing that neither reinfection nor development of micro-organisms occur at these stages.

On the crystals formed in the massecuites the number of micro-organisms increased slightly, but was represented only by spore-forming rods of the types found in the masse-cuites. A reinfection, therefore, is not traceable up to this point. And yet the molasses, the remaining mother liquors after separation from the crystallizable sugar, has a large and varied microflora. This can only be interpreted as indicating that a reinfection has taken place during or after the separa-tion of the molasses. In order to appreciate how this is possible it is necessary to recall that the separation of the crystallized sugar from its mother liquor is carried out in centrifuges in which a rapidly flowing current of air, infected with various micro-organisms, comes into intimate contact with the crystals and the mother liquor during the rotation of the centrifuge at high speeds, and that after centrifuging, the crystals are washed with a small amount of water to improve their colour. As shown by Owen this wash water is not always very clean. In the case examined by him it con-tained no less than 25,000 micro-organisms per cubic centi-metre. It is clear therefore that, apart from other sources, the centrifuge offers possibilities for the introduction of fresh infections into the process of sugar manufacture which are by no means trivial. This aspect will be dealt with in greater detail below.

It is not to be assumed, however, that conditions are invariably as clearly defined as those recorded in Owen's experiments. Even assuming that at no stage of manufacture subsequent to tempering does the temperature fall sufficiently low to allow of microbiological development, there must be occasions when a contamination of the juice can take place. This, however, has been contested in the past, for instance by Schöne,[3] who investigated the occurrence of thermophilic bacteria in sugar-beet juices. One of the likely occasions for contamination is when the juice passes the filter-press, in which the precipitate formed during tempering is removed. It will be recalled from the account given in Chapter XXI that after the settling in an appropriate tank part of the tempered juice is run off direct, while the sediment is treated in a filter-press to remove the adhering juice, the two portions of juice being subsequently mixed.

Where the filter-press and the filter-cloths are not kept scrupulously clean there is an obvious danger of the juice becoming contaminated, a possibility which is far from problematic, seeing that the microflora of the resultant press-cake may be very numerous. Owen quotes 1·5 million micro-organisms per gramme of this cake in a case examined by him.

It is on the filter-press also, and to some extent on the filters used for the clarification of the juice after its saturation with carbon dioxide and its evaporation to a syrup, that a development of *Streptococcus mesenteroides* and of other mucus-producing organisms frequently occurs. It is from these places that they are reintroduced into the now neutral or slightly alkaline juice.

Such development occurs particularly where the filtration proceeds slowly and the temperature of the juice falls below 60° C. Several writers, among them Laxa[4] and Gonnermann,[5] have drawn attention to this danger. Where filtration to ensure brilliancy is carried out through filters made of kieselguhr or of vegetable carbon a reduction of the number of micro-organisms may take place. Owen[6] observed that raw juices filtered in this way lost 99 per cent. of their microflora. Though not strictly relevant to the subject under discussion, it may be added here that when using cotton wool instead of carbon or kieselguhr, Owen found that 75 per cent. of the microflora was removed from raw juice, obviously through removal of sediment such as bagasse and other plant debris on which the micro-organisms were deposited. This experiment demonstrates very forcibly to what considerable extent the microflora of raw cane juice is influenced by the epiphytic microflora of the cane itself.

Observations, prior to those of Owen, on the reduction of the microflora of a juice through filtering, were made by Schöne.[3] In the case of the filtration of an evaporated beet-sugar juice through wood shavings Schöne found a reduction in the microflora of about 99 per cent.

Nevertheless, the juice leaving the press contains a considerable number of organisms even under normal working conditions. Church[7] records the examination of one filtered juice which showed 140 bacteria and 3,600 fungus spores per cubic centimetre.

During the actual evaporation of the filtered juice no microbiological development occurs, the temperature prevailing being sufficiently high to prevent it. This is clearly indicated by Owen's figures quoted in Table X and is supported by Schöne's observations on beet-sugar juices.

On the other hand a marked sterilizing effect, beyond a possible destruction of fungus spores, is not achieved during evaporation, no doubt owing to the limitation of the microflora at this stage to spore-producing bacteria possessing great heat resistance in their resting stage. All workers who have studied the types of aerobic soil bacilli present in boiling and boiled juice have specifically referred to the resistance of these types to high temperatures.

The microflora of the evaporated juice represents a potential danger to the preservation of the finished sugar since there is normally no step, from the stage of evaporation of the juice onwards, at which it can be eliminated. On the contrary, it is normally joined by additional types, once the massecuites have been run into the centrifuge for purposes of separating the mother liquid from the sugar crystals.

The question of the infection of the raw sugar and its molasses during centrifuging was referred to above. It was mentioned that the types composing the flora present are introduced with the flow of infected air passing through the centrifuge during its revolution at high speeds and by the water used for washing of the sugar crystals subsequent to centrifuging. It was with a view to preventing this infection of the sugar that Shorey[8] recommended the use of high pressure steam instead of water for the washing of the centrifuged crystals. His suggestion was taken up by Kopeloff, Welcome and Kopeloff,[9] who elaborated a method for the application of superheated steam to the washing of sugar crystals in the centrifuge. In their experiments, carried out on a laboratory scale, they succeeded in reducing the bacterial content of the sugar by 93 to 99·5 per cent., while the fungus spore content was reduced by 92 to 98 per cent. The flora of the mother liquor (syrup and molasses) was reduced by 50 to 80 per cent. In this process the superheated steam was allowed to pass into the centrifuge, and through the deposited sugar crystals while the centrifuge was rotating at a high speed, preferably, it need hardly be added, towards the end of the process. A very short exposure to the action of the steam, for no more than 3 minutes, caused a reduction of the microflora to the extent shown above.

After separation from the crystals the mother liquor is again evaporated to ensure a second crop of sugar crystals, and, after separation, the remaining liquor, now known as molasses, may be given one or two further evaporations for the recovery of additional crops of sugar crystals.

As the various batches of raw sugar are removed from the syrup and molasses the content of salts in solution materially increases, and it has been frequently observed that these liquors show a tendency to foam on subsequent evaporation.

This foaming, technically known as 'froth fermentation', occurs, according to Geerligs,[10] in low grade massecuites during cooling. The surface of these syrups may become convex owing to the uneven raising of the crust by gas produced in the syrup. Eventually the crust may burst under the pressure of this gas and a brown froth ooze out of the crevices formed. This froth soon covers the whole of the surface, and continuing to rise, finally flows over the top of the tank. Gases containing carbon dioxide and nitrous oxide escape from the froth and emit an unpleasant odour. The reaction of such massecuites is usually markedly acid.

It was at one time suspected that the froth fermentation was due to microbiological activity, observations by French writers, Dubrunfaut,[11] Durin[12] and others on the evolution of nitrous oxide in the fermentation of molasses in the distillery having guided attention in this direction. Subsequently Laxa[4] went so far as to associate a certain bacterium which he found capable of living in saccharose solutions of concentrations up to 40 per cent. and at temperatures of 55° C. with this type of fermentation. Lafar,[14] in his account of this aspect of the microbiology of sugar manufacture, while admitting that convincing evidence in favour of a microbiological origin of the foam fermentation is lacking, is, nevertheless, inclined to favour this explanation, at least as regards those types of foam fermentation in which, according to Durin,[12] the evolution of gas is comparatively slight, where no caramelization of the sugar is caused, and where volatile acids, probably including butyric acid, are formed. The years which have passed since Lafar's exposition of the foam fermentation have not supplied additional evidence of its microbiological origin. The present tendency undoubtedly inclines towards a chemical explanation of the phenomenon of foam fermentation.

Quite a different matter is the occurrence of a scum on the surface of molasses standing at ordinary room temperatures.

This is due to the development of fungi, and is very frequently observed. Kopeloff, Welcome and Kopeloff[9] recommended covering stored molasses with a layer of oil to prevent deterioration. It might be desirable to ascertain experimentally how far this treatment will suffice to protect molasses. That it should be capable of preventing the formation of growth of micro-organisms on the surface is likely. It is by no means certain, however, that the deeper layers could be protected in this way, seeing that both Grove[15] and Hirst[16] have observed development of micro-organisms in saccharose solutions of more than 65 per cent. concentration, that is, in concentrations considerably higher than those of molasses.

In a discussion on the microbiology of sugar manufacture there are three further subjects which must be briefly referred to, though they do not perhaps fall directly within the framework of the present thesis.

One of these is the disposal of the waste waters of sugar manufacture, another the question of the utilization of the spent plant tissues from which the sugar juice has been extracted—in other words the cossettes and the bagasse, and the third the utilization of the molasses.

The problem of the elimination or purification of the waste waters of the sugar factory is one of considerable magnitude, particularly where beet sugar is being manufactured. Here the consumption of water is of a very high order, comprising per 1,000 tons of beet, according to Owen:[17]

For the flumes and washers .	.	1,612,000 gallons
,, diffusion and wash water	.	349,440 ,,
,, the pulp presses .	. .	107,520 ,,
,, other wash and waste purposes		20,160 ,,

The greatest bulk of waste water, which as shown above comes from the flumes and washers, is fortunately not very difficult to purify. Besides stones, soil, beet rootlets and beet leaves, it contains traces of saccharose and protein in solution. In order to remove stones and soil it is customary in some places to leave the water standing in ponds for some time, a period during which various microbiological changes of the organic compounds in solution and suspension may be initiated. When the water, therefore, freed from stones, soil and larger particles, is allowed to enter a river, various microbiological processes may be in progress which require the presence of oxygen for completion. These processes, however, do not usually attain dangerous dimensions in the water from the flumes and washers, which seldom contains more than 0·05 to 0·1 per cent. of saccharose. Much more difficult is the disposal of the pulp-press water, which may contain as much as 0·5 per cent. of saccharose. Where this waste is allowed to stand for microbiological processes to be initiated, or even where it is discharged direct into a stream, the amount of oxygen required to convert the available carbohydrates into innocuous decomposition products is so large that the river water becomes incapable of supporting fish life owing to the removal of its dissolved oxygen.

The sugar-containing waste water from the presses will also encourage the development of certain fungi, such as species of *Fusarium* and *Mucor*, of sheath-producing bacteria, such as *Sphaerotilus* (Lafar[18]) and algae, notably *Leptomitus lacteus* (Kolkwitz[19]), the growth of any of which may frequently be sufficient to congest the river into which the water is flowing.

To avoid some of these disadvantages the waste waters must be subjected to treatment prior to their discharge into the river. In the case of the water from flumes and washers, this can be done, as already mentioned, by settling in ponds, or, as suggested by Owen, by carrying out a mechanical separation of the suspended solids. For this purpose Owen recommends a rotating cylindrical drum, through which the waste flows prior to filtration through a suitable filter. Owen claims that the resultant waste water may be discharged direct into a river without danger to fish life. In the case of the filter-press waste, the introduction of a fermentation process has been proposed on various occasions—for instance by Möller (see Kraisy[20]). In Möller's process a molasses solution, acidified with the acid of lactic acid bacteria, is added in quantities sufficient to increase the carbohydrate concentration of the waste by 1·5 per cent. The waste is now inoculated with a yeast and is maintained at a temperature of 27° C. to 35° C., while flowing through a set of seven vats at a rate sufficiently slow to ensure the complete conversion of the carbohydrates present into alcohol during the passage of the liquid through the plant. The yeast formed during fermentation is recovered and is claimed to be suitable as cattle food. The alcohol and other fermentation products are not recovered.

Methods of purification similar to those in use at sewage works, including septic tanks, have also been recommended (Grevemeyer[21]), but in spite of the various efforts made a fully satisfactory method has not yet come into general use.

In the cane-sugar mill the consumption of water is very much smaller than in the beet-sugar factory, and the problem of the purification and disposal of the waste water is therefore of comparatively slight importance.

On the subject of the disposal of the crushed cane residue, the bagasse, and of the extracted cossettes, very little need be said, since the problem has little bearing on the subjects under discussion. The bagasse is collected and utilized as a fuel for raising the steam required in the plant. The cossettes are valuable as a cattle food and may be consumed while still wet, after preliminary drying, or after conversion into silage. When dried the cossettes are very hygroscopic owing to their carbohydrate content. On storage, therefore, they often develop fungus growth, and become mildewed. This is avoided where the cossettes are ensilaged, a process of preservation for sugar containing plant tissues which was described in considerable detail by Thaysen and Bunker.[22]

The molasses accumulating in a sugar factory are usually disposed of by microbiological processes, through conversion into ethyl alcohol by fermentation with yeast. On a smaller scale they may be used as a cattle food, mixed with extracted cossettes or with specially prepared wood pulp.

The cattle foods may suffer microbiological changes, leading to excessive heating of the accumulated material, and perhaps even to spontaneous combustion. The microbiological changes giving rise to spontaneous combustion were also reviewed by Thaysen and Bunker.[22]

The use of molasses for the production of ethyl alcohol by fermentation dates back to the early days of the manufacture of sugar and was a well-established industry when Reiset,[23] Schloesing[24] and Dubrunfaut[25] drew attention in 1868 to the abnormal behaviour of the fermentations in cases where large percentages of nitrates were present in the molasses used. In such abnormal molasses the yeast fermentation was found to come to a premature standstill and to be replaced by the formation of lactic acid and the evolution of nitrous oxide. The phenomenon was not exhaustively studied by the writers referred to and has received little attention since. It is not possible to say therefore whether a specific microflora is responsible for the liberation of nitrogenous gases from the available nitrates, or whether this phenomenon is associated with the evolution of lactic acid in the fermenting liquid.

The remedy recommended by Reiset and Schloesing for the prevention of this abnormal fermentation consisted of the addition to the molasses of a heavy inoculant of suitable yeast and of the establishment of an optimum acidity in the molasses prior to inoculation.

LITERATURE

1. W. L. Owen, *J. Ind. Eng. Chem.*, vol. 3, p. 481, 1911.
2. N. Kopeloff and L. Kopeloff, *Louisiana Bull.*, no. 166, 1919.
3. A. Schöne, *Zeitsch. des Vereins d. D. Zuckerind. Tech. Teil*, vol. 51, p. 453, 1901.
4. O. Laxa, *Zeitsch. f. Zuckerind. in Böhmen*, vol. 24, p. 423, 1899–1900.
5. —. Gonnermann, *Zeitsch. des Vereins d. D. Zuckerind. Tech. Teil*, vol. 56, p. 600, 1906.
6. W. L. Owen, *Intern. Sugar Jour.*, vol. 26, pp. 200 and 255, 1924.
7. M. B. Church, *Zentrbl. f. Bakt.*, Abt. II, vol. 58, p. 538, 1923.
8. E. C. Shorey, *J. Soc. Chem. Ind.*, vol. 17, p. 555, 1898.
9. N. Kopeloff, C. J. Welcome and N. Kopeloff, *Louisiana Bull.*, no. 175, 1920.

10. H. C. Prinsen Geerlings, *Cane Sugar and its Manufacture*, 2nd edition. Normal Rodger, London, 1924.
11. P. Dubrunfaut, *Comptes rendus*, vol. 66, p. 275, 1868.
12. E. Durin, *Bull. Assoc. des Chim. Sucr. et Dist.*, vol. 1, p. 134, 1884.
13. O. Laxa, *Zentrbl. f. Bakt.*, Abt. II, vol. 4, p. 362, 1898.
14. F. Lafar, *Handbuch d. Tech. Mykologie*, vol. 2, p. 480. Gustav Fischer, Jena, 1907.
15. O. Grove, *Annual Report Agric. and Hortic. Research Station.* University Bristol, 1918, p. 34.
16. F. Hirst, *Annual Report Agric. and Hortic. Research Station.* University Bristol, 1927, p. 150.
17. B. J. Owen, *Desiccation of sugar beet and the extraction of sugar.* Ministry of Agriculture and Fisheries Publication, H.M. Stationery Office, 1927.
18. F. Lafar, *Handbuch d. tech. Mykologie*, vol. 3, p. 410. Gustav Fischer, Jena, 1906.
19. R. Kolkwitz, *Zeitsch. des Vereins d. D. Zuckerind. Tech. Teil*, vol. 54, p. 955, 1904.
20. A. Kraisy, *Zeitsch. des Vereins d. D. Zuckerind. Tech. Teil*, vol. 70, p. 163, 1920.
21. M. Grevemeyer, *Chem. Absts.*, vol. 19, p. 3033, 1925.
22. A. C. Thaysen and H. J. Bunker, *The microbiology of cellulose, hemicellulose, pectins and gums.* Oxford University Press, 1927.
23. J. Reiset, *Comptes rend.*, vol. 66, p. 177, 1868.
24. Th. Schloesing, *Comptes rend.*, vol. 66, p. 237, 1868.
25. P. Dubrunfaut, *Comptes rend.*, vol. 66, p. 375, 1868.

CHAPTER XXIII

THE MICROBIOLOGICAL DETERIORATION OF SUGAR IN STORAGE

It was pointed out in the previous chapter that an infection of sugar crystals may take place during their separation from the massecuites in the centrifuge and that in consequence the finished raw sugar may contain a considerable microflora.

It will be the object of the present chapter to investigate the nature of this microflora and to establish whether it affects crystallized sugar kept in storage, and if so, to what extent.

Already at the time when the introduction of sugar into Europe was fresh in men's minds it was shown (Ligon[1]) that sugar had to be kept under dry conditions if it was to be preserved. And apparently it was known also that when this was not done the sugar became discoloured, damp, and in extreme cases converted into a syrup.

Towards the middle of the last century occasional observations connected the deterioration of stored sugar with microbiological activity instead of with hydrolytic action caused by acids present in the sugar, as had hitherto been assumed.

In 1829 and 1830, according to Kopeloff and Kopeloff,[2] van Dijk and van Beek reported their observations on a sample of loaf sugar which had become blackened on standing through the action of a fungus to which they referred as *Conferva mucoroides*. Payen[3] reported to the French Academy in 1851 on two cases of sugar deterioration in which the crystals had been pitted and in some cases discoloured pink through the action of a fungus. In 1869 Dubrunfaut[4] drew attention to the presence in raw beet-sugar of 'those lower organisms so accurately described by Pasteur as the living causes of alcoholic and bacterial fermentations'. In 1880 Gayon observed various yeasts and moulds in deteriorated West Indian sugar, while in 1898 Shorey[5] detected the mycelium of what he describes as *Penicillium glaucum* on the crystals of four samples of damaged Hawaiian sugar, and attributed the deterioration to the activity of this fungus.

From that time onwards increasing interest was taken in the study of the action of micro-organisms on stored sugar, and numerous publications appeared which in the great majority of cases recorded it as definitely proved that micro-organisms were responsible for the destruction, and therefore endeavoured to throw light on various problems connected with the deterioration, rather than on accumulating fresh facts in support of the microbiological origin of the phenomenon.

It is a striking fact that but few writers, Amons[6] for instance, and Kopeloff and Kopeloff,[7] have made an effort to ascertain the destructive action of the various micro-organisms isolated by inoculating pure cultures of them on to sterilized sugar crystals. The evidence in favour of a connexion between the deterioration of sugar on storage and microbiological activity is in most cases of an indirect nature and is based partly on the observations of the presence of exceptionally large numbers of micro-organisms and partly on the failure to detect deterioration in samples of sugar stored under conditions which exclude the possibility of microbiological activity.

At first sight it might seem surprising that micro-organisms should be responsible for the deterioration of stored sugar, seeing that such sugar rarely contains more than two per cent. of moisture, an amount which, in the case of most other organic substances, would be far too small to sustain life.

Conditions are exceptional in the case of sugar, however, since the slight percentage of moisture which is found is concentrated on the surface of the crystals in a thin layer of more or less concentrated sugar solution-molasses. The moisture, of course, does not permeate the interior of the crystals, and where present, therefore, it represents a much higher percentage than would be expected. But even so it is surprising that considerable microbiological activity should be possible in the thin film of molasses to which the moisture of the sugar is limited, and which, in any case, must represent a highly concentrated solution of saccharose. High concentrations of saccharose solution have by many been regarded as in the nature of an antiseptic, preventing the growth of micro-organisms at least when exceeding concentrations of 60 to 70 per cent. Grove,[8] Hirst[9] and Meier[10] point out that the growth of most micro-organisms is prevented in such cases. This might imply that the types comprising the flora suspected as the cause of the deterioration would be limited to comparatively few forms. This is not confirmed by the available published data, however.

It is greatly to be regretted that, in their eagerness to prove their assumption, the two camps of writers, one claiming fungi and the other claiming bacteria as the more important sugar destroying types, have neglected to devote attention to a detailed study of the whole of the microflora observed. For that reason it is not possible at present to give a comprehensive review of all the types active in the deterioration of stored sugar. It is safe to assert, however, that they are far more numerous than might have been expected in view of the stringent conditions prevailing in the film of molasses in which they live.

The numbers met with, if considered per gramme of the sugar, are not excessive. They seldom exceed one to two millions, and more often vary between a few hundreds and some hundreds of thousands, numbers which could hardly give rise to marked destruction if it were not for the fact that they are distributed in the thin film of molasses surrounding the crystals, the weight of which, even in the severest cases of deterioration, does not exceed a few per cent. of the total weight of the sugar.

The concentration of micro-organisms present in this film is therefore very much higher than indicated by the figures determined in the ordinary routine estimation of numbers per gramme of material plated out.

Here, as in the raw juice, the number of bacteria greatly exceeds that of fungi, and while the latter may be entirely absent, even where the total number of organisms is high (Kopeloff, Wellcome and Kopeloff[11]), bacteria invariably occur in greater or smaller numbers, representing sometimes, it is true, a few per cent. of the total flora only.

These facts should have been thought sufficiently convincing to justify a thorough study of the subject of the bacterial types present. This, however, has not been made and a detailed account of the bacterial flora cannot be given.

In his study of the deterioration of stored raw beet-sugar Schöne[12] detected no less than 34 species of bacteria. They included cocci, in two cases even *Streptococcus mesenteroides* as well as another saccharose-inverting coccus. In addition, various spore-forming rods were found, such as lactic acid bacteria, types described as belonging to *Bact. coli commune*, and gelatine liquefying types. The latter were probably related to *Bact. fluorescens liquefaciens*. Spore formers were represented by mucus-producing types of the aerobic soil bacilli. The latter were carefully investigated by Owen,[13] who states that the two types most generally met with resemble *Bac. mesentericus vulgatus* (*Bac. vulgatus*, Migula), and *Bac. mesentericus fuscus* (*Bac. mesentericus* Lehmann and Neumann). In his earlier publications Owen did not hesitate to attribute the chief role in the destruction of stored sugar to these bacilli, remarking that other spore bearers, such as *Bac. liodermos*, *Bac. mesentericus niger* and *Bac. Megatherium*, which had also been observed by him in deteriorating sugar, take part in the destruction. Owen found justification for his deductions in the observation that the organisms referred to produce gum from saccharose and therefore liberate a certain amount of reducing sugar. A somewhat similar argument had previously been put forward by Greig-Smith,[14] who regarded his *mesentericus*-resembling organism, *Bac. levaniformans*, as one of the most important infections of deteriorating raw sugar. This argument is very misleading. It is not the synthesis of levan by these organisms which renders them dangerous enemies of the sugar manufacturer, but their property of producing saccharase.

After all, the synthesis of levan is carried out only under certain cultural conditions and cannot be regarded as an essential physiological function. The constant presence of these organisms in the thin film of concentrated molasses surrounding the sugar crystals can only be accounted for by assuming that they produce—as in fact they do—an enzyme which hydrolyses saccharose and thereby sets free monoses which can be utilized by the organisms for the liberation of the energy required for their various life functions. Synthesis of levan does not set free energy, and cannot, therefore, be an important factor.

In addition to the forms referred to above, attention was called by Browne[15] to another mucus-producing rod which he termed *Bact. invertans*, owing to its production of saccharase, and more recently by Cameron and Williams[16] to the presence in sugar crystals of true thermophilic bacteria. Their connexion with the deterioration of sugar in storage is at present obscure, though it is known from Schöne's[17] observations that microbiological activity in stored sugar may reach a pitch at which spontaneous combustion sets in. In the case to which Schöne refers, a lot of 1,000 tons of beet-sugar was destroyed in this way with almost explosive force.

The conception that bacteria are the chief type of micro-organisms responsible for deterioration of sugar on storage has never gained a firm footing among workers—in spite of the fact already referred to, that these micro-organisms dominate the microflora in the majority of cases, and in some cases may be the only type of micro-organisms present.

It is not altogether surprising that the view of the participation of bacteria should have been abandoned in favour of allocating responsibility to various fungi. The advocates propounding the bacterial theory have failed in the past to bring forward proof of their contention. It will require renewed investigation of a more exhaustive nature to establish definitely that in some cases bacteria are solely, and in other cases partly, responsible for the deterioration of sugar on storage.

The association of fungi with this phenomenon seems to have been much more definitely established.

The early microscopic observations made on the deterioration of sugar associated this phenomenon with the presence of fungi, and with the few exceptions referred to, practically every detailed study of the subject made since then has led to the conclusion that fungi were chiefly responsible.

The most frequently mentioned types are species of *Penicillium* and *Aspergillus*, which are usually found in the majority of samples, though often in surprisingly small numbers. Kamerling[18] isolated no less than nineteen types of *Penicillium* from crude cane-sugar. Schöne[12] noted the presence of *Penicillium glaucum* * in beet-sugar, but drew attention also to the importance of *Torula* types and to *Mucor* species. Scott[19] isolated species of *Penicillium* and *Aspergillus* from Brazilian, Peruvian, Jamaican and Javanese samples of crude sugar. More recently Browne,[15] Amons,[6] and Kopeloff and Kopeloff[7] have reported on the destructive activity of fungi found in crude sugar. In Amons's experiments *Aspergillus* and *Penicillium* predominated, while one type of *Mucor* was also met with. Kopeloff and Kopeloff enumerate the following fungi as having been isolated by them from cane-sugar:

Aspergillus niger
  ,, *flavus*
  ,, *nidulans*
  ,, *Sydowi*
  ,, *repens*

in addition to some unclassified strains:
Penicillium expansum
  ,, *divaricatum*
  ,, *luteum* ser.
  ,, *purpurogenum* ser. near *Penicillium pinophilum*

---

* It should be noted that the name *Penicillium glaucum* is often loosely applied in the literature.

Penicillium purpurogenum ser. near *Penicillium luteum*

    ,,   *luteum-purpurogenum* ser. near *Penicillium roseum*

Citromyces—three types

Syncephalastrum sp.

Trichoderma   ,,

Fusarium   ,,

Dematium   ,,

Monascus purpureus ser.

Monilia nigra and at least six further unidentified types.

Of these the more important were present in the percentages shown in Table XI.

Aspergillus Sydowi was thus not only the type most frequently met with, but was also the most active saccharase-producing species found.

Monilia nigra, to which Kopeloff and Kopeloff refer as a type of minor importance, was regarded by Browne[15] as very destructive, being followed closely in this respect by a related type to which he gave the name *Monilia fusca*. *Monilia nigra* was found by Browne in practically pure culture in some of the Cuban sugar examined by him. Both this and *Monilia fusca*, particularly the latter, inverted cane-sugar solutions with remarkable rapidity. In one case a 21 per cent. saccharose solution was reduced in strength to 6·5 per cent. within three weeks. Like other species of *Monilia* Browne's types produced bud cells propagating like yeast where conditions were suitable, that is, presumably, where access of oxygen was restricted. It is still an open question whether in some cases, where species of *Torula* have been found to take an active part in the destruction of saccharose, it may not have been the budding growth forms of *Monilia* which were responsible, rather than *Torula* species as defined by Hansen,[20] since the latter group does not usually invert saccharose. Browne's own work would appear to confirm this assumption. The *Torula communis*, which he described as the most common fungus found in Cuban sugar, did not hydrolyse cane-sugar, but was restricted in its action to the fermentation of invert sugars, particularly fructose. From

TABLE XI. PERCENTAGES OF SUGAR SAMPLES SHOWING PRESENCE OF:

Type of Sugar.	Aspergillus niger.	Cladosporium.	Penicillium luteum.	Unknown Fungus No. II.	Unknown Fungus No. IV.	Syncephalastrum.	Sterile Orange Fungus.	Citromyces III.	Unknown Fungus No. III.	Aspergillus Sydowi	Penicillium expansum.	Aspergillus flavus.
Plantation granulated	100	100	17	50	39	50	72	33	61	100	22	22
Plantation granulated undried	100	100	33	67	33	0	67	0	33	100	33	67
Yellow clarified	81	94	0	6	0	63	13	6	38	100	70	75
Standard granulated	60	40	0	0	0	40	20	0	80	80	0	0
Cuban raw	82	64	0	0	9	73	45	18	10	64	0	36
96°	100	83	17	67	33	33	50	17	50	100	50	67
96° washed	100	90	10	70	30	10	20	10	30	100	60	40
Second	100	100	12	75	37	12	50	50	50	100	12	60

this carbohydrate it produced a slight amount of gas and small quantities of esters. It was a *Torula* also which Owen[21] recommended as a means of protecting stored cane-sugar against deterioration. Owen found that a saccharose solution inoculated with an inverting *Hyphomycete* and a *Torula* showed practically no loss on incubation, while a corresponding solution inoculated with the *Hyphomycete* alone showed marked inversion of the saccharose.

The data referred to above on micro-organisms observed in, or isolated from, sugar crystals cannot have failed to impress the reader by the comparative variety of types, that is to say by the possibility that sugar deterioration may be due to a great variety of types—not necessarily all of them bacteria or fungi, but bacteria and fungi combined. The impression is undoubtedly gaining ground, contrary to what was at one time assumed, that this phenomenon may be due to the activity of any type of organism which can find suitable conditions for development in the concentrated solution of saccharose surrounding the individual crystal.

In the previous chapter a partial answer at least was supplied to the question of how the varied microflora is introduced into the moisture film of the sugar crystal. It was shown that the massecuite usually contains very few micro-organisms beyond a few hundred spores of aerobic soil bacilli per gramme, but that additional types are introduced in the centrifuge in which the crystals are separated from their mother liquor, partly through the large volume of contaminated air surging past the crystals at great speed and partly through the crystals being washed with badly contaminated water. It has also been suggested (Kamerling[18]) that the habit of bagging the finished sugar in infected bags might be the chief cause of infection of the crystals. While not denying the possibility of additional infections being derived from the bags, it is hardly safe to accept this assumption to the extent which Kamerling favours. If this infection actually occurred deterioration would be limited in the first instance to the crystals in direct contact with the bags, whereas actual observations show that deterioration may have proceeded for some time in the interior before being noticeable on the surface. As pointed out by Browne and by Kopeloff and Kopeloff the distribution of moisture in the sugar appears to be the factor governing the initial seat of deterioration.

At an early date in the study of the deterioration of sugar on storage the conclusion was arrived at that a sugar could not be expected to keep during storage when the moisture present appreciably exceeded the non-sugar contents of the sample. This led to the formulation of the so-called 'factor of safety' demand of the Colonial Sugar Refining Company of Australia. The factor of safety requires that the percentage of moisture in a sugar must not exceed half that of the non-saccharose constituents. It is expressed in the following formula:

$$\frac{W}{100-S-W} = 0\cdot5, \text{ or simplified } \frac{W}{100-S} = 0\cdot333;$$

where W represents the moisture content, and S the saccharose content.

As a matter of fact the figure should be put no higher than 0·3 at least in the case of Cuban and Porto Rican sugars.

In other words the requirement of the factor of safety indicates that a comparatively impure sugar may be allowed a considerably higher moisture content than a very pure sample. Thus if a sample of raw sugar, containing 90 per cent. of saccharose, had a moisture content of 2·4 per cent., the factor of safety of this sample would be:

$$\frac{2\cdot4}{100-90} = 0\cdot24;$$

while a high grade sugar of 99 per cent. saccharose content and with 2·4 per cent. moisture would show a safety factor of

$$\frac{2\cdot4}{100-99} = 2\cdot4.$$

The higher the purity of the sugar, therefore, the less moisture can it be suffered to contain, and in the same way the more will a slight change in the prevailing moisture conditions affect the factor of safety.

An absorption of 0·3 per cent. of additional moisture would make little difference in the factor of safety figure of a raw sugar of 90 per cent. purity and a moisture content of say 0·2 per cent., the factor merely rising from 0·02 to 0·05. In a high grade sugar of the same moisture content and with 99 per cent. of saccharose an increase of this order would raise the factor of safety from 0·2 to 0·5, or much beyond that at which the sugar could be stored with safety, assuming the factor of safety to be a genuine index of the keeping properties of a sugar sample.

But unfortunately it can only be claimed to be a genuine index to a limited extent. While it is correct, probably, that a sample of refined sugar is rendered more sensitive to deterioration by slight changes of moisture than low grade raw sugar, it is not possible to predict with certainty the keeping qualities of a sugar by ascertaining the factor of safety figure of the sample. Kopeloff and his collaborators[22] investigated this question and arrived at the conclusion that the factor of safety figure was effective only in 40 per cent. of the cases examined.

To some extent the reason for this would appear to be found in the fact that the deterioration at a given moisture concentration depends not only on whether micro-organisms are present in the surface film of molasses or not, but also on the numbers present per unit of the film. For example, in sugars with safety factors ranging from 0·18 to 0·50, Kopeloff and his collaborators observed deterioration in practically every case when the numbers of micro-organisms per gramme of sugar exceeded 50,000. As the numbers decreased to about 500 there was evidence of less deterioration at moisture ratios below 0·36. But even where the ratio fell below 0·3 deterioration was observed in the sugar when more than 200 micro-organisms were present per gramme. It is in samples of sugar with comparatively few micro-organisms therefore that the factor of safety is most likely to be of practical importance, and it should be applied only in combination with a bacteriological analysis of the samples.

This raises the question as to how this bacteriological analysis is to be carried out, or rather what type of nutrient medium should be used for the purpose, since it is obvious that standard conditions must be adhered to in this respect if consistent results are to be expected.

Various media have been recommended for the isolation of the micro-organisms developing on raw sugar. Browne uses a 30 per cent. solution of raw cane-sugar, Amons[6] a modified Czapek agar. This latter, which has been shown by Kopeloff and Kopeloff[7] to be of special value, contains 3 per cent. saccharose; 0·1 per cent. dipotassium hydrogen phosphate, 0·05 per cent. potassium chloride, 0·5 per cent. magnesium sulphate, 0·001 per cent. ferrous sulphate and 0·2 per cent. sodium nitrate.

Kopeloff and his collaborators finally decided on another modification of Czapek's medium in which the saccharose is increased to 5 per cent. Peptone is introduced in a concentration of 0·5 per cent. and the sodium nitrate is in part replaced by ammonium nitrate, while the magnesium sulphate is reduced by half. They claim that this medium is more effective than Czapek's for the isolation of fungi. Since it contains an appreciable percentage of peptone it will probably be found superior also for the isolation of the bacteria developing in sugar and might therefore be recommended as the standard nutrient medium in microbiological sugar analyses.

The comparative importance of the factor of safety index in the demonstration of the keeping qualities of stored sugars will have illustrated the importance of the presence of moisture for the development of micro-organisms in the film of molasses surrounding the sugar crystal. It is not to be concluded, however, that, given a sufficient concentration of moisture in a sugar, microbiological deterioration will proceed unchecked for an indefinite period. There are various factors which counteract the destruction and in time may bring it to a standstill. One of these factors is the temperature prevailing at the place of storage.

Browne refers to a consignment of moist sugar which was stored in New York from October till May without suffering deterioration, in spite of the presence of harmful micro-organisms. During this period the temperature in the store-room did not exceed $20°$ C., a figure, therefore, which may safely be placed as the minimum at which deterioration can proceed—within a reasonable period it should no doubt be added. It would be unsafe to interpret Browne's observation as establishing that no development at all is possible at $20°$ C. It is common knowledge that many fungi and bacteria not only resist, but actually develop at, temperatures down to the freezing-point of water.

Another factor which may have an important action on the progress of the deterioration of stored sugar is the actual activity of the responsible micro-organisms, or rather of the products of metabolism of these organisms. It has already been mentioned that the sphere of action is restricted to the thin film of molasses surrounding the sugar crystals. Pro-longed activity, therefore, is bound to accumulate in this thin layer a considerable concentration of products of meta-bolism, not only invert sugars, but also various fermentation products, including esters, alcohols and volatile and non-volatile acids, which in the great majority of cases cannot be removed, and therefore must arrest the activity of the various enzymes responsible for their production. That this actually occurs, at least where deterioration proceeds in a sample of sugar which is stored under conditions preventing the ab-sorption of moisture, has frequently been observed. Lewton-Brain and Deerr[23] report on a case of this type where a sugar stored for some years had, in time, become more or less sterile.

On the other hand, when an opportunity arrives for the absorption of additional moisture, a reduction in the con-centration of the accumulated products of metabolism will result and the progress of destruction can continue, other factors being favourable. This happens in many storage places, particularly in damp climates or at sea, and here it is no unusual sight to find a thick syrup oozing from the bags, spreading an infection not only from bag to bag, but through the intermediary of workmen to other consignments in storage.

Such conditions are highly dangerous and should certainly be avoided. The most obvious method of doing this might be thought to be the reduction of the humidities in the storage sheds. This may not be practicable, however, since the absorption of minute percentages of moisture suffices to support microbiological activity in sugar. Additional precautions will usually be found necessary, notably the reduction of the number of micro-organisms present. To some extent this can be ensured by the introduction of increased cleanliness in the sugar factory, particularly during those processes which start with the separation of the sugar crystals in the centrifuge. Where superheated steam, as suggested by Kopeloff and his collaborators,[11] is utilized instead of water for the removal of the adhering molasses, the very startling reduction in the microflora thereby secured, combined with the added facility of drying the hot sugar, should materially assist in securing a sugar of high resistance to decay during storage.

The economic importance of the deterioration of sugar on storage has been ascertained on various occasions and has been shown to be of considerable magnitude. For Cuban raw sugar alone it amounted to £200,000 annually, according to Browne.[15] It cannot be an exaggeration to claim, therefore, that the total world loss must be more than two million pounds sterling annually.

A destruction of saccharose occurs occasionally in chocolate-coated creams, a subject which has been studied by Weinzirl,[24] and more recently by Church, Paine and Hamilton.[25] Though this type of deterioration may not be one of great importance, it is interesting to know that it has been attributed in both cases to the activity of *Bac. sporogenes*, an anaerobic butyric acid producing bacillus, and of yeasts. Paine, Birckner and Hamilton[26] find that the destruction is prevented when a certain percentage of invert sugar is present in the creams. They secure this by the addition of saccharase to the sugar.

LITERATURE

1. O. Ligon, *History of the Island of Barbados*, London, 1673 (see N. and L. Kopeloff, *Abst. of Bacteriology*, vol. 6, p. 221, 1922).
2. N. and L. Kopeloff, *Abst. of Bacteriology*, vol. 6, p. 221, 1922.
3. A. Payen, *Comptes rend.*, vol. 33, p. 393, 1851.
4. P. Dubrunfaut, *Comptes rend.*, vol. 68, p. 663, 1869.
5. E. C. Shorey, *J. Soc. Chem. Ind.*, vol. 17, p. 555, 1898.
6. W. J. T. Amons, *Arch. u. Suikerind. Ned. Ind.*, vol. 25, p. 1225, 1917.
7. N. and L. Kopeloff, *Louisiana Bull.*, no. 166, 1919.
8. O. Grove, *Ann. Rep. Agric. and Hortic. Research Stat.*, University Bristol, 1918, p. 34.
9. F. Hirst, *Ann. Rep. Agric. and Hortic. Research Stat.*, University Bristol, 1927, p. 150.
10. A. Meier, *Zentrbl. f. Bakt.*, Abt. II, vol. 64, p. 241, 1925.
11. N. Kopeloff, C. J. Welcome and L. Kopeloff, *Louisiana Bull.*, no. 175, 1920.
12. A. Schöne, *Zentrbl. f. Bakt.*, Abt. II, vol. 17, p. 563, 1907.
13. W. L. Owen, *Louisiana Bull.*, No. 125, 1911.
14. R. Greig-Smith, *Proc. Linnean Soc. N.S.W.*, vol. 26, p. 602, 1902.
15. C. A. Browne, *J. Ind. Eng. Chem.*, vol. 10, p. 178, 1918.
16. E. J. Cameron and C. C. Williams, *Zentrbl. f. Bakt.*, Abt. II, vol. 76, p. 28, 1928–29.
17. A. Schöne, *Die Deutsche Zuckerindustrie*, vol. 36, p. 247, 1911.
18. Z. Kamerling, *Verslag over de botanische en physiologische Werksaamheden*, Proefstat. v. Suikerind in West Java, Kapok, pp. 97–104, 1899.
19. J. Scott, *Intern. Sugar J.*, vol. 14, p. 582, 1912.
20. H. Chr. Hansen, *Comptes rend. d. Laboratoire de Carlsberg*, vol. 2, p. 143, 1888.
21. W. L. Owen, *Chimie et Industrie*, vol. 11, p. 751, 1924.
22. N. and L. Kopeloff, *Louisiana Bull.*, no. 170, 1920.
23. L. Lewton-Brain and N. Deerr, *Louisiana Planter*, vol. 54, p. 282, 1915.
24. J. Weinzirl, *J. Bacteriology*, vol. 7, p. 599, 1922.
25. M. B. Church, H. S. Paine and J. Hamilton, *J. Ind. Eng. Chem.*, vol. 19, p. 353, 1927.
26. H. S. Paine, V. Birckner and J. Hamilton, *J. Ind. Eng. Chem.*, vol. 19, p. 358, 1927.

INDEX OF AUTHORS

A

Aagaard, T., *see* Bridel, M.

Abbott, O. D., decomposition of pentoses by yeasts, 164.

Abderhalden, E., assimilation of food substances, 40.

Albus, W. R., *see* Whittier, E. O.

Alekhine, A., hydrolysis of melezitose, 45.

Allemann, O., *see* Thöni, I.

Alsberg, C. L., *see also* Black, O. F.

Alsberg, C. L., and Black, O. F., synthesis of starch by *Penicillium puberulum*, 175.

Alvarez, E., hydrolysis of indican, 69.

Amelung, H., decomposition of pentoses by *Aspergillus niger*, 164.

Amons, W. J. T., deterioration of sugar by micro-organisms, 290.

—, media for bacteriological analysis of sugar, 300.

Anderson, J. A., *see* Fred, E. B.

Anderson, R. S., *see* Nelson, J. M.

Andrusiani, M., recovery of alcohol from bread, 238.

Arinstein, B., *see* Neuberg, C.

Armstead, D., and Harland, S. C., moisture requirements of mildew, 216.

Armstrong, H. E., and Armstrong, E. F., action of saccharase, 52.

—, —, effect of glycine on saccharase, 53.

Arnoldow, W. A., mould growth in stored rye, 202.

Aronowski, A., *see* Pringsheim, H.

Ashe, L. H., *see* Northrop, J. H., *and* Kohman H. A.

Atkinson, A. W., preparation of Koji, 23.

Atterberg, A., effect of moisture content on microflora of stored grain, 196, 197, 201.

Atwater, H., sour bread, 247.

Aubel, E., *see also* Cambier, R.

Aubel, E., decomposition of glucose by *Bact. pyocyaneum*, 112.

—, decomposition of hexoses by facultative anaerobes, 112.

—, decomposition of methylglyoxal by *Bact. coli commune*, 118.

—, enzymes of *Bact. coli commune*, 116, 118.

Aubel, E., pyruvic acid in bacterial fermentations, 106, 107, 119.

Aubry, A., *see also* Bourquelot, E.

—, action of maltase on *a*-glucosides, 57.

Avery, C. E., lactic acid manufacture, 131.

Ayyar, G. G., *see* Rao, T. L.

B

Bachrach, E., and Cardot, H., optimum pH for lactic acid bacteria, 132.

Bailey, C. H., *see also* Greeve, E.

Bailey, C. H., and Johnson, A. H., dough, method of testing, 235–6.

—, —, dough fermentation, effects of pH on, 233, 237.

—, —, dough fermentation, gluten in, 235.

Bailey, C. H., and Sherwood, R. C., effect of pH on diastatic activity of flour, 229.

—, —, dough fermentation, 220.

—, —, dough fermentation, effect on disaccharides of, 230.

—, —, dough fermentation, pH changes during, 236–7, 241–2.

—, —, dough fermentation, protein changes in, 240.

Bailey, G. C., and Potter, R. S., fumaric acid for synthesis of indigo, 100.

Bainier, S., *see* Sartory, A.

Baker, J. L., treatment of brewers' yeast for breadmaking, 227.

Baker, J. L., and Hulton, H. F. E., substances in flour toxic to yeast, 207, 227.

Bakes, W. E., *see* Thaysen, A. C.

Balch, R. T., *see* Paine, H. S.

Baldwin, M. E., *see* Sherman, H. C.

Banning, F., production of oxalic acid by micro-organisms, 99.

Barendrecht, H. P., isolation of lactase, 59.

Bärlund, B., *see* Virtanen, A. I.

Barthel, C., lactic acid bacteria, 125.

Baudrimont, —, yeast saccharase, 47.

Bean, P., and Scarisbrick, F., flour fermentation, 213, 214.

Beccard, E., production of rye bread, 225.

SUBJECT INDEX

A

Acetaldehyde, effect on yeast fermentation, 122.
—, formation by bacteria, 84–7, 108, 109, 111–13, 117, 119, 122, 123, 128, 129, 138, 140, 143, 145, 146, 148, 149.
—, — from methyglyoxal, 107.
— hydrate, 84.
—, occurrence in fat synthesis, 177.
—, — — hemicellulose synthesis, 178.
Acetic acid, *see also* 57, 68.
— —, addition to acetone fermentation, 147.
— —, formation by bacteria, 84, 86, 88, 90, 106–9, 112–14, 116–22, 125, 127, 129, 136–40, 142–6.
— —, occurrence in flour and dough fermentation, 213, 224, 243.
— —, — in stored grain, 206.
— —, use in bread-making, 249, 255.
Acetoacetic acid, 85, 148.
Acetone, formation by bacteria, 86, 113, 144, 146–7, 166–8.
—, — from acetic acid, 114, 147–8.
—, — from butyric acid, 148.
Acetyl bromide, action on starch and polyamyloses, 8.
Acetylmethylcarbinol, formation by bacteria, 84, 86, 106, 108, 109, 111–13, 118, 121–2, 139, 145, 148, 153.
—, — by yeast, 108, 121.
Achroodextrins, 9.
Acids, *see also* Acetic, Lactic, &c.
—, effect on takadiastase, 27.
—, formation by aerobic bacilli, 108.
—, — in dough fermentation, 237, 243.
—, — in indigo fermentation, 69–70.
—, — in stored cereal products, 203–6.
—, — in sugar manufacture, 271–2.
—, use in Amylo process, 32, 34.
Actinomyces bovis, 22.
— *diastaticus*, 22.
— *odorifera*, 22.
— *spp.*, lactase in, 59.
— — starch decomposition by, 22.
—, *see also*, 49, 65, 67, 164, 248.
Adhesives, 191, 194, 217–18.
—, phenol as antiseptic for, 217.

Aesculin, 65, 67.
Aldol, suggested formation by bacteria, 143, 145.
Algae, amylolytic properties, 16.
—, in waste from sugar manufacture, 285.
—, occurrence of inulin in, 13.
Alhagi camelorum, manna of, 45.
Aluminium sulphate, use as antiseptic, 217.
Amphiernia rubra, production of saccharic acid by, 96.
Amygdalase, 66.
Amygdalin, 65–7.
Amylase, α- and β-, 11, 12.
—, bacterial, 17–36.
—, destruction by heat, 20.
—, —, optimum temperature, 20, 21, 27.
—, effect of pH on, 17, 20, 26, 32.
—, — of temperature on, 32, 35.
—, in *Aspergillus oryzae*, 26–7.
—, in flour, 229.
—, liquefying enzymes in, 10, 26, 27, 35.
—, in malt, 26, 229.
—, in pancreas, 11, 26.
—, isolation of, 3, 20.
—, saccharifying enzymes in, 10, 12, 19, 26, 27, 35.
—, starch decomposition by, 9.
—, use in bread-making, 229.
Amylo process, 32, 36.
Amylobiose, 7.
Amylocoagulase, 12.
Amylodextrins, 9, 174.
Amylomyces Rouxii, see *Mucor Rouxii*.
Amylopectin, 4–12.
—, relationship to glycogen, 13, 36.
Amylose, 4–12.
—, α- and β-, 5, 6.
Amylotriose, 11.
Antiseptics, effect on bacterial amylase, 20.
—, use in adhesives, 217.
—, — in preparation of takadiastase, 25.
—, — in sizing of textiles, 213–17.
—, — in sugar manufacture, 274.
Arabinose, 164, 165.
—, decomposition by *Bac. acetoethylicus*, 166.
—, synthesis of starch from, 175.

Bean flour, use in preparation of Koji, 25.

Beans, *Bact. prodigiosum* on, 256.

Beer, mucus production in, 182.

Beer wort, use as leaven, 225.

Beet sugar, *see* Sugar.

'Biityn', 24.

Boletus pachypus, starch synthesis by, 175.

Botrytis cinerea, effect on germinating grain, 199.

Boulard process, 32.

Bran, 132, 159.

—, as dough improver, 232, 243.

—, bacterial development in, 197.

—, fungal development in, 202.

—, microflora of, 201–2.

—, use in takadiastase preparation, 25.

Bread, 'blood' on, 248, 255–7.

—, chalk disease of, 248, 253.

—, discoloured, 256.

—, diseases of, 246–57.

—, infection after baking, 247–8.

—, — by insects, 247.

—, microflora of, 194.

—, — —, effect of moisture content on, 247, 250.

—, moisture content of, 247–8.

—, mouldy, 253–6.

—, —, as foodstuff, 256.

—, ropiness in, 182, 203, 248–53.

—, — —, control of, 249–50.

—, — —, detection of organisms causing, 252.

—, — —, influence of moisture content on, 250.

—, — —, — of pH on, 249.

—, — —, — of storage temperature on, 250.

—, — —, organisms causing, 251.

—, rye, 220, 223, 224, 232, 251.

—, salt rising, 222, 239–40.

—, sour, 247, 253.

—, temperature of baking, 231, 246.

—, — of loaf during baking, 246.

—, wrapping of, 254.

Bread-making, microbiology of, 219–43.

Bromates, as dough improvers, 233.

Butyl alcohol, formation by bacteria, 84, 89, 91, 113–14, 138, 142–52.

— —, production by fermentation process, 152–9.

2:3 Butylene glycol, 84, 86, 106, 108, 109, 111, 113–14, 118, 121–2, 146, 148, 154.

Butyric acid, addition to acetone fermentation, 148.

—, as hydrogen acceptor, 149.

— fermentation, influence of pH on, 144, 152.

—, formation by bacteria, 84, 109, 138, 142–60.

—, formation from lactic acid, 151.

Buffer action, 27, 242.

C

Cacao shells, pentosans in, 167.

Cannizarro reaction, 119.

Capric acid, formation by bacteria, 160.

Caproic acid, formation by bacteria, 109, 160.

Caprylic acid, formation by bacteria, 160.

Caraway seed, effect on dough fermentation, 233.

Carbamide, in dough improver, 232.

Carbohydrates, reserve, 5, 12–13.

Carbon dioxide, production by bacteria, 84–6, 111–13, 116–19, 121–2, 127, 136, 139, 142, 144, 149, 154, 221.

—, — by fungi, 164.

—, — by yeasts, 164, 173, 179.

—, — in bread-making, 226, 227, 239.

— —, — in indigo fermentation, 69.

Casein, in lactic acid manufacture, 131.

Cassava, 215.

Catalase, absence of, in anaerobic organisms, 79.

—, —, in lactic bacteria, 127.

—, in propionic bacteria, 137.

Cellase, 58.

Cellobiase, 58.

Cellobiose, decomposition by microorganisms, 58.

—, formation from glucose anhydride, 11.

Cellulose, effect on maltase formation by *Monilia sitophila*, 57.

—, relation of mucus to, 183.

Cephalothecium roseum, effect on germinating grain, 199.

Cereal products, *see also* Grain, Flour, &c.

— —, addition of alkaline substances to stored, 207.

— —, chemical sterilization of, 207–8.

— —, microbiology of, 191–4.

— —, tests for damage to, 207.